INTRODUCTION TO
INSTRUMENT-TRANSFORMERS

CRC PRESS

A DIVISION OF
THE **CHEMICAL RUBBER** CO.
CLEVELAND, OHIO

INTERNATIONAL SCIENTIFIC SERIES

INTRODUCTION TO
INSTRUMENT-TRANSFORMERS

by

BRIAN D. JENKINS, B.Sc., A.M.I.E.E.

GEORGE NEWNES LIMITED
TOWER HOUSE, SOUTHAMPTON STREET,
LONDON, W.C.2

First published 1967

PRINTED IN GREAT BRITAIN
Filmset in 10/11 *pt. Times New Roman*
By J. W. Arrowsmith Ltd.
Bristol 3

PREFACE

I was very fortunate in the manner of my introduction to instrument-transformers and, in particular, to current-transformers, because, after having spent some few years on the design of distribution and power-transformers I was transferred to the switchgear department of the company I was then with and put in charge of a small section dealing with current-transformer design and application. This section had only been formed comparatively recently and thus a great deal of work other than normal production design had to be done and I met the usual number of difficulties and problems, not the least amongst them being a lack of readily available literature on the subject.

I was fortunate in having the advice of the Chief Switchgear Engineer, Mr. H. A. Lamb, now deceased, who not only helped me with my numerous problems but passed to me his own enthusiasm for the subject of current-transformers. In the same way, Mr. H. V. Rose, the Chief Transformer Engineer of the same company, helped me in the case of voltage-transformers. Any success this present work enjoys will be in no small measure due to the sympathetic and ever-ready assistance given to me by these two engineers when I first became involved in the design, manufacture and application of instrument-transformers.

Right from the start I obtained a strong impression that some electrical engineers well versed in the intricacies of rotating machines, power systems and all forms of electrical plant, even some who had a good knowledge of distribution and power-transformer theory and operation, seemed to surround the subject of instrument-transformers quite unnecessarily with an aura of mystery. This was particularly true when considering current-transformers and although I am no longer intimately connected with the design of these transformers it is an attitude I am still meeting occasionally.

There seems to be one main reason for this attitude—some instrument-transformers are specified with low errors and this, in turn, mistakenly leads engineers to believe that such 'onerous' requirements can only be met by vague and highly complex design methods. The implication is then made that the theory of the two types of instrument-transformer is also complex. Nothing could be further from the truth although this does not mean to

v

say that the design of instrument-transformers is not a highly skilled profession.

Many engineers using current- and voltage-transformers and wishing to learn something of their theory of operation, design and utilisation find the treatment given these transformers in the normal textbook on electrical technology unavoidably rather meagre and are then thwarted to learn there is no satisfactory introductory book on the subject. Numerous articles have appeared in the technical press and papers have been read before the I.E.E. and similar bodies but these are sometimes of little use to someone seeking general knowledge on the subject because they deal only with possibly obscure aspects.

Some years ago I contributed a series of articles on current-transformers to the *Electrical Times* in which I tried to present the subject in as general a manner as possible. Several readers of this series were kind enough to tell me they found it useful and I am now taking the opportunity of offering the present book in the hope that it will prove equally helpful.

One word of warning: the reader will find no startling new approach to the subject of current- and voltage-transformers because my principal aim has been to produce in this one book what I believe to be a reasonably thorough introduction to the subject which will prove to be of assistance to the user of instrument-transformers, the young designer, and to anyone else who requires such an introduction.

To fulfil this aim I have not hesitated to draw freely from numerous articles and papers that have been published over the last twenty years or so, but this book can also be claimed to be completely up-to-date, following so soon on the publication of the relevant new British Standards.

B.D.J.

TWICKENHAM

ACKNOWLEDGEMENTS

I wish to acknowledge the kind assistance given me by various institutions, companies and individuals, without whose help this book could not have been written.

My thanks, therefore, to

The British Standards Institution.
The American Standards Association.
The Verband Deutscher Electrotechniker.
The Institution of Electrical Engineers.
The American Institute of Electrical Engineers (now The Institute of Electrical and Electronic Engineers).
H.M. Stationery Office.

Also to

A.E.I. (Manchester) Ltd.
Elliott Bros. (London) Ltd.
The English Electric Co. Ltd.
Foster Transformers Ltd.
A. Reyrolle Ltd.
Dr.-Ing. Hans Ritz.
Smith Hobson Ltd.
Telcon Magnetic Cores Ltd.
Telcon Metals Ltd.
H. Tinsley & Co. Ltd.
Westinghouse Electric Corporation.

Finally, my thanks to those individuals, who by their kind help and useful criticism have encouraged me in the writing of this book: Dr. A. A. Halacsy, Dr. G. A. V. Sowter, C. Amor, E. A. Bennett, A. Martin, D. J. Price, S. J. Wilson and many others.

Considerable mention is made throughout this book to the relevant British and American standards, copies of which may be obtained from the British Standards Institution, 2 Park Street, London, W.1.

CONTENTS

LIST OF PRINCIPAL SYMBOLS AND ABBREVIATIONS

(A) COMMON TO BOTH CURRENT-TRANSFORMERS AND VOLTAGE-TRANSFORMERS

A = Gross core cross-sectional area.
B_m = Peak flux density.
E_s = Secondary induced e.m.f.
f = Frequency.
F = Form factor.
I_p = Actual primary current.
I_s = Actual secondary current.
I_e = Exciting current.
I_m = Magnetising component of exciting current.
I_w = Watt-loss component of exciting current.
K_n = Nominal ratio.
K_t = Turns ratio.
N_p = Number of primary turns.
N_s = Number of secondary turns.
P = Burden volt-amperes.
R_b = Burden resistance.
R_{sw} = Secondary winding resistance.
s = Core space factor.
X_b = Burden reactance.
X_{sw} = Secondary winding leakage reactance.
Z_b = Burden impedance.
λ = Burden power factor angle = $\cos^{-1}(R_b/Z_b)$.
ϕ = Core power factor angle = $\cos^{-1}(I_w/I_e)$.
Φ = Flux.
%R.E. = Percentage ratio error.
R.C.F. = Ratio correction factor.
T.C.F. = Transformer correction factor.

(B) FOR CURRENT-TRANSFORMERS ONLY

I_{p1} = Load component of primary current = $K_t I_s$.
I_{pn} = Nominal primary current.
I_{sn} = Nominal secondary current.
I_{poc} = Primary operating current.
I_{pf} = Primary fault current.
I_{sf} = Fault current referred to secondary.
K_c = Actual current ratio = I_p/I_s.
l = Mean length of magnetic circuit.
R_s = Total secondary circuit resistance.
X_s = Total secondary circuit reactance.
Z_s = Total secondary circuit impedance.
R_{st} = Stabilising resistance.
β = Phase error.
δ = Overall secondary circuit power factor angle
     = $\cos^{-1}(R_s/Z_s)$.

(C) FOR VOLTAGE-TRANSFORMERS ONLY

E_p = Primary induced e.m.f.
I_p' = Load component of primary current.
K_v = Actual voltage ratio = V_p/V_s.
R_{pw} = Primary winding resistance.
R_p = Total resistance referred to primary.
R_s = Total resistance referred to secondary.
V_p = Primary terminal voltage.
V_s = Secondary terminal voltage.
X_{pw} = Primary winding leakage reactance.
X_p = Total leakage reactance referred to primary.
X_s = Total leakage reactance referred to secondary.
γ = Phase error.
δ = Burden power factor angle.

Please note that certain symbols have a different significance when used for voltage-transformers compared with that when used for current-transformers.

A NOTE ON THE M.K.S. SYSTEM OF UNITS

The M.K.S. (metre-kilogram-second) rationalised system of units has been used throughout this book, but as this may be unfamiliar to some readers who are used to working in the C.G.S., or another, system, it is hoped that these brief notes will prove useful.

Similarly a great deal of the data published by the manufacturers of magnetic materials, such as characteristic curves, is not in the M.K.S. system and therefore the conversion factors included here will also prove helpful.

In the M.K.S. system the unit of flux is the *weber* and flux density is given in *webers/sq. metre*.

$$1 \text{ weber/sq. metre} = 10^4 \text{ gauss.}$$

The unit of magnetising intensity H is the *ampere-turn/metre* and may be given by

$$B = \mu_0\mu_r H \text{ webers/sq. metre,}$$

where μ_0 is termed the *absolute permeability of free space*, or alternatively the *magnetic space constant*, and has the value $4\pi \times 10^{-7}$; μ_r is the *relative permeability* of the material being considered (in this system μ_r, for air, is unity).

Thus

$$1 \text{ ampere-turn/metre} = 10^{-2} \text{ A/cm.} = 4\pi \times 10^{-3} \text{ oersteds.}$$

Magnetic characteristic curves are frequently plotted as watts-loss/kilogram, magnetising volt-amperes/kilogram and exciting volt-amperes/kilogram against flux density.

If

$$I_w = \text{watt-loss current,}$$

$$I_m = \text{magnetising current,}$$

and

$$I_e = \text{exciting current} = I_w + {}_jI_m,$$

then

$$\text{watts-loss/kilogram} = 4{\cdot}44\frac{f}{\delta}B_m(NI_w/\text{metre}),$$

$$\text{magnetising VA/kilogram} = 4{\cdot}44\frac{f}{\delta}B_m(NI_m/\text{metre}),$$

$$\text{exciting VA/kilogram} = 4{\cdot}44\frac{f}{\delta}B_m(NI_e/\text{metre}),$$

where

B_m = webers/sq. metre and is the peak value of flux density,

f = frequency in cycles/second,

δ = specific gravity in kg/cu. metre.

These equations enable one to re-plot any characteristic curve—those in ampere-turns/metre against flux density into watts or volt-amperes/kilogram against flux density and vice versa, while the introduction of suitable conversion factors enables one to move from the metric to the inch system if this latter one is preferred.

CURRENT-TRANSFORMERS

CHAPTER 1

INTRODUCTION TO CURRENT-TRANSFORMERS

The newcomer to the study of current-transformers sometimes falls into the trap of attempting to adapt the knowledge he may have already gained of the theory and operation of ordinary power-transformers. Such an approach may sometimes lead to a certain amount of confusion in his mind and to him making quite unnecessary comparisons between the two types of transformer. It is far better to consider the current-transformer on its own merits and this is made easier if it is appreciated, from the start, that while there is, inevitably, considerable similarity between the current-transformer and the power-transformer since both types depend on the same fundamental mechanism of electromagnetic induction, nevertheless there are equally considerable differences in operation which all stem from one cardinal fact. In the power-transformer the current flowing in its primary winding is largely the 'reflection' of that flowing in the secondary circuit, whereas, in the current-transformer, the primary winding is connected in series with the line whose current is being measured or indicated *and this primary current is, in the majority of applications, in no way controlled or determined by the condition of the secondary circuit.* Thus it may be said that the dominant factor in the operation of any current-transformer is the primary current.

Current-transformers must be subdivided into two main categories from consideration of their duty requirements. The first category consists of those used for metering and indicating circuits and these may be termed 'measuring current-transformers', while the second category consists of current-transformers used in association with protection equipment—trip coils, relays and the like, and these may be termed 'protective current-transformers'. There are considerable differences between the duty requirements of these two types of current-transformer and hence the design approach relevant to the one cannot be used for the other. It is therefore advisable not to compare the two types but to treat each separately, and this is done in this book. These introductory notes are, however, applicable to both measuring and protective current-transformers.

Definition and functions of the current-transformer

The current-transformer was defined in B.S. 81 as 'an instrument-transformer for the transformation of current from one value to another, usually a lower one, or for the transformation of a current which is at a voltage above earth into a proportionate current at a lower voltage'. When B.S.3938 was prepared it was felt necessary to redefine the current-transformer as 'a transformer for use with electrical measuring instruments and/or electrical protective devices for the transformation of current and in which the current in the secondary winding, in normal conditions of use, is sub-stantially proportional to the current in the primary winding and differing from it by an angle which is approximately zero for an appropriate direction of the connections'.

While the latter definition is an extremely good one in explaining the transforming function of current-transformers it is a little unfortunate that their isolating function has been ignored.

In actual practice, the adoption of certain standard secondary current ratings, of which 5 A and 1 A are the most commonly used, enables one to also employ standard relay and instrument current ratings, this rationalisation having considerable technical and commercial advantages for all the components concerned—relays, instruments and current-transformers. The very necessary elec-trical isolation of these relays and instruments in the current-transformer secondary circuit from the possibly high potential above earth of the primary circuit is obtained by the provision of major insulation between primary and secondary windings and between these windings and earth.

One can have current-transformers which are 'auto-wound', that is, the primary and secondary windings are electrically con-nected together, so that isolation from the primary circuit potential is impossible and therefore such current-transformers must never be used in other than low-voltage primary circuits.

The insulation problems met in the design and manufacture of current-transformers are, in general, no different from those encountered in other electrical equipment and are not, therefore, of first importance in this book which is principally concerned with the characteristics and performance of the electromagnetic circuit of current-transformers, or, in other words, with their transforming function. Nevertheless, from the preceding remarks it will be appre-ciated that many cases occur in practice where the primary current is of such a magnitude that one could readily use a 'directly-connected' instrument but, because of the high potential above earth of the primary circuit, a current-transformer has to be used solely for its isolating function.

Ignoring insulation, the essential components of any current-transformer are (i) the primary winding which is connected in series with the circuit, the current of which is to be transformed, (ii) the magnetic core, and (iii) the secondary winding which receives electrical energy from the primary circuit by electromagnetic induction and to the terminals of which is connected the relay, instrument, or other device, which constitutes the burden on the current-transformer. For reasons that will be discussed later, one may argue that the burden itself constitutes the fourth essential component of any current-transformer.

(i) The primary winding

For reasons also to be discussed later, current-transformers may be conveniently divided into those having a single-turn primary winding and those having a multi-turn primary winding. The simplest example of the former type is the so-called 'ring-type' or 'through-type' current-transformer which is placed over the cable or bus-bar of the primary system so that this passes through the core orifice or window, becoming the single-turn primary winding. The secondary winding is wound on the core in the normal manner. Some people seem to find it difficult to visualise that the primary conductor passed through a ring-type current-transformer in this manner does, in fact, constitute a single primary turn. The *portion* of the primary conductor actually passing through the core does not, in itself, do this, the single turn being the whole primary system of voltage source, cables and load. Anyone still doubtful about this point can reassure himself by revising on the fundamental concept of flux-linkage found in electromagnetic induction theory.

The single-turn primary winding has a number of advantages over the multi-turn type (a current-transformer using the latter is commonly called a 'wound-primary' current-transformer). A principal one is that the primary winding of any type of current-transformer is subjected to the same dynamic and thermal stresses as the rest of the primary system when large short-circuit currents are flowing and such stresses are more onerous in the wound-primary current-transformer. The ring-type or some other single-turn primary type current-transformer should be used whenever possible, but unfortunately it is often necessary to use the less desirable wound-primary construction in order to obtain the required performance.

(ii) The magnetic circuit

The performance of any current-transformer is generally deemed to mean its accuracy of transformation and is ultimately determined by the characteristics of the core material used and, to a lesser extent, by the type of core construction adopted. For this reason the magnetic alloys used in current-transformers, and allied matters, are discussed at some length in this book. For the present, it is only required that it is remembered that one important parameter in the design of a current-transformer, as with any other a.c. electromagnetic device, is the frequency of excitation, that is, the supply frequency of the primary system.

(iii) The secondary winding

In these brief introductory notes there is no need to discuss the secondary winding in any great detail. The flux density at which the core operates is a very important factor in the performance of any current-transformer and is, itself, determined by the total impedance of the secondary circuit. As the secondary winding impedance is a part of the secondary circuit impedance, sometimes the dominant part, it is therefore an important design factor.

(iv) The burden

It has already been stated that the relay, instrument or other device connected to the secondary winding is termed the 'burden' of the current-transformer. If the term 'load' is used in connection with a current-transformer it always refers to the magnitude of the primary current that is flowing.

Burdens are always specified (in Britain) in volt-amperes at the rated secondary current and at some particular power factor.

Thus, if the rated burden $= P$ volt-amperes and rated secondary current $= I_s$ amperes, then, the ohmic impedance of the burden, Z_b, is given by

$$Z_b = \frac{P}{I_s^2} \text{ ohms.} \qquad (1)$$

If the burden power factor is $\cos \lambda$, then its ohmic resistance is $R_b = Z_b \cos \lambda$ ohms and its ohmic reactance is

$$X_b = (Z_b^2 - R_b^2)^{\frac{1}{2}} \text{ ohms} = Z_b \sin \lambda \text{ ohms.}$$

The choice of volt-amperes for defining the burden may confuse the uninitiated and does, in fact, demand precise terminology. A burden of constant volt-amperes (VA) is not the same as one of constant impedance. If the burden is of constant impedance, its value, expressed in VA, will be determined by the magnitude of the secondary current, that is, if x is the fraction of the rated secondary current being considered, the burden at this current will be x^2P volt-amperes, P, as before, being the rated burden in VA at the rated secondary current.

A burden value must be specified to enable the manufacturer of the current-transformer to check its performance as agreed with the customer and as there is only a limited range of standard burdens from which to choose it is often found that the value of burden chosen for specification purposes is not the same as the actual working burden. It seems to be common practice to specify an often considerably higher burden that the working value with the idea that one then obtains a much better performance (i.e., lower errors) at the latter burden. In the absence of certain safeguards this may be incorrect, as shown later, and therefore care should be exercised in specifying a realistic burden value.

Specification data required by the current-transformer designer

From these introductory notes it will be seen that before he can proceed the designer must have the following information:

(1) Rated primary current.
(2) Rated secondary current.
(3) Rated burden.
(4) Supply frequency.
(5) The required performance, specified either in the form of a 'class of accuracy' or in some other way.
(6) Any other requirement not covered by the relevant normal specification, such as limiting dimensions.

For other than ring-type, or similar, current-transformers he also requires the following information:

(7) System voltage of the primary circuit and desired insulation level, which may include both power frequency and impulse requirements.
(8) The rated short-circuit current of the primary system and its duration for which the current-transformer must be able to withstand, without damage, the associated dynamic and thermal effects.

Naturally there will be many occasions when the customer will be uncertain about the type of construction that the designer will use, and therefore, it is sound practice to *always* include in one's inquiries the information given in items (7) and (8). It will of course be appreciated that these items (7) and (8) must be catered for with all types of current-transformers, but for ring-type and similar designs the provision of adequate major insulation and primary conductor size is the responsibility of the user and not of the designer.

One cannot emphasise too strongly that limiting dimensions must, if they exist, be given to the designer and this includes the minimum inside diameter of any ring-type transformer.

CHAPTER 2

BASIC
CURRENT-TRANSFORMER
THEORY

Practical machines or equipments and their imperfections are often better understood if consideration is first given to the pertinent ideal case and current-transformers are no exception to this approach.

The ideal current-transformer may be defined as one in which any primary condition is reproduced in the secondary circuit in exact ratio and phase relationship. An alternative definition, and possibly a better one, is that the ideal current-transformer is one in which the primary ampere-turns are exactly equal in magnitude to the secondary ampere-turns, and, furthermore, are in precise phase opposition to them. The vector diagram of such a transformer is shown in Fig. 1.

Limiting discussion, for the moment, to r.m.s. values of current; with the secondary winding connected to the burden and a primary current, I_p, flowing, an alternating flux Φ, is induced in the core. This flux is of just sufficient value to induce in the secondary winding an e.m.f., E_s, again of just sufficient magnitude to pass a secondary current, I_s, through the secondary circuit such that there is absolute equality between the primary and secondary ampere-turns and precise phase opposition between them.

Thus, arithmetically,

$$N_p I_p = N_s I_s, \tag{2}$$

where
$$N_p = \text{number of primary turns,}$$

$$N_s = \text{number of secondary turns.}$$

Although the ideal current-transformer is being considered there is no bar to assuming that the secondary winding has both resistance and leakage reactance. In fact, in some cases the secondary winding will also possess capacitance of such a magnitude that it cannot be ignored, but for the moment only resistance and leakage reactance are considered.

9

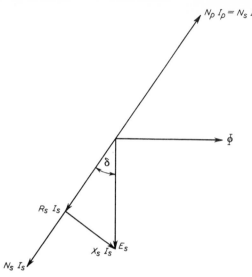

Fig. 1. Vector diagram of ideal current-transformer.

Therefore, if

R_{sw} = resistance of secondary winding,

X_{sw} = leakage reactance of secondary winding,

R_b = resistance of burden,

X_b = reactance of burden,

then the total secondary circuit impedance, Z_s, is given by

$$Z_s = (R_b + R_{sw}) + j(X_b + X_{sw}) \text{ ohms,} \qquad (3)$$

i.e.

$$Z_s = (R_s^2 + X_s^2)^{\frac{1}{2}},$$

with

$$R_s = R_b + R_{sw}; \quad X_s = X_b + X_{sw}$$

and the secondary circuit power factor, $\cos \delta$, is given by

$$\cos \delta = \frac{R_b + R_{sw}}{Z_s} \qquad (4)$$

(δ is the overall secondary power factor angle and must not be confused with λ, the burden power factor angle.)

The secondary induced e.m.f., E_s, is, therefore,

$$E_s = Z_s I_s \text{ volts.} \tag{5}$$

The peak value of the operating flux density, B_m, is easily found from the well-known transformer equation which, assuming sinusoidal conditions, is given in eq. (6):

$$E_s = Z_s I_s = 4.44 f B_m s A N_s \text{ volts,} \tag{6}$$

where

f = frequency in c.p.s.,

B_m = peak flux density in webers/sq. metre,

A = gross core cross-sectional area in sq. metres,

s = core space factor, that is, ratio of nett area to gross area.

As some confusion is caused in some minds by the use of the peak value of flux density to determine the r.m.s. value of induced e.m.f. it seems necessary to show how eq. (6) is derived.

If an alternating flux is induced in a magnetic circuit, the total flux cut per cycle per turn of the energising coil is given by $4\phi_m$ because the whole flux, from its maximum or peak value to zero, dies away in one quarter of a cycle. Thus the *average* value of the induced e.m.f. is given by $4f\phi_m N$, N being the number of turns on the energising coil, so that the r.m.s. value is then given by $4Ff\phi_m N$, F being the form factor. For sinusoidal waveforms F equals 1·11 so that one arrives at the constant 4·44 in eq. (6).

To the uninitiated the core space factor, s in eq. (6), also causes some difficulty and a brief explanation here is not out of place. The peak total flux, ϕ_m, is the product of the peak flux density, B_m, and the *nett* core cross-sectional area. This area, which may be termed the 'active or effective iron area', must be less than the gross or geometric cross-sectional area because of the laminated structure of the core and because the laminations used have some form of insulation coating. It therefore becomes necessary to include in eq. (6) a core space factor because the gross area has also been used in this equation.

For nickel-iron alloys, the oriented electrical steels and the cold-rolled non-oriented electrical steels, a space factor of 0·95 is attainable for material thicknesses 0·010 in. to 0·015 in. in wound cores, somewhat lower for built-up stacks of laminations.

In the practical current-transformer, regardless of the 'quality' of the magnetic alloy used in the core, maintenance of the induced flux requires the expenditure of exciting ampere-turns, $N_p I_e$.

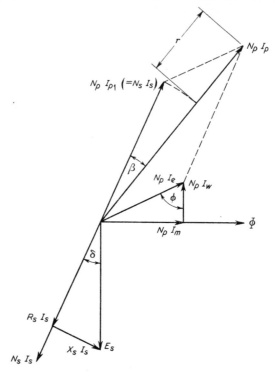

Fig. 2. Vector diagram of current-transformer with
overall lagging power factor secondary circuit.

These have two components, a quadrature or magnetising component, $N_p I_m$, and an in-phase or watt-loss component, $N_p I_w$, and
can be derived only from the available primary ampere-turns.

Thus the primary ampere-turns $N_p I_p$ must themselves now
be considered to be the vector sum of two components, (i) the
primary exciting ampere-turns, $N_p I_e$, and (ii) the primary *transforming* ampere-turns, $N_p I_{p1}$. It is only this latter component
which is transformed into secondary ampere-turns, or in other
words, it is only this component which is equal in magnitude to the
secondary ampere-turns and in precise phase opposition to them.

This is shown in Fig. 2 which is the vector diagram of a practical
current-transformer with an inductive burden and from which it
is seen that the necessity for these primary exciting ampere-turns
leads not only to the loss of equality between primary and secondary ampere-turns but also to a phase displacement between the
primary ampere-turns and the secondary ampere-turns.

Thus there is a *current error* or *ratio error*, r in Fig. 2, and a *phase error* or *phase difference*, the angle β in the same diagram. B.S.3938 uses the terms *current error* and *phase error*.

Resolving $N_p I_p$ parallel and perpendicular to $N_p I_{p1}$, then

$$N_p I_p \cos \beta = N_p I_{p1} + N_p I_m \sin \delta + N_p I_w \cos \delta \qquad (7)$$

and

$$N_p I_p \sin \beta = N_p I_m \cos \delta - N_p I_w \sin \delta \qquad (8)$$

Squaring and adding on both sides of these equations,

$$N_p^2 I_p^2 = N_p^2 I_{p1}^2 + 2N_p I_{p1}(N_p I_m \sin \delta + N_p I_w \cos \delta)$$
$$+ (N_p^2 I_m^2 + N_p^2 I_w^2)$$

dividing both sides by N_p^2, then

$$I_p^2 = I_{p1}^2 + 2I_{p1}(I_m \sin \delta + I_w \cos \delta) + (I_m^2 + I_w^2). \qquad (9)$$

Now, as $N_p I_{p1} = N_s I_s$ then

$$I_{p1} = \frac{N_s I_s}{N_p}.$$

N_s/N_p is called the *turns ratio* and is denoted by K_t, and substituting for I_{p1} in eq. (9)

$$I_p^2 = K_t^2 I_s^2 + 2K_t I_s(I_m \sin \delta + I_w \cos \delta) + (I_m^2 + I_w^2). \qquad (10)$$

I_p/I_s is the *actual current ratio*, denoted by K_c.

Dividing eq. (10) throughout by I_s^2

$$K_c^2 = K_t^2 + \frac{2K_t}{I_s}(I_m \sin \delta + I_w \cos \delta) + \frac{1}{I_s^2}(I_m^2 + I_w^2)$$

thus

$$K_c^2 = K_t^2 \left[1 + \frac{2}{K_t I_s}(I_m \sin \delta + I_w \cos \delta) + \frac{1}{K_t^2 I_s^2}(I_m^2 + I_w^2) \right] (11)$$

Now $I_m^2 + I_w^2 (= I_e^2)$ is small compared with $K_t^2 I_s^2$ and the root of the expression in the square brackets may be taken as

$$1 + \frac{I_m \sin \delta + I_w \cos \delta}{K_t I_s}$$

so that eq. (11) may be rewritten as

$$K_c^2 = K_t^2 \left(1 + \frac{I_m \sin \delta + I_w \cos \delta}{K_t I_s} \right)^2$$

and so,

$$K_c = K_t\left(1 + \frac{I_m \sin \delta + I_w \cos \delta}{K_t I_s}\right)$$

or,

$$K_c = K_t + \frac{I_m \sin \delta + I_w \cos \delta}{I_s}. \tag{12}$$

For the moment there is no need for further comment on this equation except to point out that $(I_m \sin \delta + I_w \cos \delta)$ when multiplied by N_p is substantially equal to r in Fig. 2.

Similarly, from eqs. (7) and (8),

$$\tan \beta = \frac{N_p I_m \cos \delta - N_p I_w \sin \delta}{N_p I_{p1} + N_p I_m \sin \delta + N_p I_w \cos \delta} \tag{13}$$

and this can be simplified, while maintaining ample practical accuracy, to

$$\tan \beta = \frac{N_p I_m \cos \delta - N_p I_w \sin \delta}{N_p I_{p1}}.$$

As the angle β is small, the phase error β is therefore given by

$$\beta = \frac{I_m \cos \delta - I_w \sin \delta}{I_{p1}} \text{ radians.} \tag{14}$$

At this point it must be emphasised that in eqs. (12) and (14) I_m and I_w are in 'primary amperes', that is, are referred to the primary side. These two equations may be considered to be the basic operational equations for a current-transformer but a further factor must be introduced into the ratio error equation, eq. (12), in order to obtain its final form. As it stands it gives the relationship between the turns ratio, K_t and the ratio of the actual currents, primary and secondary, K_c. Obviously *both* these actual current values cannot be equal to the *nominal or rated* values so it becomes necessary to introduce the *nominal ratio*

If

and

then

I_{pn} = nominal primary current

I_{sn} = nominal secondary current,

K_n = nominal current ratio = I_{pn}/I_{sn}.

The current or ratio error is often given in the form of a *percentage ratio error* (hereafter '% R.E.', for the sake of brevity), and in the relevant B.S. specification, B.S.3938, is expressed by

$$\% \text{ R.E. at } I_p = \left(\frac{K_n I_s - I_p}{I_p} \right) 100\%. \tag{15}$$

I_p and I_s, as before, are the actual primary and secondary currents respectively.

The National Physical Laboratory and others use an alternative method of giving the ratio error, employing a *ratio correction factor*, which is defined as the actual current ratio divided by the nominal current ratio.

Thus

$$\text{R.C.F.} = \frac{K_c}{K_n}$$

so that

$$\% \text{ R.E.} = 100 \left(\frac{1}{\text{R.C.F.}} - 1 \right) \%$$

or

$$\text{R.C.F.} = \frac{100}{\% \text{R.E.} + 100}$$

since from eq. (15)

$$\% \text{ R.E. at } I_p = \left(\frac{K_n - K_c}{K_c} \right) 100\%. \tag{16}$$

Now, substituting for K_c (from eq. (12)) in the numerator of the right-hand side of eq. (16)

$$\% \text{ R.E. at } I_p = \left[\frac{K_n - K_t - (\{I_m \sin \delta + I_m \cos \delta\}/I_s)}{K_c} \right] 100\%$$

multiplying top and bottom by I_s and rearranging

$$\% \text{ R.E. at } I_p = -100 \left(\frac{I_m \sin \delta + I_w \cos \delta}{K_c I_s} \right) + 100 \left(\frac{K_n - K_t}{K_c} \right) \%$$

$$= -100 \left(\frac{I_m \sin \delta + I_w \cos \delta}{I_p} \right) + 100 \left(\frac{K_n - K_t}{K_c} \right) \%. \tag{17}$$

Equation (17) is, therefore, the final form of the equation for $\% \text{R.E.}$ and is the basis, as will be seen later, of the design equations normally used. It will be noted that the second term,

$$100\left(\frac{K_n-K_t}{K_c}\right)\%,$$

is independent of the 'quality' of the core material and the operating flux density, and is known as the 'turns correction'.

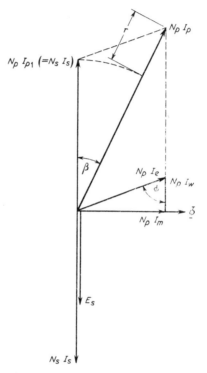

Fig. 3. Vector diagram of current-transformer with overall unity power factor secondary circuit.

If the turns ratio, K_t, is deliberately made equal to the nominal ratio, K_n, as it often is in practice, the %R.E. is then given by

$$\%\text{R.E. at } I_p = -100\left(\frac{I_m\sin\delta+I_w\cos\delta}{I_p}\right)\%. \tag{18}$$

Therefore, with an overall unity power factor or lagging power factor in the secondary circuit and $K_t = K_n$, the %R.E. is *always* negative in sign, or put another way, the actual secondary current is always less than its corresponding nominal value.

If K_t is not made equal to K_n, but slightly less, by applying the previously mentioned turns correction, the %R.E. becomes less negative by a constant amount over the whole working range of the current-transformer. Provided the amount of turns correction adopted is not large, the phase errors are not affected.

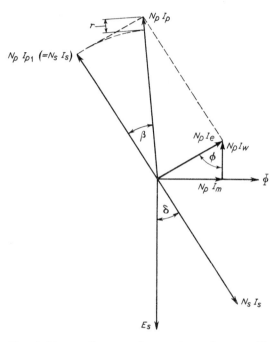

Fig. 4. Vector diagram of current-transformer with overall leading power factor secondary circuit.

When the overall secondary circuit power factor is unity, the %R.E. becomes

$$\%\text{R.E.}_{\text{u.p.f.}} \text{ at } I_p = -100\frac{I_w}{I_p}\% \qquad (19)$$

and the phase error, β, under the same condition, is given by

$$\beta_{\text{u.p.f.}} = \frac{I_m}{I_{p1}} \text{ radians.} \qquad (20)$$

The vector diagram for this condition is given in Fig. 3.

By convention, the phase error is said to be positive when the actual secondary current reversed leads the actual primary current. Thus, with an overall lagging power factor in the secondary circuit, when the secondary power factor angle δ is less than the angle between I_e and I_w, ϕ in Fig. 2, the phase error will be positive, but if it is greater the phase error becomes negative. The angle ϕ is a characteristic of the core material and varies with the flux density, but this will be discussed in greater detail later. Of course, when the overall secondary power factor is unity, the phase error will always be positive in sign.

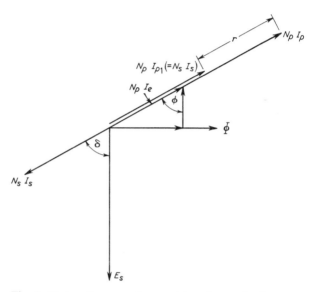

Fig. 5. Vector diagram of current-transformer having zero phase error but maximum ratio error.

Capacitive burdens are rarely met in practice but the vector diagram for such a case is given in Fig. 4 from which it is seen that the %R.E. may be positive or negative depending on the comparative values of $I_m \sin \delta$ and $I_w \cos \delta$ (if K_t equals K_n or not) but the phase error will always be positive.

There is one other very important operating condition to consider—if the secondary power factor angle δ equals the core material's characteristic angle, ϕ, the primary transforming ampere-turns, $N_p I_{p1}$, and the secondary ampere-turns, $N_s I_s$, are in direct anti-phase with each other, then while the phase error is zero in this condition the %R.E. is at its *maximum* value for that particular flux density and is given by

$$\%\text{R.E.}_\text{max.} \text{ at } I_p = -100\frac{I_e}{I_p}\%.\tag{21}$$

This condition is shown in Fig. 5.

One final point; the equations for phase error given in this chapter use radians as the unit. Many specifications, including B.S.3938, specify the phase error in minutes of arc—the conversion being 1 radian = 3438 minutes.

CHAPTER 3

MAGNETIC ALLOYS

It is not the intention in this present book to discuss the finer points of ferromagnetic theory*, a more general and practical approach being adopted. As some readers may not previously had cause to study magnetic materials in detail some brief historical notes have been included, but the main purpose of this chapter is to present the basic magnetic characteristic curves and other data of magnetic alloys commonly used in the manufacture of current-transformers. In chapter 4, on the other hand, the emphasis is on the presentation of magnetic characteristics in a more useful form, both from the designer's viewpoint and that of the user, as the curves given in that chapter immediately indicate how the errors vary with the flux density and so on.

There is one important point concerning terminology that must be mentioned. One school of thought contends that certain terms previously used in this book are incorrect, or, at the best, their usage is to be deprecated. It contends that what has been termed 'exciting current' should more properly be called 'magnetising current', and what has been termed here 'magnetising current' should, in fact, be called 'the quadrature component of the magnetising current'. Whilst sound arguments may be put forward in favour of this contention, the usage of the terms in question, as followed in this book, is so general amongst transformer engineers and others that there is ample justification in *not* changing them.

In the context of current-transformer design and operation it is, however, imperative that in studying characteristic curves of magnetic materials one is absolutely certain that the quantity concerned is the exciting current and not the magnetising current. This is because at the flux densities commonly encountered in current-transformer work the watt-loss and the magnetising currents are frequently of the same order so that there can be a substantial difference between the latter and the exciting current. Therefore incorrect identification of the quantity being read from

* See *Magnetic Alloys and Ferrites*, consulting editor M. G. Say (George Newnes, 1954).

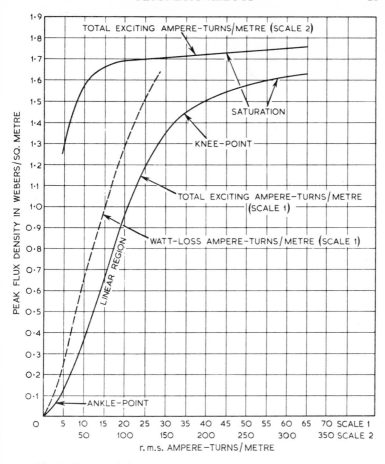

Fig. 6. Characteristic curves for a typical oriented electrical steel.

a characteristic curve could have a disastrous effect on one's calculations.

At high flux densities the watt-loss current becomes an insignificant part of the exciting current and there is no need to distinguish between the exciting current and the magnetising current. In practice, this applies above the knee-point for most alloys.

One other point—one frequently hears it commented that one magnetic alloy is 'better than another'. Such a comment is absolutely meaningless unless it is also stated which particular magnetic quality is the subject of the comparison. Therefore any comparison of magnetic alloys should be limited to a specific application and it must be appreciated that the superior alloy in one case may be inferior in another.

Figure 6 shows the excitation and watt-loss characteristic curves of a typical oriented electrical steel. It will be seen that the excitation curve may be subdivided into four main regions, (i) from the origin to the so-called ankle-point, (ii) from the ankle-point to the knee, often termed the linear region, (iii) the knee region itself, the 'knee-point' often being defined, as in B.S.3938, as where a 10% increase in flux density causes a 50% increase in exciting ampere-turns, and finally, (iv) the saturation region.

As a generalisation, a protective current-transformer may well operate over a working range of flux density extending from the ankle-point to the knee region or above, while the measuring current-transformer frequently has a working flux density in the region of the ankle-point only. There are exceptions to this, of course, and in many cases a measuring current-transformer, at its full-load primary current, may be operating not far below the knee-point. Obviously the designer attempts to use as high a flux density as possible because the higher it is the less core material is required but again generally, there is no advantage whatsoever going beyond the knee-point, which is somewhat higher than the flux density corresponding to the maximum permeability of the core material, as beyond this point the errors increase considerably with increase of primary current. In saturation, there will be little or no change in the secondary current with increased primary current, and so the current-transformer is said to 'lose ratio'.

Present-day magnetic alloys used in current transformers are conveniently subdivided into three main categories:

  (i) Hot-rolled silicon-iron alloys.
  (ii) Cold-rolled oriented silicon-iron alloys.
 (iii) Nickel-iron alloys.

Each of these alloy types will be discussed and, in addition, some notes will be given on the use of 'composite' cores, that is, cores consisting of two sections, one a nickel-iron, the other being one of the silicon-iron alloys. Usually the nickel-iron contribution is not greater that $33\frac{1}{3}\%$ of the total cross-sectional area of the core.

The silicon-iron alloys are frequently called 'electrical steels', mainly for the state of brevity, and this practice is followed here. The word 'steel' unfortunately infers the deliberate inclusion of carbon, whereas this element is most injurious in its effect on the magnetic properties of the alloys under discussion and during the manufacture of these, strenuous efforts are therefore made to exclude carbon. However, the use of the term 'electrical steel' in the present context is so widespread that it is felt no misunderstanding can arise from its continued use here.

(i) The hot-rolled electrical steels

The earliest electrical machines, including the early transformers, were produced with cores of a low carbon content mild steel which had one major disadvantage—that of 'ageing'. This is the term used to denote degradation of magnetic performance in service, caused by an increase in coercive force and hysteresis loss which in turn caused cumulative overheating and subsequent breakdown. At the turn of the present century Hadfield, Barrett and Brown did their work on the alloying of silicon with iron and it was found that the addition of silicon virtually eliminated the ageing problem, gave reduced hysteresis losses and increased the electrical resistivity (thereby giving a reduction in eddy-current losses also).

Unfortunately the addition of silicon has two serious drawbacks: as the percentage of silicon content increases it is found that there is some loss of permeability at the higher flux densities and loss of ductility; above about 5% silicon content the resulting alloy is very brittle and cannot be punched or sheared.

Thus the hot-rolled electrical steels available today vary from those having a low silicon content and therefore possessing good permeability at high flux densities, high ductility, but high losses, to those having a high silicon content and subsequently lower permeability, lower ductility, but also lower losses.

The low silicon content alloys are mainly used in rotating machines because parts of the magnetic circuit saturate and the often complex nature of rotor and stator laminations demands a high ductility. For this reason these are frequently termed the 'dynamo grades' while grades possessing higher percentages of silicon and therefore the lower losses are mainly used in transformers, including current-transformers, and these are therefore commonly termed 'transformer grades'.

Typical magnetic characteristic curves for one of these hot-rolled electrical steels are given in Fig. 7; the current-transformer designer requires information over the whole flux density range and generally prefers to have this information presented on double-logarithmic graph paper. This has been done in Fig. 7 which also indicates typical data concerning the angle between the exciting current and its watts-loss component (the core power factor angle) because, as shown previously, this angle can determine the algebraic sign of the phase error of the current-transformer. The choice of the horizontal axis for flux density is a deliberate one in order to facilitate later discussion and the development of error curves.

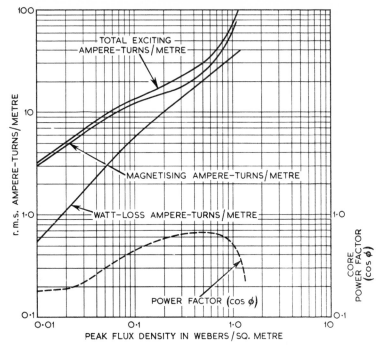

Fig. 7. Characteristics of a typical hot-rolled electrical steel 0·014 in. thickness. Frequency 50 c.p.s.

In current-transformer practice these hot-rolled electrical steels are used in a variety of forms: for ring-type current-transformers 'ring stampings' are commonly used although these can obviously be very wasteful of material, while for wound-primary type current-transformers the well-known 'T' and 'U', 'L', or 'E' and 'I' type laminations are used. In the latter type of current-transformer, it is common practice to make, when necessary, slight adjustment to the performance by removing or adding a small number of laminations. Similarly, in the case of a composite core, some adjustment of the errors may be made by the substitution of a small number of laminations in one of the alloys for some in the other alloy. Such adjustment is not possible in ring-type current-transformers where failure to meet the specified accuracy requirements means unwinding the whole secondary winding and remaking the current-transformer with a new core.

(ii) The oriented electrical steels

These oriented electrical steels, sometimes called 'anisotropic electrical steels', are correctly termed 'cold-rolled grain-oriented silicon-iron alloys' but, as previously explained, the terms used here is in such common usage that no misapprehension is caused.

The oriented electrical steels, as known today, are the result of an investigation started in the early 1930's to discover a means of manufacturing an electrical steel *in coil form* on a reversing cold mill. Limitations of the mill used and the brittleness of the material due to the silicon content of some 3% made annealing between passes essential and it was found that this series of cold reductions and intermediate annealings gave greatly improved magnetic properties in the rolling direction. Compared with the hot-rolled electrical steels it was found that the oriented electrical steels, in this rolling direction, gave not only reduced losses but also considerable increases in both permeability and the working flux density range. Thus, within the context of current-transformers and for those applications which demand an electrical steel rather than a nickel-iron alloy, these oriented electrical steels, from the purely technical aspect, are preferred to the hot-rolled electrical steels, because, with very few exceptions, the use of the former type leads to smaller cores and hence smaller current-transformers. This preference is particularly true where the core is a ring-type one and toroidal cores of oriented electrical steel have almost completely ousted ring stampings of hot-rolled electrical steel.

The improved magnetic properties of the oriented electrical steels are based on the following facts: the crystal lattice structure of a silicon-iron alloy is a body-centred cube and examination of the magnetic characteristics of a single crystal of such an alloy shows that its magnetic properties along a cube edge are superior to those across a cube face which, in turn, are better than those through a diagonal of the cube body. In the hot-rolled steels there is random orientation of the crystals in the sheet and hence there is little difference in the magnetic properties in the rolling direction compared with those across the sheet—the material is known as an isotropic one. With the oriented electrical steels, on the other hand, the cold-reduction process and intermediate annealing forces the individual crystals into a sensibly orderly array such that the easiest or 'preferred' direction of magnetisation of each crystal lies in approximately the same direction throughout the coil of material, this being the rolling direction.

Thus the magnetic properties of these anisotropic or oriented electrical steels, provided the magnetisation is in this preferred direction, are similar to those of a single silicon-iron crystal. Unfortunately the crystal lattice structure of the oriented electrical steels is such that only one easy direction of magnetisation lies in the plane of the strip, that is, parallel to the surface of the strip, as shown in Fig. 8. Thus a core of rectangles, 'T' and 'U' laminations, or 'E' and 'I' laminations, does not give the optimum properties of an oriented electrical steel; 'T' and 'U' laminations, as the worst offenders in this respect, therefore, are rarely, if ever, made from these electrical steels. From Fig. 8 the reason for this becomes plain—with the two other types of laminations the flux at the corners must pass through other than the preferred direction, while with 'T' and 'U' laminations there is a far greater part of the magnetic circuit where the flux direction is not the preferred one.

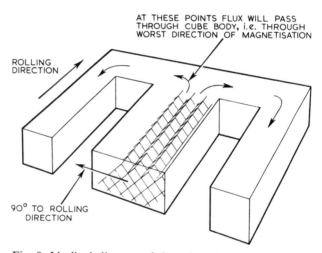

Fig. 8. Idealised diagram of the orientation of the crystal structure in the direction of rolling to show how its effect is nullified at the corners of 'E' laminations.

Figure 9 (a and b) shows comparative curves of a hot-rolled and an oriented electrical steel, and for the latter, curves are included for both preferred and non-preferred directions. It is particularly of interest to point out that the working saturation flux density is depressed in the non-preferred direction to a level no better than that obtained with the hot-rolled electrical steels.

Thus the only way in which the oriented electrical steel's magnetic properties can be fully realised is to use a strip-wound core and this form is used in the ring-type current-transformer, as opposed to the ring stampings adopted with the hot-rolled electrical steels. Although the oriented electrical steels are basically more expensive there is little or no wastage in the strip-wound core, whereas the material wastage in ring-stampings can, in some cases, make the hot-rolled electrical steel more expensive in terms of final core cost.

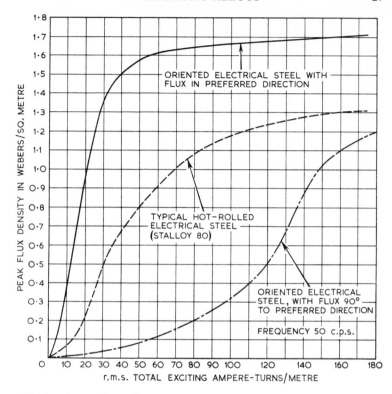

Fig. 9a. Comparison of exciting characteristics of oriented electrical steel with preferred and non-preferred flux direction. Note that worst direction is approximately 67° to preferred direction.

If 'E' and 'I' laminations of oriented electrical steel are used in a wound-primary current-transformer, instead of the more usual proportioning of such laminations in that the width of the yoke sections and the outer limbs is half that of the centre limb one can nullify, to some extent, the disadvantage of having flux in part of the magnetic circuit not in the preferred direction by increasing the yoke width. This action, of course, increases the total core weight and hence the cost. Some wound-primary current-transformers use the so-called simple construction—the core frequently being made up of 'L' laminations. In these cases oriented electrical steels are not recommended for the obvious reason that for only approximately one half of the magnetic circuit would the flux be in the preferred direction. If oriented electrical steels are to be used, such a core should be made up of plain rectangles.

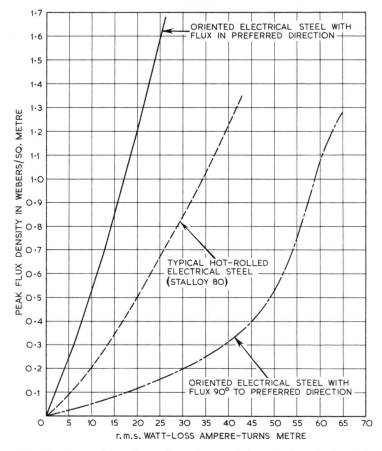

Fig. 9*b*. Comparison of watt-loss characteristics of oriented electrical steel with preferred and non-preferred flux direction.

The phosphate inter-lamina insulation used with oriented electrical steels is a very thin coating, and coupled with the very good surface finish of these steels, enables the designers to use higher stacking factors than with the hot-rolled electrical steels. Against this the oriented electrical steels are somewhat difficult to punch and are strain sensitive. Toroidal cores (ring cores) in the latter material are frequently bakelite-impregnated, resin-impregnated, edge-bonded, or resin-encapsulated, these processes being adopted to improve the mechanical rigidity of the cores for handling purposes and, in the case of the last named, to provide the current-transformer manufacturer with an already insulated core on to which he can immediately wind his secondary winding. Such processes, because of the strain sensitivity of the oriented electrical steels, inevitably cause some degradation of magnetic performance, that is, cause increased losses and decreased permeability, but by careful selection of the materials used and the manufacturing techniques that are employed this degradation has been kept down to such a low level that the final product still exhibits lower losses and higher permeabilities than similar-sized cores using 'E' and 'I' or similar laminations.

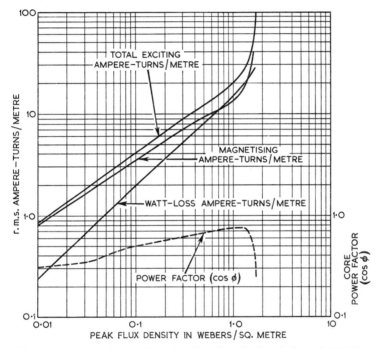

Fig. 10. Characteristics of grade 51 oriented electrical steel 0·014 in. thickness. Frequency 50 c.p.s.

A number of grades of oriented electrical steel are available in 0·013 in. material, while the thinner gauges, 0·004 in., 0·002 in. and 0·001 in. are not graded. The grading of the 0·014 in. material is done by selection, unlike that of the hot-rolled electrical steels which is caused by the deliberate changing of the silicon content.

Performance curves for one grade of 0·014 in. material are given in Fig. 10 and information is again given on the material's power factor angle.

Some wound-primary current-transformers using oriented electrical steel are now made with cut strip-wound cores—commonly called 'C-cores'. The initial processes employed in the manufacture of these C-cores are the same as for toroidal cores of the same material. Ribbon, gang-slit to the required width, is wound on a

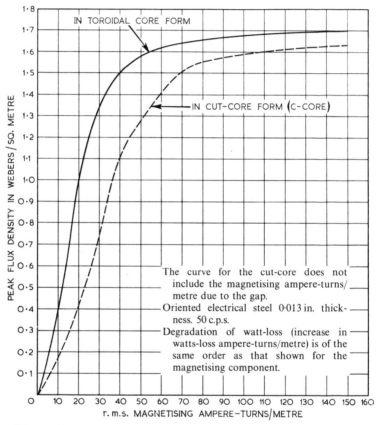

Fig. 11. Showing degradation of magnetic characteristic due to bonding and cutting.

mandrel to the correct radial depth or 'build-up' and the core is then stress-relief annealed. This annealing process is extremely important as all stresses caused by the gang-slitting and winding processes must be removed in order to attain the optimum magnetic properties of the oriented electrical steel. Toroidal cores are supplied in this state or undergo a finishing process as already described. The 'C-core', on the other hand, *must* be bonded with an epoxy resin prior to cutting. The bonding and cutting cause some degradation but again the techniques adopted minimise this degradation. After cutting, the core gap faces are lapped and the core then tested. A typical performance curve for C-cores is given in Fig. 11 and while the specific watts-loss is constant for a given core material at any particular flux density, the core permeability will depend on the core size, or, in other words, on the ratio of the gap length to the total mean length of the core. Figure 11 includes the material's magnetic characteristics so that the previously mentioned degradation may be gauged.

A particularly interesting application of cut strip-wound cores, sometimes C-cores having rectangular windows, other times cut toroids, is in the production of so-called 'split-core' current-transformers which are installed around existing bus-bars or cables thus eliminating possibly expensive dismantling of switchgear and the like.

One final note on the silicon-iron alloys—certain grades of the hot-rolled electrical steels are now available in a cold-reduced non-oriented version and in coil form, so that these may be supplied in the usual lamination types or in strip-wound cores, either toroids or C-cores. These non-oriented cold-reduced electrical steels have essentially the same magnetic characteristics as the equivalent hot-rolled grades but with marginally better permeabilities at the higher flux densities. They also possess better surface finish, enabling the designer to use higher space factors and, when used for laminations, give a longer tool life.

(iii) The nickel-iron alloys*

The early development of the magnetic nickel-iron alloys was due to the need for stable magnetic materials for use in the loading of submarine telegraph and telephone cables, it being essential that these materials, because of the low-energy levels encountered in this type of work, should possess both low electrical losses and high permeability, the latter so that high inductance levels could be attained. Obviously these desiderata apply equally to many other applications and today there is a wide range of magnetic nickel-iron alloys of differing characteristics in use in many fields outside that of submarine cables.

One of these alloys—Mumetal—has been widely used in the manufacture of current-transformers, particularly those for metering and high-accuracy applications. The adoption of Mumetal, in point of fact, enabled designers to readily attain accuracies previously almost impossible to attain commercially and made some

* Sowter, *Proc. J.E.E.*, **98** (1951), part II, p. 714.

techniques of error compensation virtually obsolete. This is particularly important when it is remembered that at the time Mumetal was introduced the only alternative materials were the hot-rolled electrical steels.

With the nickel-iron alloys there are two methods by which one may alter the magnetic properties, (i) by altering the alloy composition, or (ii) by modifying, for the same composition, the production technique such as the heat-treatment, or by annealing in a magnetic field or by heavy cold-rolling.

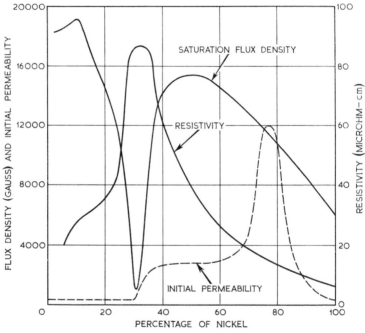

Fig. 12. Showing effect of nickel content on magnetic performance.

The choice of composition is not unlimited. It has been pointed out for the silicon-iron alloys that increase of the silicon content causes some decrease in the saturation flux density but the alloying of nickel with iron is far more complex as shown in Fig. 12 where it is seen that there is a small range of nickel content, around 30%, at which the resulting alloy is of little use magnetically. It is not the intention in this book to detail the complicated metallurgical problems encountered in the production of these nickel-iron alloys and the techniques used to overcome them, but certain basic points must be mentioned. The purity of the alloy constituents is of

Table 1. Table of nickel-iron alloys

Magnetic properties	Supermetal 100	Supermumetal 50	Mumetal 40	Mumetal	Super-Radiometal 50	Radiometal 50	Radiometal 36	Permendur
Initial permeability	100,000	50,000	50,000	40,000	10,000	3,500	3,000	1,000
Maximum permeability	250,000	200,000	120,000	100,000	100,000	30,000	20,000	7,000
Saturation ferric induction (Webers/sq.m.)	0·8	0·8	0·8	0·8	1·6	1·6	1·2	2·36
Remanence, B rem, from saturation (Webers/sq.m.)	0·5	0·5	0·47	0·47	1·1	1·0	0·5	1·5
Coercivity, Hc. (ampere-turns/metre)	0·056	0·08	0·20	0·32	0·32	1·2	1·6	16·0
Hysteresis loss at B sat. (erg/c.c./cycle)	9	13	23	38	400	1,000	1,000	12,700
Maximum energy product (gauss-oersteds) (B.H.) max.								
Curie point (°C)	390	390	390	390	500–550	500–550	280	980
Physical properties								
Coefficient of linear expansion (per °C)	13×10^{-6}	13×10^{-6}	13×10^{-6}	13×10^{-6}	10×10^{-6}	10×10^{-6}	$2·0 \times 10^{-6}$	9×10^{-6}
Resistivity (microhm-cm.)	60	60	62	62	40	45	80	47
Density (g./c.c.)	8·8	8·8	8·8	8·8	8·3	8·3	8·1	8·05
Density (lb./cu. in.)	0·318	0·318	0·318	0·318	0·300	0·300	0·293	0·291
Thermal conductivity (c.g.s. units)	0·08	0·08	0·08	0·08	0·03	0·03	0·02	—
Specific heat (cal/g./°C)	0·105	0·105	0·105	0·105	0·115	0·115	0·112	—

Approximate composition
Mumetal: 76Ni+4Mo+Cu+Fe+Mn.
Radiometal: 50Ni+50Fe.
Permendur: 49Fe+49Co+2Va.

Note: Permendur is frequently linked to the nickel-iron alloys, but actually this is a cobalt-iron alloy. *Telcon Metals Ltd.*

extreme importance and considerable pains are taken to remove impurities by such methods as slag reactions during melting which removes, to some extent, carbon, sulphur, phosphorous and oxygen. Further reduction of these impurities is obtained by melting in reduced or controlled atmospheres and by suitable heat-treatment during the rolling processes.

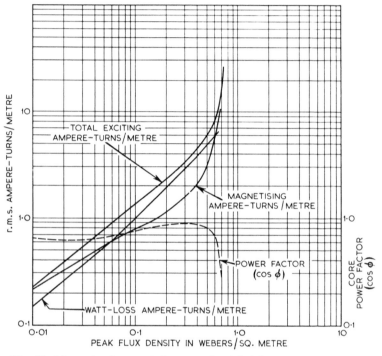

Fig. 13. Magnetic characteristic curves for 0·015 in. Mumetal. Frequency 50 c.p.s.

All these magnetic nickel-iron alloys must have some form of stress-relief annealing process in order to attain optimum magnetic properties and such annealing must be carried out after all mechanical operations have been completed. These include winding into a ring core, bending, forming, and stamping into laminations. The nickel-iron alloys are even more strain sensitive than the oriented electrical steels and when using nickel-iron cores of any type care must be exercised to see that minimum strains are put on the core by undue mechanical pressure and wherever possible the core should be protected against the ingress of impregnant or

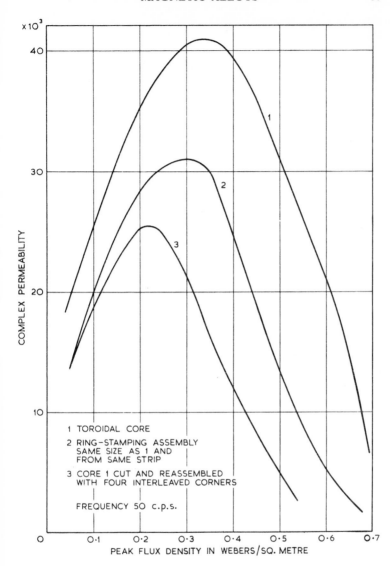

Fig. 14. Effect on permeability of 0·015 in. Mumetal of various types of core construction. (Note that the initial permeability of 1 indicated in this diagram does not coincide with that given in Table 1. This is due solely to improvements in values of initial permeability since the data upon which Fig. 14 are based were obtained.)

resin as failure to observe this rule will inevitably cause some degradation in magnetic properties.

Typical properties of the nickel-iron alloys are given in Table 1, but while Radiometal and Permendur (a cobalt-iron alloy) have been used in current-transformers the most commonly adopted nickel-iron alloy for this purpose is Mumetal and this is mainly used in toroidal core form, its magnetic characteristics being shown

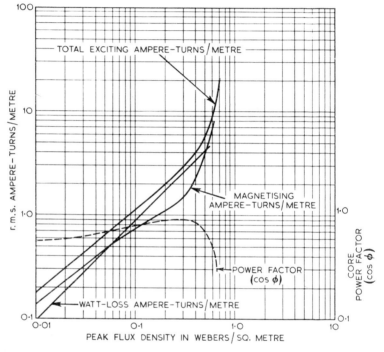

Fig. 15. Magnetic characteristics of 0·015 in. Mumetal 40. Frequency 50 c.p.s.

in Fig. 13. This type of core should be used whenever possible as the type of core construction plays a very important part in the attained levels of magnetic performance. Some indication of the degradation caused by other constructions is given in Fig. 14. Cut strip-wound cores (C-cores) are being manufactured from Mumetal and, as in the case of similar cores of oriented electrical steel, degradation of both permeability and watts-loss occurs due to the stress set up by the interlaminar bonding necessary before cutting. Figure 15 gives the characteristics for Mumetal 40 in spiral or toroidal core form, this material being a comparatively recent addition to the range of nickel-iron alloys and is particularly useful to the current-transformer designer because not only does it offer higher permeability and lower losses and hence lower errors compared with Mumetal, but also a reduction in the variation of these over the operating flux density range.* This is not the 'spread' or non-uniformity of magnetic properties encountered in all magnetic materials, but the difference between the permeability and watts-loss exhibited at the lower level of the operating flux density and those at the upper level, corresponding therefore to the variation of errors over the specified range of primary current, this variation being limited in the case of the metering accuracies. The improved performance of Mumetal 40 compared with those of Mumetal are indicative of what may be done by altering manufacturing processes but not the alloy composition— Mumetal 40 being vacuum melted and subjected to some additional heat-treatment.

A brief comparison between the characteristics of the electrical steels and those of Mumetal immediately shows the advantages of the latter. For a particular core weight and volume, the same number of primary ampere-turns and the same burden, the ratio and phase errors obtainable with a Mumetal core are very much lower than those obtained with any of the electrical steels, provided, of course, the flux density does not exceed the knee-point level of Mumetal. Alternatively, to obtain the same errors, the use of Mumetal leads to a much smaller core being required. The lower saturation flux density of Mumetal compared with that of the hot-rolled and the oriented electrical steels is often an advantage as it serves to give a much lower maximum secondary current when a primary fault current is flowing. On the other hand, there are many applications, particularly in protective circuits, where for a given primary current and amount of available space the most important requirement is the highest possible secondary voltage at saturation and the errors, are, themselves, of relatively minor importance. Other protective circuits depend not on the errors or exciting currents in a current-transformer but on the differences of these in two opposed current-transformers, and in both these cases one would use one of the electrical steels.

Mumetal is more expensive than the electrical steels and sometimes purely commercial considerations, apart from those of a technical nature, preclude its use. It is only these commercial aspects that limit the use of another of the alloys, Permendur, in current-transformer applications. This material has a higher satura-

* The latest nickel-iron alloy is Satmumetal, which has a higher saturation than either Mumetal or Mumetal 40.

tion flux density than the oriented electrical steels and but for its comparatively high cost would be the preferred material in many cases.

Thus it is necessary to stress the fact that while, as a general rule, protective and low-accuracy current-transformers employ the electrical steels and Mumetal is used for high accuracy and metering current-transformers, the final choice of the correct magnetic material is not always automatic or clear cut and one can only repeat the comment made earlier in this chapter that each particular application should be treated on its own merits.

Composite cores*

Within the context of current-transformers there is one important type of core that must be mentioned. This is the so-called 'composite core' which consists partly of a nickel-iron alloy (usually Mumetal) and partly of one of the electrical steels. The composite core technique enables the designer to obtain, very readily, magnetic characteristics lying between those of an all-Mumetal core and those of a core consisting solely of the appropriate electrical steel. Composite cores may have any of the mechanical forms of construction already mentioned; if of the toroidal core form the Mumetal portion may have the same inside and outside diameters as the electrical steel portion or alternatively the Mumetal portion is fitted inside the latter. Yet a third method is sometimes used when the Mumetal portion is sandwiched radially between the electrical steel which is therefore now in two separate toroidal cores.

When 'T and U', 'E and I' or 'L' laminations are adopted for the electrical steel it is usually the practice to employ plain rectangular ('I') laminations for the Mumetal thus avoiding expensive wastage of the material, almost inevitable if other lamination forms were used. The use of a built-up laminated core construction has some slight advantage when considering composite cores because the current-transformer errors may be modified, if it is found necessary, by the substitution of a small number of laminations in Mumetal for some in the electrical steel, or vice versa. Composite cores are employed mainly for metering classes of current-transformers when an all-Mumetal core would give a much higher accuracy than actually required and because of the cost difference between Mumetal and the electrical steels a composite core is the cheapest way to obtain the desired performance. There are no technical reasons why these cores may not be used in some protective applications and they are employed in these cases, particularly

* 'Composite Core Current Transformers', by Halacsy, *Electrical Times*, 11 October 1951.

in some earth leakage protective circuits in order to improve sensitivity.

The magnetic characteristic curves for a composite core may be obtained in two ways—by direct measurement in the usual manner of the watts-loss and magnetising current or by calculation from the magnetic characteristic curves of the two component alloys.

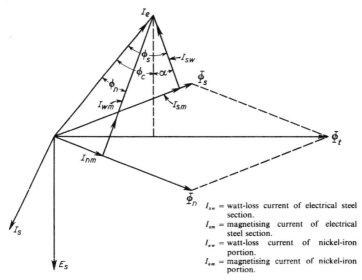

I_{sw} = watt-loss current of electrical steel section.

I_{sm} = magnetising current of electrical steel section.

I_{nw} = watt-loss current of nickel-iron portion.

I_{nm} = magnetising current of nickel-iron portion.

Fig. 16. Vector diagram for composite core.

The analysis of the magnetic circuit conditions in a composite core is a simple matter particularly when the mean magnetic paths of the component materials are equal. As the exciting current is unique and because the two materials will have different loss angles, the two corresponding flux components are not in phase and therefore the total flux in the core is the vector sum of these component fluxes as shown in Fig. 16.

Let I_e be the unique exciting current;

B_n = corresponding peak flux density of the nickel-iron alloy portion;

B_s = corresponding peak flux density of the electrical steel portion;

A_n = cross-sectional area of nickel-iron portion;

A_s = cross-sectional area of electrical steel portion.

Then the total flux Φ_t is given by the vectorial sum $(A_n B_n + A_s B_s)$; now $A_n B_n = \Phi_n$ and $A_s B_s = \Phi_s$ and if the total cross-sectional area is given by A_t the 'composite flux density', B_c, is given by

$$B_c = \frac{\Phi_t}{A_t} = \left[\frac{\Phi_n^2 + \Phi_s^2 + 2\Phi_n\Phi_s \cos(\phi_s - \phi_n)}{A_t} \right]^{\frac{1}{2}}. \qquad (22)$$

The composite loss angle ϕ_c is given by

$$\phi_c = \phi_s - \alpha,$$

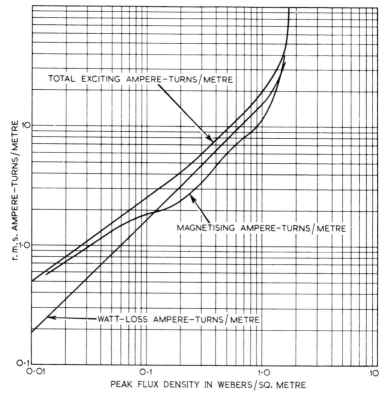

Fig. 17. Typical characteristics for a composite toroidal core consisting of $66\frac{2}{3}\%$ oriented electrical steel and $33\frac{1}{3}\%$ Mumetal.

where

$$\alpha = \sin^{-1}\frac{\Phi_n \sin(\phi_s - \phi_n)}{\Phi_t}. \qquad (23)$$

The 'composite' watt-loss ampere-turns/metre, NI_{cw}/metre, and the 'composite' magnetising ampere-turns/metre, NI_{cm}/metre, are then easily found from

$$NI_{cw}/\text{metre} = NI_e/\text{metre}.\cos\phi_c \qquad (24)$$

and

$$NI_{cm}/\text{metre} = NI_e/\text{metre}.\sin\phi_c. \qquad (25)$$

NI_{cw}/metre, NI_{cm}/metre and NI_e/metre plotted against the corresponding values of B_c then give the desired magnetic characteristic curves for the particular composite core in question and these may be universally applied provided the mean length of magnetic path of the nickel-iron component is the same as that of the electrical steel. For unequal magnetic path lengths a similar technique, but in a different form, must be used and the resultant characteristic curves are no longer universal but apply only to certain core configurations in respect of the precise method of subdivision of the total core cross-sectional area into the two component materials concerned.

Examples of the universally applicable characteristic curves for composite cores are given in Figs. 17 and 18 and these are used in exactly the same way as the curves of any 'single-material core' in one's design calculations. In practice, composite core curves are generally obtained by actual test rather than by calculation and particular care must be taken in both obtaining and using any composite core curves when the flux density in the nickel-iron portion passes its saturation level as considerable distortion of the exciting current waveform then occurs. The excitation characteristic curves of a composite core for the often-employed percentage contents of nickel-iron alloy—25% and $33\frac{1}{3}$%—show only relatively small decreases in the apparent saturation flux density compared with that of the electrical steel component material. This means the loss of the advantage of a lower saturation voltage of a similar-sized Mumetal core in limiting secondary currents under primary fault conditions—or in other words—it may be said that beyond the Mumetal saturation point the electrical steel 'takes over'.

Departure from sinusoidal waveform of the exciting current (and hence of the secondary current) once the Mumetal saturation flux density is exceeded also prevents the use of composite cores in those applications where the waveform of the secondary current materially affects the performance of the associated relay equipment such as in the preservation of the timing characteristics of certain relays at various over-current values, these time-current characteristics being considerably affected by waveform.

While only curves for 25% and $33\frac{1}{3}$% Mumetal content have

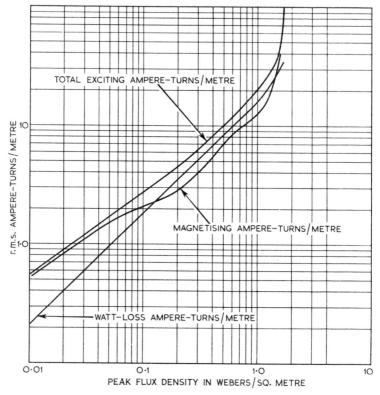

Fig. 18. Typical characteristics for a composite toroidal core consisting of 75% oriented electrical steel and 25% Mumetal.

been shown, much lower values are also used in practice and particularly when laminations are used a 10% Mumetal content is frequently encountered in these composite cores.

One advantage of composite cores not immediately apparent from the foregoing is that the use of such cores in metering current-transformers leads to lower variation in errors, an important consideration in these current-transformers. This is due to the 'straightening' of the magnetic characteristic curves as the concave part of the silicon steel component characteristic is filled by that of the convex portion of the Mumetal component.

Spread of characteristics and testing for exciting current

The current-transformer designer must have a detailed knowledge of the characteristics of the various magnetic alloys over the whole range of flux density—from very low inductions up to, and including, saturation. It is inevitable that all the alloys exhibit 'spread' or 'scatter' of characteristics, that is, exhibit non-uniformity to some degree and in the case of the electrical steels of which the bulk of the produced tonnage is sold and used on the basis of a guaranteed watts-loss at one flux density level only, he frequently has no realistic information on the permeability of the alloy. While everything is being done to alleviate this situation by the manufacturers of toroidal cores it has become standard practice with a number of current-transformer manufacturers to specify a grading system based on exciting current measurements at a number of flux density levels. Thus they purchase, for instance, toroids produced from Grade 51 oriented electrical steel but to be graded by means of these measurements of exciting current, typical flux density levels being 0·1, 0·6 and 1·5 webers/sq.metre.

It is really immaterial whether the cores are bought on such a basis or not, but some such selection of cores should be carried out prior to applying the current-transformer windings, particularly where the final characteristics of a number of current-transformers must 'match up' to each other to a close degree.

It is, of course, very important that when comparing excitation characteristics from different sources, due account is taken of the possible dissimilarity in the test-circuits and instruments used as these will considerably influence the results obtained.

A typical method of testing to obtain the excitation characteristic consists of either winding a small number of temporary turns on the core or using a suitably connected plug-and-socket arrangement or some other mechanical device to give the desired number of turns so that the exciting current is of convenient magnitude for the ammeter range, the ammeter reading r.m.s. values. The flux density in the core is determined by the measurement of the voltage appearing across a search-coil of a known number of turns on the core. It must be remembered that the peak flux density corresponds to the average value of the voltage and not to its r.m.s. value and for this reason the search-coil voltage is measured by means of a rectifier type voltmeter (reading average volts), through a voltage amplifier when necessary. Simultaneous measurement of this voltage by means of a r.m.s. voltmeter gives the form factor as this is the ratio of r.m.s. to average voltage.

In order to maintain as near a sinusoidal voltage waveform as possible a resistance can be placed across the exciting winding of such a value that it takes approximately 10 to 15 times the actual exciting current, but if this resistance is a variable one then the form factor may be altered at will. By this means one may obtain a very accurate measurement of exciting current corresponding to sine-wave conditions using the following method: The r.m.s. exciting current is measured at two different form factors but at the same average voltage across the search-coil; then, if the form factors are F_1 and F_2, and the corresponding exciting currents are I_1 and I_2, the desired value of exciting current with sine-wave voltage is given by I_e where

$$I_e = I_2 - \frac{I_2 - I_1}{F_2 - F_1}(F_2 - 1\cdot 11).$$

One is able to use this method because there is a substantially linear relationship between r.m.s. exciting current and the form factor of the voltage waveform, the higher the form factor the higher the r.m.s. exciting current.

Similar care must be taken when measuring iron-losses which are, like the exciting current, influenced by the waveform of the test voltage. While peaked voltage waveforms (that is, form factors greater than 1·11) give pessimistically high exciting currents this is not true of the watts-loss and thus it becomes of even greater importance to preserve a sine-wave voltage or be able to reduce the test results to a sine-wave basis when measuring watts-loss than when measuring the exciting current.

The hysteresis loss is a function of the maximum flux density in the core and is independent of the flux wave shape so that provided the test voltage as measured by an average-reading voltmeter is the same as the average value of the desired sine-wave voltage the hysteresis loss will be the correct one, corresponding to sine-wave conditions.

The eddy-current loss varies with the square of the r.m.s. value of the excitation voltage, but is also substantially independent of the voltage wave-shape. However, when the correct average value of the voltage is held and as measured by the average-reading voltmeter, the actual r.m.s. value of this voltage may not be the correct value due to non-sinusoidal conditions and thus some correction will have to be applied to this component of the total iron loss.

Thus if there is waveform distortion in the voltage the total loss P is found from the following equation:

$$P = \frac{P_m}{P_h + KP_e}\ \text{watts},$$

where P = total sine-wave excitation loss at rated voltage;
$\quad\ P_m$ = measured loss with average reading voltmeter at correct value;
$\quad\ P_h$ = hysteresis loss;

P_e = eddy-current loss;
$K = (E_m/E)^2$;
where E_m = test voltage (r.m.s.) as measured during test;
E = rated voltage (r.m.s.) corresponding to required flux density.

As discussed elsewhere separation of total loss into hysteresis and eddy-current losses presents certain problems and for this reason strenuous efforts should be made to ensure sinusoidal conditions of test, obviating the need for a further separation test.

These brief notes on magnetic materials have been limited to discussion on those which are currently in use. Improvements in the nickel-iron alloys and the electrical steels are being made continually, and one is always hearing of new types of core construction, but this chapter indicates the main types of core at present being used and the present characteristics of the magnetic alloys which are commercially available.

It is a temptation to discuss interesting developments such as the double oriented and magnetostriction-free electrical steels, but as these are not yet in ready supply there seems to be no necessity to discuss these here. Similarly, some particularly interesting core constructions have been developed, particularly for the oriented electrical steels, but patents frequently preclude their general adoption so that there seems to be no immediate practical reason why they should be detailed here.

CHAPTER 4

DERIVATION OF DESIGN FORMULAE AND CURVES

The main difference between the measuring current-transformer and the protective current-transformer is that while in both types the primary winding must be able to withstand the thermal and dynamic stresses associated with a primary system fault current possibly many times the current-transformer's rated full-load value, in the measuring current-transformer the specified accuracy of transformation must be maintained only for a limited range of the primary current—in B.S.81 this was from 10% to 120% of its rated value but in B.S.3938 this becomes 5% to 125%. With protective current-transformers, on the other hand, reasonable accuracy must be maintained over a much wider range, sometimes up to twenty times full-load primary current, or even higher. There are other differences which will become apparent later and this chapter is generally limited to showing the derivation of design formulae and curves specifically for measuring current-transformers although they are also applicable, under certain operational conditions, to protective current-transformers.

For measuring current-transformers, the accuracy of transformation is specified by the adoption of 'Classes of Accuracy' and Table 2 reproduces those given in B.S.3938, from which it is seen that each class of accuracy is defined by placing a maximum permissible value on the % R.E. and on the phase error at each of several percentages of the *nominal or rated* primary current. For class D, only the % R.E. is limited in this manner, there being no stipulation regarding the phase error. For the so-called 'metering classes' (that is, classes AM, BM and CM) there is, however, a further limitation placed on the *variation* of both the % R.E. and phase error over the specified range of primary current.

Now, because the errors are specified at various percentages of the *nominal* primary current the designer is theoretically barred from the direct use of eqs. (14) and (17) in chapter 2 for the predetermination of those errors. He has to determine I_m and I_w, the

Table 2. *Accuracy classes in B.S.3938*

Class	Absolute errors								Variation in error	
	From 125% to 20% of rated current		From 125% to 10% of rated current		Below 20% and to 10% of rated current		Below 10% and to 5% of rated current		From 125% to 5% rated current	
	Current error (per cent + or −)	Phase error (minutes + or −)	Current error (per cent + or −)	Phase error (minutes + or −)	Current error (per cent + or −)	Phase error (minutes + or −)	Current error (per cent + or −)	Phase error (minutes + or −)	Current error (per cent)	Phase error (minutes)
AL	—	—	0·1	5	—	—	0·2	10	—	—
AM	—	—	0·5	30	—	—	0·75	40	0·5	20
BM	—	—	1·0	40	—	—	1·5	60	1·0	30
CM	—	—	1·5	120	—	—	2·0	150	1·5	75
C	1·0	120	—	—	2·0	180	—	—	—	—
D	5·0	—	—	—	—	—	—	—	—	—

magnetising and watt-loss currents respectively, but before he can do this he must first calculate the flux density, B_m, and he is therefore forced to work from the secondary side.

Let it be assumed that he has already chosen the core dimensions, the number of secondary turns and the secondary winding conductor. He is immediately able to calculate the secondary winding resistance so that knowing the burden details he is able to obtain the total impedance of the secondary circuit, Z_s, and its power factor. For the present it has been assumed that the secondary winding leakage reactance and capacitance are negligible.

The designer now assumes a value of *actual* secondary current, I_s, and the obvious choice is to take its nominal value and calculate the secondary induced e.m.f. and hence the peak flux density, B_m. This enables him to obtain I_m and I_w, in some form or other, from the magnetisation and watt-loss characteristics of the core material being used. Knowing the turns ratio, K_t, eq. (12) in chapter 2 supplies him with the actual current ratio, K_c, and, finally, substitution in eq. (17) in the same chapter gives him the % R.E. at some primary current I_p. Unfortunately this I_p equals $K_c I_s$ and not $K_n I_s$, or, in other words, as he took the nominal secondary current for his calculations this I_p will not be the corresponding nominal primary current. As the errors are specified at the nominal primary current and percentages of this, a completely rigorous method entails repeating the foregoing process for various percentages of the nominal secondary current and plotting the resulting calculated % R.E. against the calculated actual primary current, I_p. Then, to determine compliance with the requirements of the specified class of accuracy this curve would have to be interpolated for the specified percentages of the *nominal* primary current. (The phase error is more straight forward.)

This rigorous method is not used in actual practice, a far easier approach being adopted by using a simple modification to the equations concerned. Whilst the resulting equations are fundamentally incorrect their departure from the academic equations has such little practical significance that they offer a very realistic method of predetermining current-transformer errors.

The design method is as previously described except that the turns ratio is initially made equal to the nominal current ratio, that is, $K_n = K_t$. Using I_{pn} and I_{sn} now as the *full-load* nominal primary and secondary currents respectively, and letting x be the fraction of full-load being considered, then

$$E_s = xI_{sn}Z_s = 4{\cdot}44fB_m sAN_s \text{ volts}, \qquad (26)$$

from which B_m is calculated. As before, I_m and I_w are then obtained from the magnetic characteristic curves of the core material being used and the errors *immediately* calculated from the following equations:

$$\%\text{R.E. at } xI_{pn} = -100\left(\frac{I_m \sin \delta + I_w \cos \delta}{xI_{pn}}\right)\% \qquad (27)$$

and

$$\text{phase error at } xI_{pn} = 3438\left(\frac{I_m \cos \delta - I_w \sin \delta}{xI_{pn}}\right)\text{minutes.} \qquad (28)$$

This is done for sufficient values of x to prove compliance with the accuracy class requirements. Equations (27) and (28) are fundamentally incorrect, as already mentioned, because I_m and I_w have been based on a flux density calculated for the various percentages of the nominal secondary current so that eq. (27), for instance, ignores the presence of the very quantity it is being used to calculate, namely the ratio error. This departure from the academically correct equations, as a percentage, is of the same order as the %R.E. itself, so that compared with the associated practical uncertainties such as variation from the estimated value of the secondary winding resistance and of the effective core area, and again, the 'spread' of the magnetic characteristics of the core material, no great inaccuracy is caused by the use of eqs. (27) and (28), particularly for the small errors specified for the metering and indicating accuracies in B.S.3938.

In eqs. (27) and (28) I_m and I_w are in primary amperes—some designers prefer to use I_m and I_w referred to the secondary side, these equations then becoming

$$\%\text{R.E. at } xI_{pn} = -100\left(\frac{I_m \sin \delta + I_w \cos \delta}{xI_{sn}}\right)\%; \qquad (29)$$

$$\text{phase error at } xI_{pn} = 3438\left(\frac{I_m \cos \delta - I_w \sin \delta}{xI_{sn}}\right)\text{minutes.} \qquad (30)$$

Similar simplification is carried out on the error equations for an overall secondary circuit power factor of unity and for this condition

$$\%\text{R.E.}_{\text{u.p.f.}} \text{ at } xI_{pn} = \frac{-100 I_w}{xI_{sn}}\% \qquad (31)$$

and

$$\text{phase error}_{\text{u.p.f.}} \text{ at } xI_{pn} = \frac{3438 I_m}{xI_{sn}} \text{ minutes.} \qquad (32)$$

For the condition of maximum %R.E.,

$$\%\text{R.E.}_{\text{max.}} \text{ at } xI_{pn} = \frac{-100I_e}{xI_{sn}}\%; \qquad (33)$$

I_m, I_w and I_e now in secondary amperes in eqs. (29) to (33).

If the designer decides to modify the %R.E. by using turns correction he uses a simplified version of the relevant term previously given in eq. (17) in chapter 2; the percentage turns correction instead of being

$$100\left(\frac{K_n - K_t}{K_c}\right)\%$$

is now calculated from

$$100\left(\frac{K_n - K_t}{K_n}\right)\%.$$

The *general* equation for %R.E. is, therefore,

$$\%\text{R.E. at } xI_{pn} = -100\left(\frac{I_m \sin \delta + I_w \cos \delta}{xI_{sn}}\right) + 100\left(\frac{K_n - K_t}{K_n}\right)\%. \quad (34)$$

It has now been shown that the performance of a current-transformer, in terms of its ratio and phase errors, is ultimately determined by the magnetising and watt-loss ampere-turns required to maintain the excitation of the core. These are, in their turn, determined by the core material chosen, the type of core construction and the operating flux density, the last named being dependent on the burden and secondary winding impedances, the power factor of the secondary circuit, the core dimensions, the number of secondary turns and the supply frequency.

This multiplicity of factors, some of which are interdependent to some degree or other, coupled with the non-linear nature of the magnetisation and watt-loss characteristics of the core material, often leads to a certain amount of confusion in the mind of the newcomer to current-transformers, particularly on the question of the relative importance of any of these factors compared with the others.

Various attempts have been made to overcome this difficulty, one method being to approximate the core magnetisation and watt-loss characteristics to mathematical functions and to then use these in any design analysis.*

* 'Instrument Transformers', by Hobson, *J.I.E.E.*, **91** (1944), part II, p. 182; also 'The Predetermination of Current Transformer Errors', by Freeman, *J.I.E.E.*, **91** (1944), part II, p. 190.

From the previous chapter it has been seen that these magnetic characteristics, when plotted on double logarithmic graph paper, approximate reasonably closely to straight lines, at least over a limited range of flux density. Therefore one may write

$$NI_w/\text{metre} = KB_m{}^a \tag{35}$$

and

$$NI_m/\text{metre} = K_1 B_m{}^b. \tag{36}$$

This method of approximation applies to most magnetic materials, the constants K, K_1, a and b having different values for different materials.

It must be remembered that the characteristic curves, and in particular the magnetisation curve, are only *universally* applicable if the core construction is such that there are no interleaved corners or butt joints in the magnetic circuit so that any formulae finally derived from eqs. (35) and (36) suffer the same limitation.

Let it be assumed that the core meets this requirement and furthermore that the secondary winding leakage reactance and capacitance are negligible. Thus with the unity power factor burdens specified for the metering and indicating accuracies in B.S. 3938 the overall power factor of the secondary circuit is also unity and the error equations (31) and (32) apply.

Now, I_w is given, in secondary amperes, by

$$\left(\frac{NI_w/\text{metre}}{N_s}\right)l,$$

where l is the mean magnetic length of the magnetic circuit in metres:

Substitution for I_w in eq. (31) gives

$$\%\text{R.E.}_{\text{u.p.f.}} \text{ at } xI_{pn} = -100\left(\frac{NI_w/\text{metre}}{xN_s I_{sn}}\right)l\%$$

and as $NI_w/\text{metre} = KB_m{}^a$

$$\%\text{R.E.}_{\text{u.p.f.}} \text{ at } xI_{pn} = -100\frac{KB_m{}^a l}{xN_s I_{sn}}. \tag{37}$$

From eq. (26)

$$B_m = \frac{xZ_s I_{sn}}{4\cdot44 fs A N_s} \text{ webers/sq. metre.} \tag{38}$$

Combining eqs. (37) and (38) one then obtains

$$\%\text{R.E.}_{\text{u.p.f.}} \text{ at } xI_{pn} = \left[\frac{-100K}{(4\cdot44fs)^a}\right]\left[\frac{x^{a-1}I_{sn}^{a-1}Z_s^a l}{A^a N_s^{a+1}}\right]\%. \quad (39)$$

Similarly, it can be shown that the phase error is given by

$$\text{phase error}_{\text{u.p.f.}} \text{ at } xI_{pn} = \left[\frac{3438K_1}{(4\cdot44fs)^b}\right]\left[\frac{x^{b-1}I_{sn}^{b-1}Z_s^b l}{A^b N_s^{b+1}}\right] \text{ minutes.} \quad (40)$$

For any given core material, once the constants K, K_1, a and b have been determined, eqs. (39) and (40) may be used for design work. However, they are of more use in proportional form for comparison purposes.

Thus for any given frequency (applicable also to the original characteristic curves), a particular value of both core space factor and nominal secondary current, one may write

$$\%\text{R.E.}_{\text{u.p.f.}} \propto \frac{x^{a-1}Z_s^a l}{A^a N_s^{a+1}} \quad (41)$$

and

$$\text{phase error}_{\text{u.p.f.}} \propto \frac{x^{b-1}Z_s^b l}{A^b N_s^{b+1}}. \quad (42)$$

These proportionality expressions are of considerable assistance to the designer in obtaining, fairly rapidly, some indication of the change in errors he may expect if one or more of the factors influencing those errors are changed. Unfortunately, the value of these expressions is limited, not only by the incomplete flux density range for which the approximate mathematical functions hold good, but also by the fact that some of the factors are interdependent. For instance, change of core cross-sectional area A, will affect the secondary winding resistance and hence the total secondary impedance; change of area may also influence the mean length of the magnetic circuit, l, and so on. Nevertheless, even with these limitations, the equations prove useful to the designer and may be shown quite readily in graphical form.

Similar proportionality expressions may be developed for other than unity power factor conditions, the first step in the case of the ratio error being to plot from the two basic magnetic characteristic curves a third curve of

$$[(NI_m/\text{metre}) \sin \delta + (NI_w/\text{metre}) \cos \delta]$$

against flux density, $\cos \delta$ being the secondary circuit power factor under consideration. For the phase error one first plots the graph of the expression

$$[(NI_m/\text{metre}) \cos \delta - (NI_w/\text{metre}) \sin \delta]$$

against flux density. Having obtained these two new curves the procedure is exactly as before.

There are, obviously, many variations on this theme—one, in particular, is worth mentioning: For toroidal cores, if D_o is the outside diameter, D_i is the inside diameter and the diameter ratio, D_o/D_i is given by d, then the mean length of the magnetic circuit, l, is given by

$$l = \tfrac{1}{2}\pi(D_o + D_i)$$
$$= \tfrac{1}{2}\pi D_i(d + 1)$$

also

$$A = \tfrac{1}{2}sW(D_o - D_i)$$
$$= \tfrac{1}{2}sW D_i(d - 1),$$

where s = core space factor and W = axial length of core.

Substitution for l and A in eq. (41) then gives

$$\%\text{R.E.}_{\text{u.p.f.}} \propto \frac{x^{a-1} Z_s{}^a(d+1)}{W^a D_i{}^{a-1}(d-1)^a N_s{}^{a+1}},$$

so that for particular values of x, Z_s, N_s and W

$$\%\text{R.E.}_{\text{u.p.f.}} \propto \frac{(d+1)}{D_i{}^{a-1}(d-1)^a}.$$

As, for any one comparative exercise, the inside diameter, D_i will also be constant, then finally

$$\%\text{R.E.}_{\text{u.p.f.}} \propto \frac{(d+1)}{(d-1)^a}. \tag{43}$$

Similarly,

$$\text{phase error}_{\text{u.p.f.}} \propto \frac{(d+1)}{(d-1)^b}. \tag{44}$$

These expressions obviously give the change of errors with increase in outside diameter because the inside diameter is held constant. The important point is that the advantage gained in the reduction of errors by increase of the diameter ratio (and hence of the outside diameter) must be carefully compared against the resultant increase in weight and cost of the larger core, remembering that weight is proportional to $(d^2 - 1)$, provided that again the inside diameter is kept constant.

Another approach leading to very useful design curves, but again limited to cores having no interleaved corners or butt joints, is as follows:

From eq. (26)

$$xI_{sn} = \frac{4 \cdot 44 f B_m s A N_s}{Z_s} \text{ amperes}$$

and, as

$$I_w = \frac{(NI_w/\text{metre})l}{N_s} \text{ amperes,}$$

$$I_m = \frac{(NI_m/\text{metre})l}{N_s} \text{ amperes}$$

then, taking the unity power factor condition first, substitution for these in the error equations (31) and (32) give

$$\%\text{R.E.}_{\text{u.p.f.}} \text{ at } xI_{pn} = \left(\frac{-100}{4 \cdot 44 fs}\right)\left(\frac{lZ_s}{AN_s^2}\right)\left(\frac{NI_w/\text{metre}}{B_m}\right)\% \quad (45)$$

and

$$\text{phase error}_{\text{u.p.f.}} \text{ at } xI_{pn} = \left(\frac{3438}{4 \cdot 44 fs}\right)\left(\frac{lZ_s}{AN_s^2}\right)\left(\frac{NI_m/\text{metre}}{B_m}\right)\text{minutes.} \quad (46)$$

Similarly, for the condition of maximum ratio error, from eq. (33),

$$\%\text{R.E.}_{\text{max.}} \text{ at } xI_{pn} = \left(\frac{-100}{4 \cdot 44 fs}\right)\left(\frac{lZ_s}{AN_s^2}\right)\left(\frac{NI_e/\text{metre}}{B_m}\right)\%. \quad (47)$$

Consideration of these three equations shows that the first term in each will be a constant as the magnetisation and watt-loss characteristic curves which are the source of these equations are applicable to only one particular frequency and the core space factor, s, will also be constant.

The second term lZ_s/AN_s^2 is common to all three equations and consists solely of design parameters. The third term in each of these equations is obtained immediately from the relevant basic characteristic curve. Thus it is an easy matter to produce *error curves* from the original curves in the following manner:

The functions

$$\left(\frac{NI_w/\text{metre}}{B_m}\right), \quad \left(\frac{NI_m/\text{metre}}{B_m}\right) \quad \text{and} \quad \left(\frac{NI_e/\text{metre}}{B_m}\right)$$

are calculated from the original curves and plotted on a base of the flux density, B_m. The vertical scale, multiplied by the appropriate factor

$$\left(\frac{-100}{4\cdot44\,fs}\right)\left(\frac{lZ_s}{AN_s{}^2}\right)$$

for the %R.E. curve, and

$$\left(\frac{3438}{4\cdot44\,fs}\right)\left(\frac{lZ_s}{AN_s{}^2}\right)$$

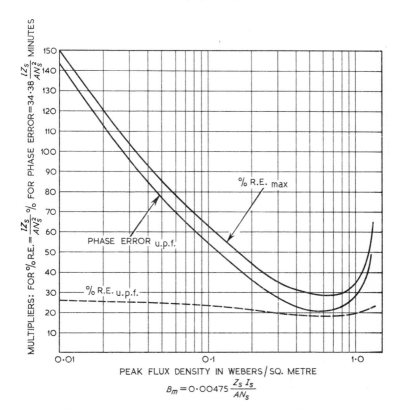

Fig. 19. Error curves for a hot-rolled electrical steel 0·014 in. thickness. Frequency 50 c.p.s. Material in ring-stampings.

for the phase error curve, immediately give the errors. The constants of these 'multipliers' can, of course, be taken into account when first plotting the error curves so that the multipliers become, quite simply

$$\left(\frac{lZ_s}{AN_s^2}\right) \quad \text{and} \quad 34{\cdot}38\left(\frac{lZ_s}{AN_s^2}\right),$$

respectively. Notice particularly the change to 34·38 enabling one to use a common scale for both ratio and phase errors, as in the diagrams.

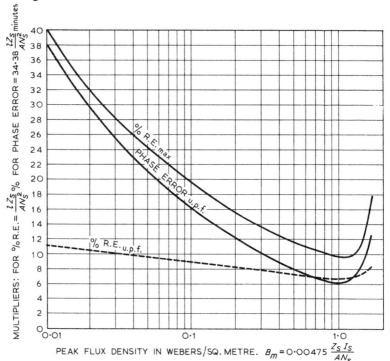

Fig. 20. Error curves for grade 51 oriented electrical steel 0·014 in. thickness. Frequency 50 c.p.s. Material in toroidal core form.

Figures 19–22 show such error curves for commonly used magnetic alloys *and as the flux density is directly proportional to the secondary current, I_s, and therefore to the primary current (to the same degree of approximation as the error equations)*, these curves have the tremendous advantage over the usual magnetic characteristic curves in that they immediately show how the errors vary with primary load current. They also indicate quite clearly the effect on the errors of the various factors influencing them.

The use of these error curves is very simple. Let it be assumed the designer has already chosen values of l, A, and N_s. Knowing the burden impedance and being able to calculate the secondary winding resistance he is able to calculate the total secondary impedance, Z_s. Thus he immediately obtains the 'scale multipliers'.

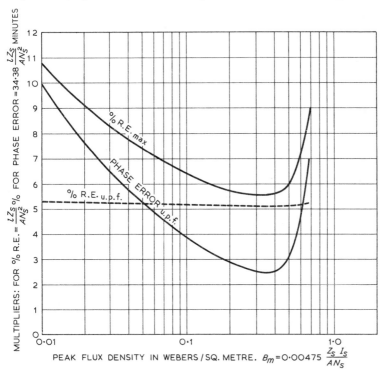

Fig. 21. Error curves for Mumetal 0·015 in. thickness. Frequency 50 c.p.s. Material in toroidal core form.

He is also able to calculate the operating flux densities for various percentages of the full-load secondary current and therefore, by inspection of the appropriate curve, he obtains the phase error or the %R.E. A useful accessory to employ with these curves is based on the fact that one cycle of the flux density logarithmic scale is equivalent to a range of secondary current from 10% to 100%. Thus a piece of Perspex marked with one logarithmic cycle of flux density scale allows the designer to calculate only the flux density corresponding to, say, the full-load current and by suitably placing this accessory over the error curves he can immediately obtain the errors at any percentages of full-load current he wishes.

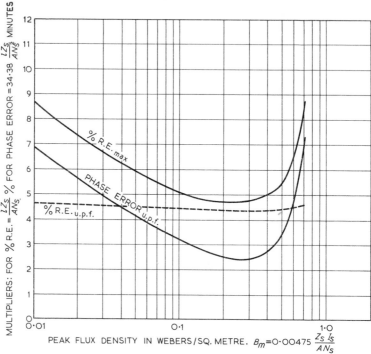

Fig. 22. Error curves for Mumetal 40 0·015 in. thickness. Frequency 50 c.p.s. Material in toroidal core form.

Similarly, the general equations for the %R.E. and phase error, eqs. (29) and (30) respectively, are now given by

$$\%\text{R.E. at } xI_{pn} = \left(\frac{-100}{4\cdot44\,fs}\right)\left(\frac{lZ_s}{AN_s{}^2}\right)$$

$$\times \left[\frac{(NI_m/\text{metre})\sin\delta + (NI_w/\text{metre})\cos\delta}{B_m}\right]\% \quad (48)$$

and

$$\text{phase error at } xI_{pn} = \left(\frac{3438}{4\cdot44\,fs}\right)\left(\frac{lZ_s}{AN_s{}^2}\right)$$

$$\times \left[\frac{(NI_m/\text{metre})\cos\delta - (NI_w/\text{metre})\sin\delta}{B_m}\right]\text{minutes.} \quad (49)$$

The graphical representation of these general equations necessitates a family of curves in each case and typical examples are shown in Figs. 23 and 24, these curves being particularly useful in showing how the errors change with the secondary circuit power factor.

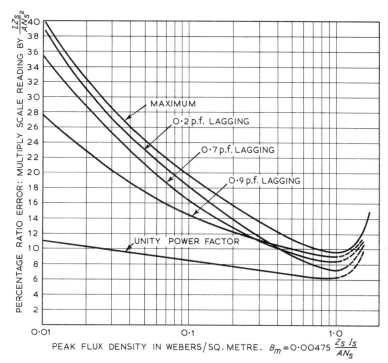

Fig. 23. Error curves for percentage ratio errors showing effect of secondary power factor. Material: grade 51 oriented electrical steel. Frequency 50 c.p.s.

Returning for a moment to Figs. 19–22 one may calculate the errors at any power factor from these curves. For any particular value of flux density and for a secondary circuit power factor of $\cos \delta$ the %R.E. is given by

$$\%\text{R.E.}_{\cos \delta}$$

$$= -[\%\text{R.E.}_{\text{u.p.f.}} \cos \delta + (\%\text{R.E.}^2_{\text{max}} - \%\text{R.E.}^2_{\text{u.p.f.}})^{\frac{1}{2}} \sin \delta]\%$$

and

$$\text{phase error}_{\cos \delta}$$

$$= (\text{phase error}_{\text{u.p.f.}} \cos \delta) - (34 \cdot 48 \,\%\text{R.E.}_{\text{u.p.f.}} \sin \delta) \text{ minutes.}$$

These equations, though, should only be used in association with these special curves as more general use could lead to unnecessary confusion. They are, nevertheless, perfectly correct equations.

For each particular value of secondary circuit power factor there is a further extension to these design curves, leading to another set

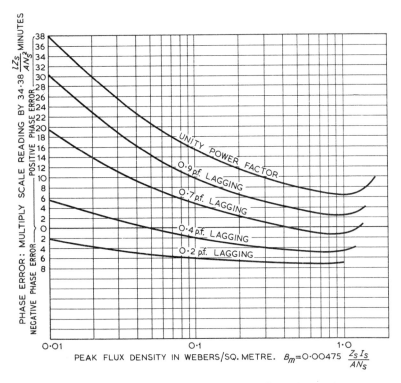

Fig. 24. Error curves for phase errors showing effect of secondary power factor. Material: grade 51 oriented electrical steel. Frequency 50 c.p.s.

of curves of possibly even greater help in design. The obvious choice to take for illustration is the unity power factor case as the classes of accuracy to B.S.3938 are specified at this value.

At this power factor, eqs. (45) and (46) are applicable and may be modified by multiplying top and bottom of each by I_{sn}. Rearrangement then gives

$$\%\text{R.E.}_{\text{u.p.f.}} \text{ at } xI_{pn} = \left(\frac{-100}{4\cdot44\,fs}\right)\left(\frac{l}{N_s I_{sn}}\right)\left(\frac{Z_s I_{sn}}{AN_s}\right)\left(\frac{NI_w/\text{metre}}{B_m}\right)\% \quad (50)$$

and

$$\text{phase error}_{\text{u.p.f.}} \text{ at } xI_{pn}$$

$$= \left(\frac{3438}{4 \cdot 44 fs}\right)\left(\frac{l}{N_s I_{sn}}\right)\left(\frac{Z_s I_{sn}}{A N_s}\right)\left(\frac{NI_m/\text{metre}}{B_m}\right)\text{minutes} \qquad (51)$$

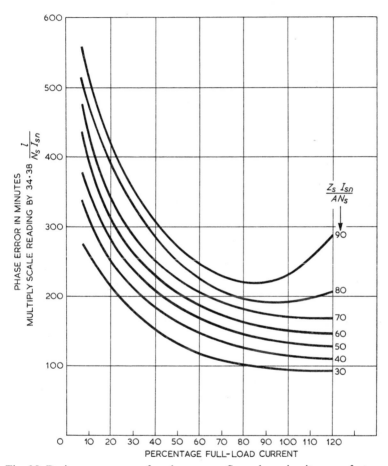

Fig. 25. Design error curves for phase error. Secondary circuit power factor of unity. Material: Mumetal 0·015 in. thickness. Frequency 50 c.p.s.

and the flux density, B_m, is given by

$$B_m = \left(\frac{x}{4 \cdot 44 fs}\right)\left(\frac{Z_s I_{sn}}{A N_s}\right)\text{webers/sq. metre.} \qquad (52)$$

It will be seen that in each of these three equations the term $Z_s I_{sn}/AN_s$ appears and therefore for each assumed value for this term a %R.E. curve and a phase error curve may be obtained from the earlier curves as already explained. The resulting families of curves for two of the magnetic alloys previously described are

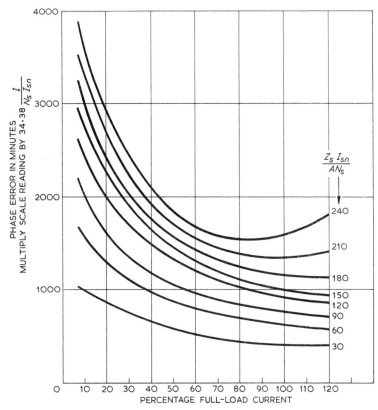

Fig. 26. Design error curves for phase error. Secondary circuit power factor of unity. Material: grade 51 oriented electrical steel 0·014 in. thickness. Frequency 50 c.p.s.

shown in Figs. 25 and 26, only the phase error curves being given. For Mumetal there is no real need to produce the corresponding ratio error curves as the %R.E. is sensibly constant and independent of flux density. The %R.E. for this material may be taken as directly proportional to lZ_s/AN_s^2 when the overall secondary power factor is unity.

The most important point about these families of curves is that they are now plotted on a base of *percentage full-load current* and the variable portion of the error scale multipliers has now become $l/N_s I_{sn}$.

The designer has to determine the size of core for a given ratio to meet a certain class of accuracy at some burden value and let it be assumed he is attempting to use a single-turn primary, that is, a ring-type current-transformer. He therefore knows the factors N_s and I_{sn} in the error scale multipliers and from his knowledge of the rated full-load primary current and likely size of primary bus-bar he is able to make an intelligent estimate of the inside diameter of the core. He then assumes a mean diameter from which he immediately has the mean length of the magnetic circuit, l, the third factor in the error scale multipliers.

As adjustment of the % R.E. may be made by the adoption of turns correction one need only concentrate on the phase error. Knowing the class of accuracy required and having calculated the phase error scale multiplier, by inspection of the pertinent family of curves, he is able to establish the *worst* curve he can tolerate and hence the maximum permissible value of $Z_s I_{sn}/AN_s$. N_s and I_{sn} are already known so the problem has been effectively reduced to the determination of the maximum tolerable value of Z_s/A. As the unity power factor case is being considered, the secondary circuit impedance is purely resistive and is the sum of the burden resistance, R_b, and the secondary winding resistance, R_{sw}. The latter component is unfortunately dependent, to some extent, on the core cross-sectional area, A, in as much as the mean length of turn of the secondary winding conductor is determined by the core proportions, but remembering that the assumption of values for the inside and mean diameters automatically gives a value of outside diameter and therefore of the radial build-up of the core, then a process of trial and error rapidly gives the correct value of core area. 'Correct' is possibly not the best term to use as there are numerous values of Z_s and of A which satisfy the maximum permissible value of Z_s/A.

The minimum value of secondary winding resistance (and therefore the total secondary resistance) occurs when the core cross-section is a square, but such a section does not necessarily give the minimum errors. For any particular value of core cross-sectional area and of inside diameter, departure from the square by making the axial length greater than the build-up increases the secondary winding resistance but decreases the core weight because the mean diameter is now reduced. Thus the total watts-loss and magnetising volt-amperes may be reduced and this, in turn, would mean a reduction in the errors, but whether the nett result is an increase or decrease in errors depends on a number of factors—what proportion the secondary winding resistance is of the total secondary impedance, the core inside diameter and the operating flux density. It is immediately obvious that there is never any theoretical justification in making the departure from the square in such a manner that the radial build-up exceeds the axial length of the core because such an action would increase both the secondary winding resistance and the core weight, thus causing a twofold increase in the errors. In practice, limitations placed on overall dimensions may, of course, force the designer to make the radial build-up greater than the axial length.

There is, however, another very good reason why there is some advantage in making the radial build-up less than the axial length and this is to reduce the non-uniformity of the flux distribution in the core. Take, for example, a toroidal core, the reluctance of that portion of the core nearest the inside diameter is obviously less than that of a section near the outside diameter and there is therefore a tendency for the induced flux to 'crowd' towards the inside diameter, causing non-uniform flux distribution across the core cross-section. All the error equations and curves have naturally been based on the assumption of uniform flux distribution and errors so calculated are, in fact, optimistic. Correction factors to allow for maldistribution of flux can be used but as these are small compared with the scatter of magnetic properties of the core material and other practical uncertainties, there is little to be gained in their use except for very high-precision current-transformers. This maldistribution of flux increases with the ratio of the outside diameter to the inside diameter and it can be shown that the flux density at the inside diameter is approximately given by

$$B_{\text{inside diameter}} = B_{\text{mean}} s \left(\frac{D_m}{D_i} \right),$$

where B_{mean} = flux density calculated on the basis of uniform distribution, that is, from the transformer equation;
s = core space factor;
D_m = mean diameter;
D_i = inside diameter.

A commonly accepted but quite arbitrary rule is that the outside diameter should not be greater than 1·5 times the inside diameter.

All other forms of core construction suffer from this maldistribution of flux and in cores built up from laminations there is the further complication of flux disturbance at the corners.

Similarly, some toroids have a cruciform or stepped sectional area which accentuates the non-uniformity of the flux distribution. The industrial designer invariably does not attempt any form of strict analysis but establishes design data for various core constructions based on experimental results.

There are other factors the designer has to take into account—there may be difficulty in making a core where the ratio of strip width to build-up is high or it may not be possible to use a number of separate cores of smaller strip width together. Too high a value of this ratio also presents difficulty in applying the secondary winding. Or there may be limiting dimensions he has to meet or he has to keep within a rationalised range of designs.

Sometimes the time taken to determine the optimum proportions cannot be justified from the commercial aspect, so while the technique suggested still requires further trial and error it can be used to give, reasonably quickly, a good idea of the core area required and it is not intended to discuss further refinements to it.

When the current-transformer is, of necessity, a wound-primary type there are further complications in determining the core size and proportions because the relative costs of the core and the copper content must be considered, but again the final decision may be ultimately determined by other than technical considerations.

With many measuring current-transformers, there is no limitation placed on the phase error and whilst this leaves only the ratio error to worry the designer, because he can use turns correction the direct use of these design curves does not necessarily assist him quite as much as when the class of accuracy does include phase error. Nevertheless, assuming a value for N_s, the designer is able to immediately determine the percentage turns correction effected by the removal of one or more secondary turns and a reasonable amount of trial and error will, as before, indicate the best values for the core dimensions.

One minor criticism of the design curves given in Figs. 25 and 26 is that they do not indicate the flux density level and in those cases where there may be an additional requirement concerning limitation of secondary current with primary fault currents flowing it may be advisable to use the appropriate design curve in the series Figs. 19–22. One other point, already mentioned, in favour of these latter design curves but one which requires emphasis, is that they immediately indicate how the errors vary with flux density and hence with primary load current, over the whole available range of flux density. Re-examination of these curves show that from the aspect of accuracy of transformation an overload condition, that is, one in which the primary current exceeds its normal rated value, is not necessarily an onerous one.

All the characteristic curves have been based on toroidal cores or similar types where there are no interleaved or butt joints in the magnetic circuit. When such joints are present in the adopted core construction similar curves may be drawn but they are no longer universal in their application. Usually the designer is mainly interested in a range of current-transformer designs, associated for instance, with a range of switchgear, and in such a case the alternative approach is to produce design curves indicating performance levels on a given size and type of core against varying values of available primary ampere-turns.

For cores of toroidal or similar construction the use of characteristics of the type shown in Figs. 19–22 have been found extremely useful while Figs. 25 and 26 and similar curves are generally of more use in determining trial values of design parameters.

CHAPTER 5

FURTHER THEORETICAL CONSIDERATIONS

The information given in the preceding chapter has been sufficient to show how the various design parameters affect the performance of a current-transformer, some comparisons have been drawn of various magnetic alloys and appropriate design curves have been derived from the error equations. While these design curves have been limited to a unity power factor total secondary impedance, sufficient information has been given to enable one to produce similar families of design curves for any secondary power factor, but with the tacit understanding that the reactive component of this total secondary circuit impedance does not include any secondary winding leakage reactance. Thus these curves are strictly limited to those types of current-transformers where this leakage reactance is negligible.

In many wound-primary current-transformers the secondary winding leakage reactance is not negligible and this, with the allied subject of winding capacitance, must be discussed.

Discussion of another important aspect of current-transformer practice, that of the voltage induced in an open-circuited secondary winding when primary current is flowing is also essential, but before proceeding with these various points it is advisable to introduce the concept of the equivalent circuit of a current-transformer as this will materially assist the future discussion of at least some of them. Similarly this equivalent circuit offers a convenient means of summarising certain aspects that have already been discussed.

The equivalent circuit of a current-transformer

Figure 27a shows the first stage in the determination of the equivalent circuit, although, again, no capacitances are included. On the primary side there is the source impedance, Z_g, the primary winding resistance and reactance, R_p and X_p respectively, and the load impedance, Z_l. This source impedance Z_g is usually low and the primary load impedance Z_l is high except under fault conditions when the latter is also low, but whether the primary circuit is healthy or not, the primary winding impedance, or as it is sometimes called, the current-transformer series impedance, will be negligible in comparison to these and therefore R_p and X_p may be

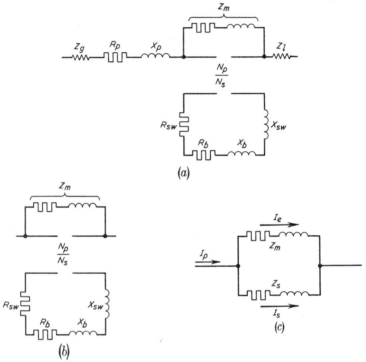

Fig. 27. Derivation of equivalent circuit for a current-transformer.

deleted. This explains why the vector diagrams used in previous chapters show a complete absence of primary voltages and voltage drops. Put another way, although the current-transformer and its burden are an additional load on the primary circuit this is normally negligible compared with the main load and, in any case, does not influence the errors. (In some specialised applications current-transformers may be inserted into low-power circuits such that the current-transformer and its burden form an additional primary load appreciably affecting primary circuit conditions.)

The current through the primary winding of the current-transformer is generally, therefore, solely determined by the source and load impedance of the primary circuit and is not influenced in any way by the condition of the secondary circuit.

The magnetisation of the core takes the exciting current from the primary just as the secondary burden extracts the secondary load current from the primary. Thus the load caused by the core magnetisation can be represented by an impedance and this, being in parallel with the secondary impedance Z_s, is a shunt impedance, Z_m. It has already been shown that this exciting current varies non-linearly with the flux density, which in turn is determined by a number of factors previously discussed in some detail. Therefore the shunt impedance is a variable and non-linear quantity and furthermore, because the exciting current possesses in-phase and quadrature components it must, itself, possess a resistive and a reactive component in order to maintain the desired equivalence. Remembering that the primary current is determined by factors unconnected with the actual current-transformer, the equivalent circuit of the current-transformer and its burden is now as shown in Fig. 27b.

On the secondary side there is no need to maintain the segregation of the various components of the total secondary impedance, as has been shown in previous chapters. The transformer windings have been deleted because they can be replaced either by the current-transformation ratio of the transformer, or the exciting current may be referred to the secondary side, so that the final form of the current-transformer equivalent circuit is as shown in Fig. 27c.

This equivalent circuit offers a very convenient means of explaining the operational characteristics of a current-transformer in a somewhat different manner than previously adopted and, as will be shown later, is particularly helpful in discussing protective current-transformers.

The shunt impedance is easily found by test or in the case of a current-transformer using a continuous magnetic circuit, by calculation from the magnetic characteristic curves of the core material. Assuming that the current-transformer is of the ring-type, with no primary bar through the orifice (or, if there is a primary winding, with this open-circuited) the secondary winding is connected to an a.c. supply and the current measured for various values of input voltage until the core saturates. The voltages and corresponding exciting currents are plotted against each other and the resultant curve is known as the current-transformer excitation curve, or less correctly, as its 'open-circuit curve'. As the secondary winding resistive drop will be negligible, this curve, for a continuous wound core, will be sensibly the same as the excitation characteristic of the core material as such, provided too, that no process has been used in the manufacture of the current-transformer causing degradation of the magnetic properties, as discussed in chapter 3. The input voltage may also be taken as the secondary induced voltage, E_s, and the shunt impedance, Z_m, at any particular value of E_s is simply given by

$$Z_m = \frac{E_s}{I_e} \text{ ohms.} \tag{53}$$

Thus the shunt impedance effectively has the same identity as the permeability of the core material and this explains the limitation in type of core. (For built-up cores of laminations with interleaved corners or for cores with butt-joints one cannot use the material permeability in this manner.)

When one is able to use the material characteristic curve,

$$Z_m = \frac{4\cdot 44f\,B_m s A N_s^{\,2}}{(NI_e/\text{metre})\,l} \text{ ohms} \tag{54}$$

and from eq. (54) Z_m may be calculated for any value of flux density.

For the magnetic alloys previously described appropriate curves of $B_m/(NI_e/\text{metre})$ may be easily obtained from the normal characteristic curves and are then indicative of the variation of the shunt impedance, Z_m, with the flux density.

For any particular and constant value of secondary circuit impedance Z_s, at low levels of primary current and hence of flux density, the shunt impedance is relatively low and the *proportion* of the primary current absorbed by the shunt impedance is relatively high. As the primary current increases the shunt impedance also increases and therefore the *proportion* of the primary current taken by it decreases until the maximum value of the shunt impedance is reached, corresponding to the maximum permeability flux density. This gives the characteristic decrease of errors with increase of primary current when the corresponding range of flux density is that from zero to the knee-point value, as noted in earlier chapters.

Further increase of primary current such that the flux density exceeds its maximum permeability value leads to a decrease of shunt impedance and it therefore takes an increasingly greater proportion of the total primary current leaving less and less to pass into the burden impedance. In other words, it is in this saturation region that fewer of the primary ampere-turns are available for transformation, the errors increase considerably to such an extent that eventually the current-transformer is said to lose ratio. When this happens any further increases in primary current lead to no corresponding increases in the secondary current.

Practical burdens must have a linear or resistive component, namely the resistance of leads interconnecting the actual burden to the current-transformer, the resistance of the instrument or relay coil and the resistance of the secondary winding. They frequently have a non-linear or reactive component because they themselves have a magnetically saturable core, this component decreasing in magnitude with increase of current through the burden. Design curves for other than unity power factor burdens described in previous chapters are, however, based on the assumption of constant burden impedance, this constancy being a practical impossibility due to the burden non-linear or reactive component.

Thus as the primary current increases the secondary circuit reactance and impedance will decrease, the overall power factor increases and the %R.E. will be lower than that calculated with the assumption of constant impedance, or in other words, a reactive component in the secondary circuit impedance assists in limiting the proportion of the primary current taken by the shunt impedance and increases the magnitude of the primary current at which the current-transformer will lose ratio.

Consideration of the phase error in the same terms is rather more complex. As the working burden impedance is not constant but decreases with increase of primary current the secondary induced e.m.f. and the flux density will be less than the values calculated on the assumption of constant burden impedance, but any modification of calculated phase error will be determined as much by the corresponding increase in the overall secondary power factor angle and change in the core material power factor angle as by the reduction in the secondary induced e.m.f.

Even the equivalent circuit with its conception of a shunt impedance does not automatically indicate one other important aspect of current-transformers—namely that of waveforms. The primary current, controlled solely by the source and load impedances, will be sinusoidal under normal steady-state operating conditions. Up to the maximum permeability level of flux density the current taken by the shunt impedance, that is, the exciting current, will also be substantially sinusoidal and therefore the secondary current will not depart from the sinusoidal waveform either, whether the total secondary impedance is predominantly resistive or not. As the flux density increases beyond this point— over the knee-region and into saturation the current into the shunt impedances departs increasingly from the sinusoidal with an increase in the third-harmonic content of its waveform. As the secondary current is the vector subtraction of the shunt-impedance current from the primary current this will also become increasingly rich in harmonics.

At the flux densities commonly used in measuring current-transformers the secondary current and the shunt exciting current are both substantially sinusoidal (with sinusoidal primary current) and usually it is only in protective current-transformers that one encounters *in normal operation*, the high flux densities required to cause significant departure from sinusoidal conditions.

The relationship between the secondary induced e.m.f. and the secondary current, in terms of their waveforms, is then determined by the impedance characteristics of the burden, that is, by the ratio of its resistive and the reactive components and at the same time the secondary induced e.m.f. and the exciting current waveforms must satisfy the demands of the core material's dynamic hysteresis loop.

Open-circuit voltages in current-transformers

An important aspect of current-transformer operation concerns the voltage appearing at the secondary terminals when the secondary winding is open-circuited, that is, is not connected to any burden. It is all too infrequently appreciated by the newcomer to current-transformers that while the terminal voltage across the secondary winding under normal operation is often very small, if, for some reason, the burden is disconnected, thus open-circuiting the secondary winding, then this voltage will rise considerably, sometimes to a level of kilovolts rather than volts, if the primary current is still flowing. It is for this reason that in the introductory remarks in chapter 1 the comment was made that the burden may be regarded as the fourth essential component of any current-transformer.

A current-transformer, for instance, having a 5 A rated secondary current and supplying a 15 VA burden will, at full-load primary current have a seondary terminal voltage of only 3 volts, but if the secondary winding becomes open-circuited the *peak* voltage appearing across the secondary terminals may now be kilovolts. This is due to the fact that all the primary ampere-turns have become exciting ampere-turns and saturation of the core occurs, sometimes 'high' or 'heavy' saturation. Although saturation as shown by the usual current-transformer excitation curve limits the effective or r.m.s. value of the voltage development by the secondary winding, Fig. 28 shows that the flux waveform is very flat-topped and as the voltage is directly proportional to the rate of change of flux this gives rise to a very 'peaky' voltage waveform, the crest value being many times the r.m.s. value. It may be of such a magnitude as to cause breakdown of insulation and at the same time the eddy-current losses increase considerably, causing general overheating of the core. It has therefore become a common requirement that a current-transformer shall be capable of withstanding continuously the effects of an open-circuited secondary winding, although the usual test specified is for a one minute period with rated full-load primary current flowing.

In order to examine this problem more closely one must first develop the equivalent diagram of the current-transformer by first examining the various components of the shunt impedance.

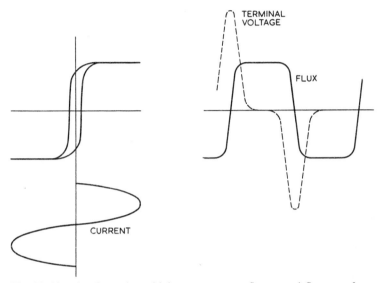

Fig. 28. Showing how sinusoidal current causes flat-topped flux waveform, but a 'peaky' voltage waveform.

The d.c. or static hysteresis loop and its derivation are well known as is the fact that its area gives the hysteresis loss per cycle of the material concerned. This hysteresis loss is a fundamental 'quality' of a magnetic alloy and up to the knee-point flux density is given by the Steinmetz empirical rule: hysteresis loss per unit volume per cycle equals $\eta B_m{}^n$, where η is the Steinmetz coefficient for the particular material and the exponent n lies between 1·6 and 2·8 for different materials. Above the knee-point flux density the relationship between the hysteresis loss and the flux density becomes approximately linear.

The a.c. or dynamic hysteresis loop differs from the d.c. loop because it must include the eddy-current losses. These eddy-current losses are due to the fact that the magnetic core is itself a conductor being cut by lines of flux so that small e.m.f.s are set up in the core causing local circulating currents, known as eddy-currents, and as the eddy-current paths have electrical resistance there is a loss of power. These eddy-current losses are minimised by trying to obtain the highest possible resistivity in the core material and by using the thinnest possible lamination commensurate with commercial considerations. For any particular magnetic alloy and gauge of material the eddy-current losses are directly proportional to $f^2 B_m{}^2$.

The traditional technique for separating the hysteresis loss from the eddy-current loss is based on the assumption that the former loss is independent of frequency so that for any particular value of flux density, if

$$W_h = \text{hysteresis loss/kg/cycle};$$

$$W_e = \text{eddy-current loss/kg};$$

and

$$W_t = \text{total watts loss/kg}.$$

Then

$$W_e = kf^2,$$

where k is a constant and the total watts-loss/kg/cycle is given by

$$\frac{W_t}{f} = kf + W_h \text{ watts/kg/cycle}. \tag{55}$$

Thus the usual method of separation of losses has been to obtain the total losses for a core at a particular flux density but at various frequencies. Plotting losses per cycle against frequency gives a straight line of the form $y = mx + c$ and where this intersects the watts-loss per cycle axis gives the hysteresis loss per cycle; this latter being assumed to be independent of frequency, its graph is a straight line parallel with the frequency axis. However, the *apparent* eddy-current loss per cycle resulting from this method of separation does not agree with the appropriate *calculated* value (calculated, that is, from fundamentally correct and well-known equations). The difference between the apparent and calculated values is commonly called the 'extra loss' or the 'anomalous loss' and present-day opinions favour the calculated eddy-current loss as being more accurate than that obtained by the separation technique and that the extra loss already described is a hysteresis effect.

While some little time has been spent on this subject it is an extremely important one because it is the eddy-current paths which are, in effect, a concealed high-resistance burden on a current-transformer when its secondary winding is open-circuited and they are therefore the predominant influence in determining the secondary open-circuited voltage.

For a given frequency, as the eddy-current losses are proportional to B_m^2 and hence E_s^2, they may be represented by a constant resistance R_e. The hysteresis losses, varying non-linearly with B_m and dependent on the hysteresis loop, are preferably kept separate, and are therefore represented by a second resistance R_h in series with the shunt reactance X_u, previously discussed, and based on the r.m.s. current and voltage. The equivalent diagram for a current-transformer with its secondary winding open-circuited *but not saturating* is shown in Fig. 29a together with the associated VA and power loss vector diagram.*

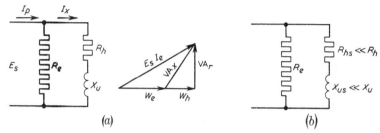

(a)   (b)

Fig. 29a. Equivalent and vector dia-   Fig. 29b. Equivalent diagram in
grams in unsaturated region.   saturation region.

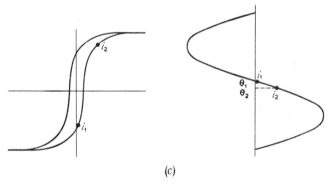

(c)

Fig. 29c. Sinusoidal current (I_p) waveform.

Thus, if at some voltage E_s (r.m.s.) in the unsaturated region, the eddy-current loss is W_e and the hysteresis loss is W_h, as determined by the separation technique previously described, and the exciting current is I_e (also now the primary or line current), then the volt-amperes into the reactance branch are given by

$$\mathrm{VA}_x = (W_h^2 + \mathrm{VA}_r^2)^{\frac{1}{2}},$$

* 'Overvoltages in Saturable Series Devices', by Boyajian and Camilli, *Trans. American I.E.E.*, **70** (1951), part II, pp. 1845–51.

where VA_r are the overall reactive volt-amperes, that is,

$$VA_r = [E_s I_e^2 - (W_h + W_e)^2]^{\frac{1}{2}}.$$

The current into the reactive branch, I_x, is then given by

$$I_x = \frac{VA_x}{E_s} \text{ amperes}$$

and

$$R_h = \frac{W_h}{I_x^2}; \quad X_u = \frac{VA_r}{I_x^2} \quad \text{and} \quad R_e = \frac{E_s^2}{W_e} \text{ ohms.}$$

It is commonly known that in a non-linear magnetic device one must distinguish between two types of reactance—the 'ordinary' one, in this case X_u, and the other is the *incremental* reactance, based on the slope of the dynamic loop. It is equally well known that in the unsaturated region these two reactances are approximately equal but in saturation the incremental reactance decreases considerably and it becomes necessary to differentiate between these two regions, the demarcation between them being given approximately by the knee-point of the normal excitation curve. The magnitude of the primary current is such that the current-transformer is saturated for most of the cycle and the hysteresis loss actually incurred during this period of saturation is very small compared with the total hysteresis loss per cycle. Therefore not only does X_u have to be modified to the incremental and much smaller value X_{us}, but also must R_h be similarly decreased to a value R_{hs} and the equivalent diagram during the period per cycle when the core is saturated is given in Fig. 29b. R_e, it will be noticed, is assumed to remain constant at its previously determined value for the unsaturated core condition.

Figure 29c shows the dynamic hysteresis loop with the associated exciting current waveform showing two instantaneous currents, i_1, and i_2, the former being the current at which the core comes out of the 'negative' saturation region and i_2 is that at which the core commences to enter the 'positive' region of saturation. When the core is saturated most of the primary current will flow through the much-reduced reactive branch consisting of X_{us} and R_{hs} and with negligible voltage drop. Let it be assumed this saturation is caused by the negative part of the sinusoidal primary current, then as this becomes less negative and passes zero value the condition changes to the unsaturated case given in Fig. 29a, i_1, being assumed to be approximately equal to zero. Obviously the current in X_u cannot change suddenly and it therefore possesses a transient component which circulates in the loop R_e, R_{hs} and X_u, as this cannot flow in the external primary line. While this transient current is decaying the primary line current is diverted through the eddy-current resistance R_e, until it reaches the value i_2, when the core again saturates, i_2 almost wholly flowing through X_{us} and R_{hs}. At this current i_2 it may be shown that the voltage across R_e is given by

$$e_{Re} \simeq 1\cdot4\sqrt{I_c i_2 X_u R_e} \text{ peak volts} \tag{56}$$

and as the change to the saturated condition, when X_u reverts to its much lower saturation value of X_{us} may be interpreted as a short-circuit across R_e, then the maximum voltage developed across the secondary terminals will be that given by eq. (56). This may be further modified to

$$e_{oc} \simeq 1\cdot4\sqrt{I_c E_k R_e} \text{ peak volts.} \tag{57}$$

A closer approximation for e_{oc} requires inspection of the dynamic hysteresis loop in order to determine i_1 and θ_1, the electrical angle corresponding to i_1,

$$i_1 = I_o \sin \theta_1,$$

now $i_2 = E_k/X_u$ and θ_2 the corresponding angle, is then found from

$$i_2 = \frac{I_c R_e}{Z}\left[\sin(\theta_2 - \phi) + \left\{\frac{i_1 Z}{I_c R_e} - \sin(\theta_1 - \phi)\varepsilon^{-R_t(\theta_2 - \theta_1)/X_u}\right\}\right],$$

where

$$Z = [(R_e + R_h)^2 + X_u^2]^{\frac{1}{2}},$$
$$R_t = R_e + R_h,$$
$$\phi = \tan^{-1}\frac{X_u}{R_t},$$

then

$$e_{oc} = (I_c \sin \theta_2 - i_2)R_e. \tag{58}$$

Interesting curves based on experimental data are given in Fig. 30 for these open-circuit secondary voltages and for different materials. These show that the nickel-iron alloy, Mumetal, although having a lower saturation flux density than the silicon-iron alloys, gives higher open-circuit secondary voltages.

This may be most easily explained by referring back to Fig. 28 which showed that a highly saturating primary current gives an almost rectangular flux waveform. This in turn gives the extremely 'peaky' secondary voltage waveform due to the relationship between this voltage and the rate of change of the flux. This rate of change of flux will be considerably greater in Mumetal than in the silicon-iron alloys for the same core size, secondary turns and magnitude of the saturating current.

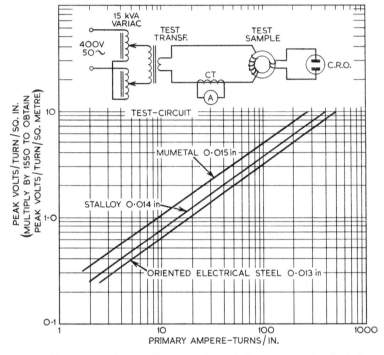

Fig. 30. Secondary voltages when secondary winding is open-circuited when primary current is flowing. (*By courtesy of the English Electric Co. Ltd.*)

Secondary winding leakage reactance

In chapter 2 the basic operation of a current-transformer was described in the same manner that one commonly encounters in general tranformer theory, namely that flux is set up in the core, induced by the primary ampere-turns, this flux, in turn, inducing an e.m.f. in the secondary winding such that the resulting secondary ampere-turns are ideally equal and opposite to the primary ampere-turns.

In all transformers it is physically impossible to completely confine the flux to the magnetic core and there is, inevitably, so-called 'leakage' of the flux into the surrounding air space. The main flux in the core may be looked upon as having been set up by the resultant of the primary and secondary ampere-turns and in addition each winding is linked by a leakage flux set up by the ampere-turns of the winding in question. Therefore the primary and secondary windings have corresponding voltage drops (corresponding that is, to the leakage fluxes), and both windings thus possess leakage reactance.

With most other types of transformer there is no need to segregate primary leakage reactance and secondary leakage reactance from each other, the usual method being to calculate, and use, either 'total leakage reactance' or 'total percentage leakage reactance'. For current-transformers, on the other hand, this segregation is essential for the reasons already given when discussing the equivalent circuit. It also has already been shown in chapters 2 and 4 how the errors of a current-transformer are considerably affected by the secondary leakage reactance and thus it is very important that one must be able to make either a reasonable estimate as to its magnitude or alternatively be at least able to gauge its effect on one's calculated errors.

Secondary leakage reactance in a current-transformer presents two problems, (i) its determination in a completed transformer by some particular test procedure, and (ii) its calculation at the design stage.

Consider the first of these: as with any other type of transformer the equivalent impedance of a current-transformer may be easily determined by the well-known short-circuit test in which one winding is short-circuited and the other winding supplied from a source of variable voltage until full-load current is flowing in the short-circuited winding. The applied voltage at which this occurs gives the current-transformer impedance and from a knowledge of the winding resistances the total leakage reactance is obtained. This is the sum of the secondary winding leakage reactance X_{sw}, and the primary winding leakage reactance X_{pw}, which if referred to the secondary side is given by

$$X_t = X_{sw} + K_t^2 X_{pw},\tag{59}$$

where K_t, as before, is the turns ratio.

With this test, segregation of the two component reactances is not possible and neither is the turns ratio known precisely in many cases.

There is one test technique of interest: if current is passed through the secondary winding and a current in phase-opposition to this is passed through the primary winding such that the primary and secondary ampere-turns are equal (and opposite), the main flux in the core, as shown by a search coil, is then substantially zero. Furthermore, the working leakage fluxes and those obtained during this test will, to all intents and purposes, be identical, and thus measurement of current and voltage on the secondary side will give its 'leakage impedance' and hence its leakage reactance. This reactance must be due to leakage flux because the main flux has been made zero.

It is important to appreciate that because these leakage fluxes use parts of the core in their paths the total flux is not constant over the magnetic length of that core. These leakage fluxes may be measured by means of search coils around various parts of the core and by the use of a suitable instrument such as a separately excited reflecting dynamometer voltmeter the phase relationships of these fluxes as well as their magnitudes are determined. It has been shown that these leakage fluxes are nearly in-phase with the respective currents and are proportional to those currents.

The degree of leakage and hence the obtained leakage reactance are determined by the relative disposition of the primary and secondary windings on the core and by their similarity or other-wise in shape, but before dealing with this aspect it is of interest to discuss one further test technique based on the Möllinger and Gewecke (M. & G.) current-transformer diagram.*

This is shown in Fig. 31 from which it is seen that its basis is the 'ampere-turn' vector diagram of a current-transformer in which the vectors have been divided by I_s and by N_p. The example shown is corresponding to Fig. 2 in chapter 2 which is the vector diagram with a lagging power factor burden or when the current-transformer possesses leakage reactance so that even with a unity power factor burden the overall power factor of the secondary circuit is still a lagging one.

Thus the vector N_pI_{p1} becomes K_t, N_pI_p becomes K_c and N_pI_e, N_pI_m and N_pI_w become respectively I_e/I_s, I_m/I_s and I_w/I_s. The secondary induced e.m.f. E_s and its resistive and reactive compo-nents become an impedance triangle Z_s, R_s and X_s.

Resolving K_c upon and perpendicular to K_t, then for small phase errors, that is, for small values of $\hat{\beta}$, the errors, to a close degree of accuracy are given by

$$K_c = K_t + OA \tag{60}$$

and

$$\beta = OB/K_c \text{ radians.} \tag{61}$$

These equations are, of course, identical to those given in chapter 2.

For any particular secondary impedance triangle the perpendi-cular to K_t drawn through O becomes the *phase error axis*, while the vector K_t and its extension becomes the *ratio error axis*. For

* See also Hague, *Instrument Transformers* (Pitman). See also note on page 92 below.

various values of I_s the corresponding secondary induced e.m.f. E_s, and flux densities are easily calculated as already described and from the appropriate magnetic characteristic curves the ratios I_m/I_s and I_w/I_s are easily found. Because of the non-linearity of the magnetisation curve I_m/I_s also varies non-linearly with I_s, but examination of the error curves given in chapter 4 shows that the u.p.f. ratio error is sensibly constant, or in other words, the ratio I_w/I_s is sensibly constant and independent of I_s.

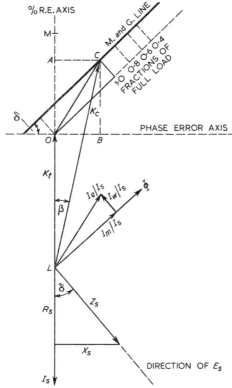

Fig. 31. Möllinger and Gewecke diagram for a current-transformer supplying a lagging power factor burden.

Thus if a line is drawn through O parallel to the flux vector for any particular value of Z_s and of δ, the secondary circuit power factor angle, one can measure along this line, to some suitable scale, the various values of I_m/I_s, now corresponding to various percentages of full-load secondary current.

As I_w/I_s is constant the locus of the point C is a second line through C again parallel to the flux vector, at the angle δ to the phase error axis and as this line, the M. & G. line, may be immediately marked in divisions representing the various percentages of full-load secondary current so can the respective perpendiculars to the phase error and ratio error axis be drawn and the errors measured at these various percentages.

Now the percentage ratio error is given by

$$\%\text{R.E.} = \left(\frac{K_n - K_c}{K_c}\right)100\%, \tag{61a}$$

where, as before, K_n = nominal ratio and K_c = actual current ratio and when $K_n > K_c$ the %R.E. is said to be positive.

If, along the K_t vector a distance LM is marked off corresponding to K_n, then the distance MA represents the deviation of the actual ratio K_c from the nominal ratio K_n and MO is the deviation of the turns ratio K_t from the nominal ratio.

Obviously there is no need to draw the complete vector diagram and in its simplest form the M. & G. diagram is as shown in Fig. 32.

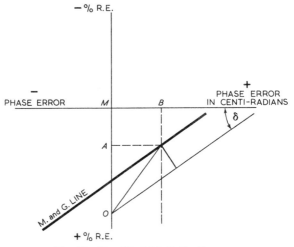

Fig. 32. Simplified M. & G. diagram.

While this M. & G. diagram may be used at the design stage this means estimating the secondary leakage reactance. In the context of the present discussion the M. & G. diagram is used to determine the secondary leakage reactance and the turns ratio from test results obtained on the current-transformer concerned, in the following manner.

A current-transformer of which only the nominal ratio and secondary winding resistance are known is tested for %R.E. and phase error with a burden of which the resistance and reactance are known. The errors are then plotted on a suitably scaled grid giving one M. & G. line, and if then a line is drawn perpendicular to this M. & G. line to some scale it represents the total secondary impedance and a second line parallel to the ratio error axis represents the total secondary resistance, only the length of this second line being known. Thus the impedance triangle can be completed, as shown, and from which the total secondary circuit reactance is measured; subtraction of the external reactance then gives the required secondary winding reactance.

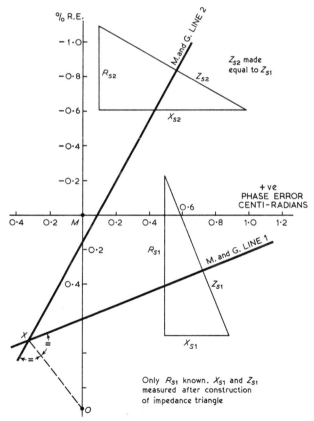

Fig. 33. Determination of X_{sw} and K_t from two M. & G. lines.

The burden resistance and reactance are now changed such that the total secondary impedance is unaltered and the %R.E. and phase errors again measured and plotted giving a second M. & G. line meeting the first at some point X. Where the bisector of the angle at X cuts the ratio axis it gives the point O. Now

$$K_t\left(1+\frac{MO}{100}\right) = K_n,\tag{62}$$

from which the turns ratio K_t is immediately found.

The scales chosen for the M. & G. grid are very important, but as seen from Fig. 33 the use of the centi-radian unit for phase error simplifies the matter. If on the %R.E. axis 1 inch equals $x\%$, then 1 inch on the phase error axis represents x centi-radians or $34\cdot38x$ minutes.

Other test techniques based on the M. & G. diagram have been evolved but it is felt that the one already discussed is sufficient for most readers. One by-product of this M. & G. diagram derived from tests is that once the point O has been determined a line drawn through it parallel to the M. & G. line for either of the two test conditions enables one to produce the 'excitation triangles' for the core corresponding to the various percentages of full-load current enabling the designer to determine the magnetising and watt-loss characteristics of the core material being used.

The precise calculation of secondary leakage reactance is not possible, as is immediately apparent if one examines the usual technique adopted for the calculation of total leakage reactance. Figure 34 shows a cross-section through one side of a concentric

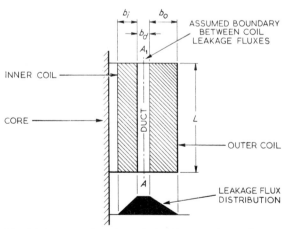

Fig. 34. Cross-section through double-wound transformer showing leakage flux distribution.

winding, it being assumed that the leakage fluxes are confined to the paths indicated and since these pass through the space between the primary and secondary coils in the same direction, because the ampere-turns in these coils are in opposition, it is further assumed there is a cylindrical boundary surface given by $A-A_1$, but its precise position is indeterminate.

Now the m.m.f. diagram shown in Fig. 34 also represents the flux density distribution, the leakage flux being directly proportional to m.m.f. and the indeterminate position of $A-A_1$ is of no importance in the calculation of the total leakage reactance.

If the total leakage reactance, referred to the secondary side is denoted by X_t, as before, then

$$X_t = \frac{4.44 f N_s \Phi_t}{I_s} \text{ ohms.} \tag{63}$$

Φ_t = peak value total leakage flux in webers

and

$$\Phi_t = \Phi_d + \Phi_i + \Phi_o \text{ webers,}$$

where

Φ_d = peak total flux in inter-coil duct,
Φ_i = peak total flux in inner coil,
Φ_o = peak total flux in outer coil;

if

b_d = radial depth of duct (in metres),
b_i = radial depth of inner coil (in metres),
b_o = radial depth of outer coil (in metres),
M_d = mean periphery of duct (in metres),
M_i = mean periphery of inner coil (in metres),
M_o = mean periphery of outer coil (in metres),
L = axial length of duct and coils (in metres);

then it can be shown that

$$\Phi_d = \frac{4\pi}{10^7} \sqrt{2} \frac{N_s I_s}{L} b_d M_d,$$

$$\Phi_i = \frac{4\pi}{10^7} \sqrt{2} \frac{N_s I_s}{L} \frac{b_i M_i}{3},$$

$$\Phi_o = \frac{4\pi}{10^7} \sqrt{2} \frac{N_s I_s}{L} \frac{b_o M_o}{3},$$

I_s being the r.m.s. secondary current.

So that

$$\Phi_t = \frac{4\pi}{10^7}\sqrt{2}\frac{N_s I_s}{L}\left(b_d M_d + \frac{b_i M_i}{3} + \frac{b_o M_o}{3}\right). \tag{64}$$

$N_s I_s$ has been used throughout because, of course, $N_s I_s = N_p I_p$ and there is no need to distinguish between them. Substitution for Φ_t in eq. (63) then gives

$$X_t = \frac{7 \cdot 9}{10^6} \cdot f \cdot \frac{N_s^2}{L}\left(b_d M_d + \frac{b_i M_i}{3} + \frac{b_o M_o}{3}\right) \text{ ohms.} \tag{65}$$

This equation immediately shows that the method employed by some people in assuming that the secondary winding leakage reactance X_{sw} is $\frac{1}{2}X_t$ is without foundation and should this relationship be found it is quite fortuitous. If the inner coil in this analysis is the secondary winding then that part of the secondary leakage flux denoted by Φ_i not only may or may not be equal to Φ_o depending on the radial depths of the windings but also the portion of the duct leakage flux Φ_d due to the secondary ampere-turns is indeterminate.

In some designs of current-transformers there may be a considerable difference in the axial lengths of the primary and secondary windings and this affects the accuracy of eq. (65) in the calculation of total leakage reactance. Then again, in some designs the disposition of the windings or their shape is such that it becomes impossible to calculate reactance with any accuracy; a good example of this is when the secondary winding is uniformly wound on a toroidal core in the same way as for a ring-type current-transformer, but the primary turns are concentrated over a short length of the core. It is of interest to point out here that even for high-rated primary currents where the primary winding is a bar through the core orifice the actual position of this primary bar and of the return leads can affect the leakage flux and hence the ratio and phase errors.

As the leakage flux varies with the primary load current its effect on the shape and magnitude of the ratio and phase-error curves will also vary, but provided the addition of the leakage flux to the main flux does not cause the flux density in any part of the core to go beyond that corresponding to the maximum permeability then, in general, the ratio error calculated on the basis of no leakage is too high and similarly the calculated phase error is too large.

The industrial designer is frequently concerned with a standard range using a particular size of lamination, a particular disposition of primary and secondary windings and catering for a range of secondary turns. In this case the secondary leakage reactances corresponding to various values of secondary turns are found by test and the results plotted as shown in Fig. 35 and therefore actual calculation of secondary leakage reactance is not carried out.

One technique sometimes employed is to first measure the leakage reactance by means of a search coil as shown in Fig. 36a and with the secondary winding short-circuited.

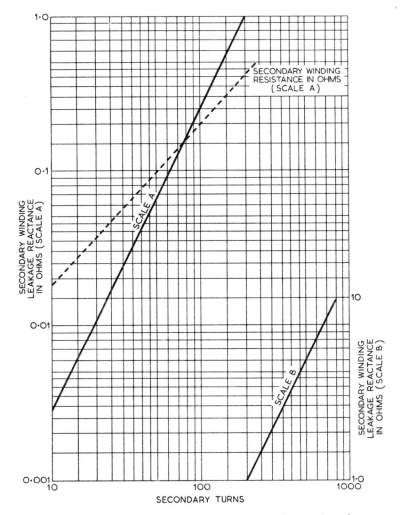

Fig. 35. Secondary leakage reactance. Secondary coil wound on former 2¾ in. diameter; winding length 2½ in.; 16 s.w.g. conductor. For comparison purposes the secondary winding resistance is also shown dotted.
(*By courtesy of the English Electric Co. Ltd.*)

If

E_e = induced voltage in search coil,

N_e = number of turns on search coil,

then

$$X = \left[\left(\frac{E_e N_s}{N_e I_s} \right)^2 - R_{sw}^{\ 2} \right]^{\frac{1}{2}}$$

and the equivalent circuit is then assumed to be as shown in Fig. 36b. The flux density for that part of the core with no leakage flux is calculated, the total impedance being the sum of the burden impedance and the secondary winding resistance. From the usual magnetic characteristic curves the magnetising and watt-loss currents are obtained and the procedure repeated for that part of

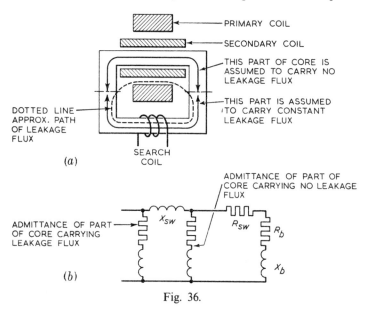

PRIMARY COIL

SECONDARY COIL

THIS PART OF CORE IS ASSUMED TO CARRY NO LEAKAGE FLUX

THIS PART IS ASSUMED TO CARRY CONSTANT LEAKAGE FLUX

DOTTED LINE APPROX. PATH OF LEAKAGE FLUX

SEARCH COIL

(a)

ADMITTANCE OF PART OF CORE CARRYING NO LEAKAGE FLUX

ADMITTANCE OF PART OF CORE CARRYING LEAKAGE FLUX

X_{sw}

R_{sw}

R_b

X_b

(b)

Fig. 36.

the core assumed to be carrying leakage flux, remembering that the total secondary impedance is now the sum of the burden impedance, the secondary winding resistance and the equivalent reactance determined by the test described. Thus the flux density and the core power factor will also be altered as well as the secondary overall power factor. Equations (29) and (30), or derivatives of these, are then used to calculate the ratio and phase errors for each branch and the actual ratio and phase errors are taken as the sum of these so calculated, or, if in obtaining the watt-loss and magnetising currents for each branch the *total* core magnetic length had been used the average of the calculated errors is then taken.

The presence of leakage flux in a core means that the excitation characteristic of that current-transformer cannot be used to pre-determine its performance, particularly at high levels of apparent flux density, corresponding to high overcurrents in the primary circuit and thus, for protective current-transformers to B.S. 2046, two categories were introduced, 'low-reactance' and 'high-reactance', the demarcation between these two categories being quite an arbitrary one while some changes in the manner of presentation were made in the new standard, B.S. 3938.

The capacitance of current-transformer windings*

The vast majority of current-transformers is used at the normal power frequencies—25 c.p.s., 50 c.p.s. or 60 c.p.s., and it is for this reason that little has been written in this book on current-trans-formers for use at the higher frequencies where winding capaci-tances are an important factor in determining performance. In most power-frequency current-transformers one may completely disregard the effect of the various capacitances present, one excep-tion being high-accuracy current-transformers having rated cur-rents less than 5 A, 'high-accuracy' here meaning Class AL to B.S. 3938 or similar.

It is beyond the scope of this book to discuss in any great detail the work that has been carried out on this aspect of current-transformers and the following discussion is therefore of a very general nature.

There are three basic forms of capacitance in any current-transformer—the first is the interwinding capacitance, i.e., that between primary and secondary windings, the second is the self-capacitance of each winding and the third is the capacitance between each winding and earth. The interwinding capacitance may be reduced by increasing the duct between the primary and second-ary windings, although there is a limit to the usefulness of this technique because it also causes some increase in secondary wind-ing leakage reactance and possibly in core size. The self-capacitance of the windings may be reduced by spacing out the turns although, again, this sometimes leads to an increase in the overall size of the current-transformer. Other methods have been used in trying to minimise the self-capacitances of the windings, usually by the

---

* 'Dielectric Admittances in Current-transformers', by Arnold, *Proc. I.E.E.*, **97** (1950), part II, p. 727; 'The Effect of Capacitances on the Design of Toroidal Current-transformers', by Arnold, *Proc. I.E.E.*, **97** (1950), part II, p. 797.

adoption of special winding techniques, one simple example of this is to so wind that the voltage between adjacent turns is kept to a minimum by winding in sections. Some advantage is gained if the outer winding, usually the primary, is so wound that the middle of this winding is adjacent to the other (secondary) winding.

This problem of capacitance is exceedingly complex, for two reasons; the first of these is that it is virtually impossible to determine the distribution of the various capacitances present and the second is the relative effect of these capacitances on performance. It becomes necessary to use in one's analysis an approximate system of lumped admittances as shown in Fig. 37. The self-capacitance of the windings has been included with the excitation admittance of the current-transformer to give Y_1, because this capacitance is largely independent of the relative potentials of the primary and secondary circuits.

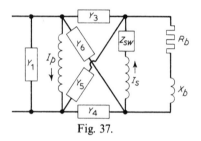

Fig. 37.

The effect of the interwinding capacitances is influenced by these relative potentials and by the presence or otherwise of a low-resistance connection between the windings, such a connection being required in many of the test-circuits used for the determination of the errors of a current-transformer. These capacitances may be represented by four admittances connected across the primary and secondary winding terminations as shown in Fig. 37.

If the winding self-capacitances and the interwinding capacitance are negligible (also those between primary and secondary windings and earth) and if the capacitance between primary and secondary circuits external to the current-transformer is also negligible, then there will be no change in the errors of that current-transformer if the primary and secondary circuits are connected together or to earth at one point. This is the condition generally encountered in most current-transformers for power-frequency operation and thus there is no need for a critical examination of these capacitances.

On the other hand, if the capacitance between primary and secondary circuits (and between either of these and earth) external to the current-transformer is negligible but the internal capacitances are not, then the errors measured in any test-circuit requiring interconnection between the primary and secondary windings will be different to those obtained in actual operation, when, of course, there is no such interconnection. There are two other cases one should consider, but the two mentioned are the most important. Taking the latter case there are five ratios to be considered, the first of which is that obtained with no interconnection between windings, given by K, the other four are for the various methods by which interconnection between the primary and secondary windings may be made, given by K_{ll}, K_{mm}, K_{lm} and K_{ml}, where the first letter of the suffix gives the primary terminal and the second letter gives the secondary terminal which are linked.

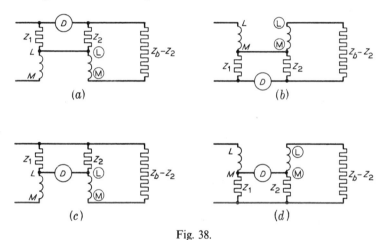

Fig. 38.

The basic test-circuit is shown in Fig. 38, where Z_1 and Z_2 are variable impedances and D is a detector, such as a vibration galvanometer or valve detector. The impedances Z_1 and Z_2 are adjusted until the detector indicates zero current and the voltages drops across these impedances are then equal. Thus if Z_1 and Z_2 at balance are known, then the ratio of the currents through them is also known. When connected as Fig. 38a this gives K_{lm}, while the connection shown in Fig. 38b gives K_{ml}. The ratios K_{ll}, K_{mm} and K are not obtainable by this method, but if the current ratios at balance in the connections shown in Figs. 38c and 38d are K_a and K_b respectively, then it can be shown that

$$K = \frac{K_{lm} K_{ml} - K_a K_b}{K_{lm} + K_{ml} - K_a - K_b}.$$

To determine K_{ll} and K_{mm} the turns ratio and the current-transformer internal impedance must be known, although there is a technique whereby K, K_{ll} and K_{mm} may be obtained by direct measurement, but there is no real need to proceed further with this.

If the current-transformer is such that the capacitance between primary and secondary circuits are negligible both internal and external to the current-transformer, the ratios found in the tests shown in Figs. 38a to 38d will be the same. Alternatively, if ∂K is an arbitrarily chosen permissible difference between these ratios and the other three (dependent, of course, on the specified class of accuracy), then the current-transformer will be acceptable as having negligible capacitance if

$$\frac{(1 + K_t)(I_{lm} + I_{ml})}{I_s} < \partial K,$$

where K_t is the turns ratio and I_{lm} and I_{ml} are the currents measured by an ammeter in a low-resistance link between L and Ⓜ and between M and Ⓛ respectively. Of course, these linkages are not carried out simultaneously, but the two separate tests are quite rapidly completed. The secondary is connected to the rated burden and in these tests the previous impedances Z_1 and Z_2 are omitted.

NOTE: The Möllinger and Gewecke diagram for current-transformers discussed in this chapter and the similar diagram for voltage-transformers discussed later in the book were first described by the originators in volumes 33 and 32 (1911–12) respectively of *Elektrotechnische Zeitschrift* (V.D.E.-Verlag).

CHAPTER 6

SOME OPERATIONAL NOTES

At this stage it is advisable to examine various aspects of current-transformer operation and theory from the user's viewpoint, perhaps recapitulating some already mentioned but in a different form and, far more importantly, emphasising some points that may have been obscured in the general theoretical approach hitherto adopted. Most of these remarks, unless otherwise stated, apply equally to both measuring and protective current-transformers.

Selection of secondary current rating

There is sometimes confusion in the user's mind on the advantages and disadvantages of the adoption of 5 A as the nominal or rated secondary current compared with 1 A or lower. For any particular value of rated primary current and for a given core size, the same flux density in the secondary winding and the same mean length of secondary turn, the performance of the current-transformer in terms of its ratio errors and phase errors, when tested at its rated burden in accordance with the relevant specification, becomes independent of the value chosen for its rated secondary current. The *working* burden, however, consists of the relay or instrument and the leads connecting this to the current-transformer. If the distance involved is great then the lead resistance becomes an important factor in the working performance of that current-transformer and this is equally true when the lead resistance is still a significant portion of the total secondary impedance even though the distance between current-transformer and burden is not great. Should the working burden have a reactive component, as is often the case, probably because it possesses a saturable core, this reactance decreases with primary load current and the corresponding secondary current and the lead resistance would then become the predominant factor in determining the performance, particularly in some protection applications.

It is general standard practice to use 7/0·029 conductor in the secondary wiring circuits of switchgear and the like, and for a given length of connecting lead the burden imposed on the current-transformer is directly proportional to the secondary current squared. Thus for a given distance between burden relay or instrument and the current-transformer the adoption of 1 A as the rated secondary current reduces the lead burden to $\frac{1}{25}$ its value at 5 A rated secondary current. Obviously there are occasions when this reduction in effective burden may give the designer considerable assistance but it must be remembered this particular advantage in a lower rated secondary current comes from the standardisation of conductor size for secondary wiring circuits.

There is another advantage in adopting a lower value of rated secondary current. For any particular rated primary current and selected value of primary ampere-turns, the lower the rated secondary current the finer the adjustment to the ratio error by the use of turns correction. For instance, let it be assumed a ring-type current-transformer has a ratio of 50/5 amperes, giving ten secondary turns. The lowest or minimum turns correction one can obtain by straightforward means is one turn, that is, 10%, which may be too 'coarse', whereas adoption of 1 A as the rated secondary current, giving fifty turns reduces the minimum turns correction to 2% and at the same time allows the designer a far greater choice of possible levels of turns correction (in 2% increments).

There are two disadvantages in lowering the rated secondary current. First, a more expensive, finer gauge wire is required and the secondary takes longer to wind, therefore adding to the factory cost of the current-transformer although from the foregoing it may be possible to reduce the core size because the effective working burden may have been lowered by the adoption of this lower rated secondary current. The second objection is of more importance and concerns the peak voltage developed across an open-circuited secondary winding. While open-circuiting should not happen, accidents do occur in practice and then the insulation between windings and earth and the secondary interturn and interlayer insulation suffer possibly considerable dielectric stress. It has been seen in Fig. 30 in chapter 5 that for a given number of primary ampere-turns per unit length of core magnetising that core and with the secondary winding open-circuited, the peak voltage developed across the secondary terminals is proportional to the core area and to the *number of secondary turns*. Thus a 1 A secondary would, all other things being equal, develop five times the peak voltage of a 5 A secondary and the time for which the various insulations could withstand the stresses set up by this condition may be considerably shortened. It must also be remembered that if the open-circuit occurs near the burden relay or instrument the interconnecting leads would also suffer the increased dielectric stressing due to the lowering of the secondary current rating.

It is not possible to lay down general rules on the selection of the rated secondary current except to point out that 5 A should always be considered first and a lower value chosen only if it is felt necessary. The final choice may well rest with the designer rather than with the user.

Selection of primary current rating

The performance of any current-transformer is considerably influenced by the number of the primary ampere-turns. It has already been shown that the ratio errors and phase errors of a measuring current-transformer are influenced by the number of these 'available' primary ampere-turns to a greater extent than by any other single factor and this is equally true of the performance of protective current-transformers. Thus there is a minimum level of primary current for any particular application for which a ring-type or similar current-transformer may be used without making it unduly large or expensive. Should the rated primary current be below this level then a wound-primary construction has to be adopted but again there is a minimum limit determined this time by the maximum dynamic and thermal stresses which the particular construction employed is capable of withstanding, again without making the current-transformer unduly expensive. Then again, the designer for some reason or other may not be able to fit wound-primary current-transformers into a particular type of equipment and, even for ring-type current-transformers, space limitations in the equipment are often such that they place severe restrictions on the designer's final proposals. The higher the primary system voltage the more important it becomes to try and use the ring-type or similar construction because insulation costs involved in a wound-primary current-transformer will be considerably greater than in the former type and sometimes are prohibitive.

The user should therefore specify the highest possible rated primary current commensurate with the operational demands of his distribution system and associated equipment in order to ensure the most economical design of current-transformer. It must be remembered that the bar-primary or ring-type construction is, for higher primary system voltages, cheaper than any wound-primary construction and it is *always* the more robust. Insistence on a low rated primary current may lead to an unduly large and expensive current-transformer, possibly accompanied by some loss of performance.

Multi-ratio current-transformers

In the laboratory there is obvious need for current-transformers in which a number of different ratios may be obtained and as the primary circuit is rarely a permanent one then the ratio may be changed in one of three ways:

(i) Keeping the secondary turns constant and having tappings or series and parallel arrangements on the primary side;

(ii) keeping the primary turns constant and having tappings or series and parallel arrangements on the secondary side; or

(iii) a combination of (i) and (ii) in that tappings or series and parallel arrangements are on both primary and secondary windings.

With current-transformers used in switchgear and the like it is frequently impracticable to have tappings or a series-parallel arrangement on the primary side and in the main the different ratios required are obtained by tappings or series-parallel arrangements on the secondary side. Both methods have the disadvantage that the current-transformer performance, dependent to a great extent on the number of secondary turns, will vary from ratio to ratio. Again these methods sometimes makes suitable turns correction difficult. For a dual ratio current-transformer where one rated primary current is half the value of the other a series-parallel secondary winding (now of two equal sections) has a lot to commend it because although the number of secondary turns will still not be the same for both ratios, at the lower ratio the secondary winding resistance with the parallel condition will be a quarter of that obtained with the series connection applicable to the higher ratio, and this will reduce to some extent the difference in performance at the two ratios.

The only way in which the number of secondary turns can be held constant is to alter the primary turns for the different ratios and this method should always be adopted when practicable.

Multi-ratio current-transformers should not be confused with either 'double-primary current-transformers' or 'double-secondary current-transformers'. The first term refers to those current-transformers having two entirely separate primary windings fully insulated from each other but linking the same magnetic circuit. One frequent use for this type of current-transformer in some countries is the metering of single-phase three-wire systems. The second term, 'double-secondary current-transformers' refers to those current-transformers possessing a single primary winding embracing two entirely separate magnetic circuits each having its own secondary winding. Each secondary circuit therefore operates completely independently of the other and this type should always be considered when it is required to operate a relay with, for instance, an ammeter or other instrument because the operational demands of the protective circuit are dissimilar to those of the measuring circuit and segregation of these two functions by using a double-secondary current-transformer may be the only sensible answer. This type of current-transformer obviously takes up less space than two separate current-tranformers (when wound-primary type) and sharing the same primary winding affords considerable saving in manufacturing cost—this saving increasing with the primary system voltage.

Selection of rated burden

The selection of the correct value for the rated burden is not always quite so simple as it may seem at first glance. For measuring current-transformers to B.S.3938 the burden is specified at unity power factor whereas practical burdens frequently have a reactive component and it is this difference between specified and actual values of the burden power factors that causes the trouble.

Confining discussion to unity and lagging power factors because capacitative burdens, as already indicated, are rarely found in practice, examination of the various curves in chapter 4 shows that the ratio error, for any particular value of flux density, is lowest for an overall secondary power factor of unity. If the rated and the actual burdens have the same value but the latter is at a lagging power factor then the actual ratio errors will be greater than those obtained when the current-transformer is tested with its rated u.p.f. burden.

The difference between these actual and test values of ratio error will depend on a number of factors: the flux density, the proportion of the total secondary circuit impedance supplied by the secondary winding, the core material and the type of core construction. The issue is further confused because there is some interrelation between some of these factors. It may seem that the difference between maximum possible ratio error and the u.p.f. ratio error is least when a continuously wound core is used, because in any core with interleaved corners the magnetising component of the exciting current increases causing a corresponding increase in the maximum ratio error and as the watts-loss is not unduly affected the u.p.f. ratio error is not altered. Such cores, however, are mainly used for wound-primary current-transformers and in which there may be an appreciable secondary leakage reactance so that although the rated burden may be a u.p.f. one the overall secondary circuit power factor will be a lagging one. Therefore the *difference* between test and actual ratio errors may well be less in such a current-transformer than in a ring-type current-transformer. A further factor that must not be forgotten is that turns correction may have been adopted. In such cases increasing the rated burden over the working value does not necessarily give numerically lower ratio errors at the lower working burden. The ratio error becomes less negative than at the rated burden but the extent of the turns correction may well mean that the errors become positive to a greater value than the negative error at the higher burden (i.e. the test burden).

As far as the phase error is concerned, and again considering only unity and reactive power factor conditions, the maximum phase error occurs at the former.

Another important point that must be remembered is that in calculating the total burden some allowance must be made for connecting leads, which in some switchgear installations may be a significant portion of the total burden. As already indicated, reduction of lead burden may often be most effectively carried out by reducing the rated secondary current—a 5-yard route length of 7/0·029 cable constitutes a 1·3 VA burden at a rated secondary current of 5 A, but only 0·05 VA at 1 A.

Manufacturers of instruments and meters frequently recommend VA ratings to be used and, of course, large-scale users of current-transformers often standardise on a limited number of VA ratings and of ratios so that, on occasions, the best possible current-transformer is not used; this is the usual price one has to pay for the advantages implicit in standardisation. It is hoped these brief notes will indicate some of the problems encountered in the selection of the VA rating and how it is partly influenced by the relative importance of the ratio errors and the phase errors in the working circuit concerned.

From what has been written it is obvious that in any application demanding high accuracy the errors of the current-transformer must be measured whenever possible with the working burden and not the rated burden and this is frequently done in the case of metering current-transformers by the user after receiving the current-transformers from the manufacturer.

Choice of class of accuracy

It has already been pointed out that the choice of a burden for specification purposes considerably larger than the actual burden does not necessarily give better results at the lower burden and even if it did the better accuracy might be quite unnecessary so that one has a totally uneconomic current-transformer. Similarly the class of accuracy should be chosen equally carefully, but one can do no better than reproduce the pertinent data given in

B.S. 3938. Table 3 therefore is the same as Table 11 in Ap
of that specification.

One interesting point here is that some people for duty
times specify 'Class C Ratio Error Only', this practice
considerable assistance to the designer when the ratio is
meeting the phase-error requirements of Class C is of embarrass-
ment to him.

The advent of B.S. 3938, as that of B.S. 2046 before it, has done
much to limit the often unfortunate use of B.S. 81 Classes of
Accuracy for protection applications.

Table 3. *Selection of suitable class of accuracy*

	Application	Class of accuracy
(I)	Precision testing or as a standard for testing other current-transformers	AL
(II)	Meters of precision grade in accordance with B.S. 37	AM
(III)	Meters of commercial grade in accordance with B.S. 37	BM or CM
(IV)	Precision measurement (indicating instruments and recorders)	AL or AM
(V)	General industrial measurements (indicating instruments and recorders)	C
(VI)	Approximate measurements	D

The polarity of a current-transformer

If a current-transformer is supplying some burden and the
secondary circuit is such that it is not associated with any other
current-transformer then in most cases a knowledge of its polarity
is not required. On the other hand, there are many practical cases
where there is interconnection between the secondaries of two or
more current-transformers and in these cases a knowledge of the
polarity of the current-transformers concerned is essential, otherwise incorrect connection is possible leading to mal-operation of
the burden or burdens being supplied.

The polarity of a current-transformer is a means of designating
the relative instantaneous directions of the currents in its primary
and secondary leads and these leads are said to have the same
polarity when at some instant the current enters the primary lead
in question and leaves the secondary lead in question in the same
direction *as if the two leads formed a continuous circuit.*

Put another way and using the simplest case of a current-transformer supplying an ammeter as in the example shown in Fig. 39. If at the instant concerned the primary terminal P1 is positive to P2, then the secondary terminal S1 is also positive to S2, or if the current flow in the primary circuit is from P1 to P2, then it will also be from S1 to S2 on the secondary side *via the ammeter*, that is, *the external burden*. Thus at the instant concerned the direction of the current through the ammeter would

Fig. 39. Polarity of a current-transformer.

Fig. 40. Polarity test on current-transformer using d.c.

be the same as if the terminal connected to S1 had been directly connected to P1 and that connected to S2 had been connected to P2 so that all the current-transformer has done is to alter the *magnitude* of the current passing through the ammeter.

Numerous polarity check methods are in existence, one commonly used is shown in Fig. 40, where a centre zero d.c. moving-coil voltmeter is connected to the secondary side of the current-transformer, the primary side being supplied from a battery. Depression of a key switch in series with the primary winding and battery will cause a momentary reading of the voltmeter, the direction of this indicating correct or incorrect polarity. One disadvantage of this method is that the core may be left in a magnetised state and any measurements of ratio and phase errors taken after such a polarity check would give incorrect results. The same thing happens when d.c. measurements are made of the secondary winding resistance and therefore after d.c. polarity and resistance tests the current-transformer should be immediately demagnetised.

For this reason a.c. methods of checking polarity are preferred. Relative methods for determining ratio and phase errors automatically check the polarity at the same time and numerous other methods exist when a standard current-transformer or one of known polarity is available. Sometimes this is not so but a simple test one can then use is shown in Fig. 41. From this diagram it is immediately apparent that if the polarity is correct the ammeter will give a higher reading when the selector switch is in position x than when it is in position y.

The terminal nomenclature used, namely, P1, P2, S1 and S2 is that recommended by B.S. 3938. T_1, T_2, Ⓣ₁ and Ⓣ₂ were the markings recommended by B.S. 81, although one even finds today the markings used previous to that specification, namely M, L, Ⓜ and Ⓛ.

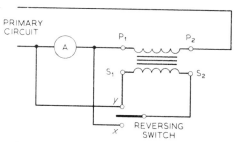

Fig. 41. Polarity test on current-transformer
using a.c.

For primary windings with tappings the markings are P1, P2, P3, etc. If there is more than one secondary winding one set of secondary terminals is marked 1S1 and 1S2—the second set 2S1 and 2S2, and so on.

Overload and overcurrent operational considerations

While the accuracy limits for measuring current-transformers were specified in B.S. 81 over a range of 120% down to 10% of rated primary current, there was no continuous overload rating because the limitations in temperature rise were related to 100% rated primary current. In measuring current-transformers the iron loss is negligible because of the low flux densities normally used and thus the main source of heating is the copper loss in the primary and secondary windings. These copper losses are proportional to the square of the respective currents and during continuous operation the temperature attained by the windings substantially follows the same law.

In many current-transformers of the wound-primary type the copper cross-sectional area of the primary winding conductor is determined not by the rated primary current but by the overcurrent factor and its associated time rating, so that in such cases the current density of the primary winding at rated primary current may be quite low and the ability of the current-transformer to meet its temperature-rise requirements, under normal operating conditions, is mainly determined by the thermal characteristics of the secondary winding. Due to saturation of the core during primary overcurrents the secondary current will not, of course, experience the same overcurrent factor as the primary.

It is, of course, extremely difficult, if not impossible, to generalise on this matter because the temperature rise characteristics of any current-transformer depends not only on the type and disposition of the windings and of the core but also on how the current-transformer is enclosed or mounted in, for instance, a switchgear cubicle, or control board. With these limitations in mind, Fig. 42 indicates the overload capacity of a range of air-insulated or dry-type current-transformers.

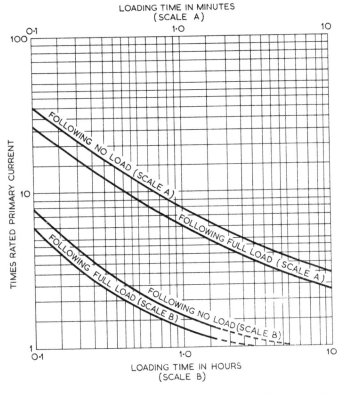

Fig. 42. Typical recommended values for permissible short-time currents for dry-type current-transformers. (Overload not occurring more than once a day.)

For a current-transformer to meet a continuous overload rating means some increase in the overall dimensions of that current-transformer although this increase would, in many cases, be small, while for a ring-type current-transformer there may be no need to increase its physical dimensions because in these cases the thermal characteristics are such that a continuous overload may be easily accommodated provided the location of the transformer is not a restricted one.

This question of overload capacity is of considerable importance in the current-transformer, possibly more so than in other types of equipment. First, there is no great difficulty in maintaining accuracy at an overload value of primary current provided the flux density in the core does not exceed that corresponding to maximum permeability as examination of the error curves given in chapter 4 shows. In fact, the current transformer may be more accurate at say 150% rated primary current than at the 100% value. Furthermore, for a given maximum primary current, if the current-transformer rated primary current is reduced to such a value that some permissible continuous overload is not exceeded this means that the range of primary current for which the accuracy limits apply is also extended at the lower end. Of course, these advantages are not obtained for nothing: the size of core will be determined by the rated primary current and for a given class of accuracy and burden the lower the rated primary current the larger the core required.

This can be best shown by means of an example: let it be assumed that the maximum primary current is 500 A so that normally one would employ a current-transformer having a rated primary current of 500 A and the limits of accuracy would apply to a range of primary current of 50 A to 500 A (the test-point at 120% primary current refers only to accuracy requirements and not to a continuous overload at this level). Now if a current-transformer having a rated primary current of 400 A also had a permissible continuous overload rating of 125% the accuracy range of primary current would be from 500 A down to 40 A. As already indicated the latter current-transformer would probably be larger than that having a rated primary current of 500 A. Again, although it is dangerous to generalise, this technique although offering, as it does, an important extension of accuracy range at the lower primary current levels, does not offer any advantage over the obvious alternative of increasing the accuracy range from that of 120% down to 10% to one of 120% down to 5% without offering a continuous overload capacity. Thus, in the example already used, it may be easier to provide a current-transformer with a rated primary current of 500 A and an accuracy range of 500 A to 25 A than the suggested

current-transformer of 400 A primary current rating with a 125%
continuous overload being permitted and it would be obviously
considerably easier to produce than a current-transformer, again
of 400 A rated primary current and an accuracy range of 500 A
down to 20 A (with 125% permissible continuous overload). This
is due solely to the sharply rising errors at low flux densities as
shown in the various error curves in chapter 4.

It is of interest to note here that in the new standard, B.S. 3938,
although the range of primary current over which the accuracy
limits apply is greater than that in B.S. 81, the new standard still
allows no permissible continuous overload, in relation that is, to
the permissible operating temperatures.

The term 'overcurrent' in B.S. 81 applied to primary currents
possibly many times the rated full-load value associated with
primary system short-circuit or other fault conditions and of short
duration. Thus B.S. 3938 replaces 'overcurrent' and the associated
'overcurrent factor' by two new terms 'rated short-time current'
and 'short-time factor (s.t.f.)'. When the primary current increases
the copper losses in the current-transformer windings immediately
increase, but there is some time-lag before there is a corresponding
rise in the winding temperatures. First of all the loss is stored in the
copper then dissipating into the insulation, the core and the
surrounding cooling medium. Under overcurrent conditions, when
the current increases very suddenly to a possibly very high value,
it is usually assumed that all the heat generated is stored in the
copper.

The temperature rise in the primary winding, $\theta°C$, is then given by

$$\theta°C = \frac{KtI_F^2}{A^2},\qquad(66)$$

where

K = some constant,
I_F = fault current,
A = primary conductor cross-sectional area,
t = time in seconds.

Thus for any particular value of temperature rise

$$\frac{I_F}{A} \propto \frac{1}{\sqrt{t}}.\qquad(67)$$

A well-known equation, sufficiently accurate for temperatures
up to 350°C, is given in eq. (68), $\theta°C$ again being the temperature
rise

$$\theta°C = Ft\left[\frac{m}{2(\theta_0 + 234·5)} + \frac{618·4K}{m}\right],\qquad(68)$$

where

θ_0 = initial temperature °C,

t = time in seconds,

k = ratio of eddy-current loss to the I^2R loss at 75°C,

$F = \dfrac{\text{watts per pound}}{180}$ (at θ_0°C),

$m = 2(\theta_0 + 234\cdot5) + Ft.$

From eq. (67) the short-circuit current rating (from thermal considerations only) for any other time rating may be easily found. If a current-transformer withstands a short-circuit current of I_{F1} for x seconds, then the current for x_1 seconds is I_{F2}, given by

$$I_{F2} = I_{F1}\left(\frac{x}{x_1}\right)^{\frac{1}{2}}. \tag{69}$$

In addition to the thermal stresses caused by the passage of these large short-circuit currents there are also considerable mechanical forces acting on the conductors, and with wound-primary type current-transformers the number of primary turns one may use is limited by the maximum short-circuit current likely to occur. It cannot be too strongly emphasised that although the current-transformer user may sometimes compromise on the ratio, burden and class of accuracy he specifies there can be no such compromise on the short-circuit rating as embodied in the short-time factor (s.t.f.) for current-transformers of the wound-primary type. They must be able to withstand the thermal and dynamic stresses set up by the maximum possible short-circuit current and while the *time* rating is capable of variation, depending upon the type of protection in the primary circuit, the short-circuit *current* rating must never be less than that corresponding to the breaking capacity of the associated circuit breakers.

If the mechanical design of the current-transformer is such that the maximum possible number of primary turns one can use is insufficient to enable a certain class of accuracy to be met for a particular rated primary current with a particular s.t.f., then either the class of accuracy, ratio or burden must be changed.

Put another way, for any standard range of wound-primary current-transformers, then for a particular short-circuit current rating, there is a minimum rated primary current below which one cannot meet some particular class of accuracy at some particular burden and should it be necessary to use a lower rated primary current then either the class of accuracy or the burden, or both, must be altered.

The study of the mechanical forces set up in a wound-primary current-transformer is a complex one and only the broadest outline is possible here. It is well to remember that when such current-transformers are situated relatively close together, as in a three-phase switchgear cubicle, there will also be interaction between the current-transformers as well as the stresses set up in the individual transformers, but the study of these interphase forces is even more complex. When testing current-transformers for their 'short-circuit strength' they should be mounted in exactly the same manner and at the same phase-centres as in normal operation.*

The short-circuit forces in a wound-primary current-transformer are (i) a radial force on the primary coil, tending to burst it or in other words, if the primary winding is not circular in shape, tending to make it so; (ii) a radial force on the secondary coil opposite in effect to (i), as it tends to compress the secondary coil; and (iii) axial forces on both primary and secondary coils, these again being compressive.

The effect of the first two forces may be minimised by making the primary and secondary coils as circular in shape as possible and in the case of the primary coil one frequently uses the primary winding conductor as strip, wound 'on edge'. As the three forces are adversely affected by any radial and axial dissymmetry the assembly of a wound-primary current-transformer must aim at the lowest possible dissymmetry between primary and secondary coils. It must be emphasised here that if the primary and secondary conductors are of different widths the 'pitch' at the ends of both coils is where one experiences these axial forces, even if the axial lengths are nominally the same.

These forces occurring under primary system short-circuit conditions are greatest when the short-circuit current attains its first peak and are proportional to the square of this peak value, which if the transient primary current is fully offset (possesses full assymmetry) is twice the peak symmetrical current and 2·82 times the r.m.s. symmetrical current.

Thus if the associated circuit breaker is rated for a breaking capacity of x kiloamperes r.m.s. short-circuit current, the current-transformers must be able to withstand a maximum possible force proportional to $(2·82x)^2$ peak amperes. This force is of very short duration and as the subsequent current peaks are considerably lower than the first the dynamic forces associated with these are also much lower than the initial 'shock' force and some designers do use a somewhat lower figure than 2·82. B.S.3938 states that the short-time current is the r.m.s. value of the a.c. component of the primary fault current which the current-transformer is capable of withstanding for the rated time without damage, the peak value of

* 'The Calculation of the Magnetising Force', by Halacsy, *Trans. American I.E.E.*, **71** (1952).

the major loop of the first cycle of this current being not less than 2·55 times the symmetrical r.m.s. current.

The analysis of the effect of the short-circuit force is made more complicated by the fact that the elastic limit of copper varies with temperature and that under short-circuit conditions the core saturates so that the primary and secondary ampere-turns are no longer equal, considerably affecting the leakage flux condition in the intercoil space, that is, the space between the primary and secondary coils.

If one assumed that the primary and secondary ampere-turns are equal, the total radial force F_r is given by

$$F_r = 202 \times 10^{-9} a^2 l \lambda^2 D m^2 \alpha^2 \text{ kilogrammes}, \qquad (70)$$

this giving rise to a peripheral force F_p, where $F_p = F_r/2\pi$, that is,

$$F_p = 32 \times 10^{-9} a^2 l \lambda^2 D m^2 \alpha^2 \text{ kilogrammes}. \qquad (71)$$

The hoop tensile stress caused by F_p, and which must be less than the elastic limit of the primary conductor material if deformation of the primary coil is to be avoided, is given by

$$P_p = 32 \times 10^{-9} a \lambda D m^2 \alpha^2 \text{ kilogrammes/sq. cm}, \qquad (72)*$$

where

a = winding depth of primary coil,
α = current density in primary coil due to the r.m.s. rated primary current,
m = ratio of the short-circuit r.m.s. current density to the normal current density (α),
D = mean diameter of primary coil,
l = axial length of primary coil,
λ = space factor of primary coil.

Equations (70), (71) and (72) give pessimistic results and other equations have been evolved with the assumption that the core saturates to such a level that practically all the primary ampere-turns become magnetising ampere-turns and the secondary current is therefore negligibly low.

Many practical designs of wound-primary current-transformers are such that the coils are not circular in shape and inevitably there is a difference between the axial lengths of the primary and secondary coils so that while some estimation of dynamic strength may be made there is only one reliable course of action one may take in practice. This is the testing under the correct short-circuit conditions of sample current-transformers representative of the range concerned in order to determine the dynamic strength of the design used—this dynamic strength frequently being quoted

* Hague, *Instrument Transformers* (Pitman).

in terms of maximum permissible r.m.s. symmetrical overcurrent ampere-turns.

From the foregoing remarks it will be appreciated that in any standard range of wound-primary current-transformers there are two limitations placed on the number of primary turns that can be used, the one due to the mechanical strength of the assembly, the second due to the winding space needed to meet the short-circuit current density requirements demanded by the short-circuit rated time specified.

The effect of frequency on performance

Current-transformers are normally designed for one specific supply frequency and as such are subject to the normal small fluctuations of that frequency, but the errors are not materially affected. Some current-transformers however may be required to operate over a range of frequency or a current-transformer designed specifically for use at one frequency may occasionally be energised at some other value, this latter case being particularly true of current-transformers used in the laboratory and it is important that one then appreciates what happens in such circumstances.

Consider first the case of a current-transformer possessing negligible secondary leakage reactance supplying a purely resistive burden designed to operate at a frequency of f_1 c.p.s. The peak flux density corresponding to, say, full-load primary current is B_1 webers/sq. metre, but should the frequency be changed to f_2 c.p.s. the flux density for the same primary current changes to B_2 webers/sq. metre, where $B_2 = (f_1/f_2)B_1$ webers/sq. metre. The watt-loss and magnetising currents change and hence both the ratio error and phase error alter. This change in the watt-loss and magnetising currents is a twofold one—first, there is the actual change in flux density and secondly there is the change in the relationship between these currents and flux density which is inherently dependent on the frequency. As far as the watt-loss current is concerned it will be remembered that the hysteresis loss is proportional to frequency while the eddy-current loss is proportional to the square of the frequency and the manner in which the total loss is split up into these plays an important part in the relationship of the errors with frequency.

As 50 c.p.s. is the most commonly specified and used frequency it is instructive to indicate the changes in errors experienced by a current-transformer designed specifically for this frequency if the frequency is changed to either 25 c.p.s., 60 c.p.s. or 400 c.p.s.

The errors become worse at the 25 c.p.s. frequency for the same primary current and burden, and the core saturates at a lower value of secondary current and hence of primary current, while at the higher frequencies the errors decrease and there is later saturation. One must use such comment with some degree of circumspection—no indication is given of the high specific core watts-loss incurred at the higher flux densities at 400 c.p.s. or higher frequencies, but as a general rule current-transformers designed for 50 c.p.s. are perfectly satisfactory for operation at 400 c.p.s. at the same burden. Should a larger burden be used at the higher frequency then it is possible that the current-transformer will be able to handle this without increasing the errors or the temperature rise but it is advisable that in such cases the manufacturer of the current-transformer be consulted.

The presence of secondary winding leakage reactance or of an inductive component in the burden complicates matters because both these are themselves proportional to frequency, thus it must be remembered that in the case of the operating frequency being less than the design frequency the secondary winding and burden reactances will decrease, but should the operating frequency be greater than the design frequency they will increase. As previously discussed, although such increase in reactance will increase the required flux density, it may have a beneficial effect on the errors.

Test windings on current-transformers

In practice one frequently wishes to check whether or not an installed current-transformer and its associated equipment is functioning correctly, this requirement being particularly true of protective current-transformers. However, it also frequently happens that it is not practicable to use the normal primary winding to energise the current-transformer core to the desired level of excitation, not the least of the problems encountered here is the provision of a suitable portable test-set capable of delivering possibly many hundreds of amperes for such testing and the ready connection of this equipment to the normal primary circuit.

For this and other reasons it is common practice to specify that a 'test-winding' or 'test-secondary' is included in the current-transformer. The latter term is to be strongly deprecated for the simple reason that in use the test-winding becomes a temporary *primary* winding. It is usual for such a test-winding to be nominally rated at twice the rated secondary current so that the turns on this test-winding are one-half those of the secondary winding. With a test-winding it becomes an easy matter to check the performance of the installed current-transformer and the provision of a suitable variable current supply for such testing presents little difficulty.

Test-windings suffer from some disadvantages—for any given available volume the provision of a test-winding means that there will be some reduction in the core cross-sectional area one can accommodate, or put another way, the inclusion of a test-winding increases the overall size of the current-transformer. It will be appreciated that the test-winding must be fully insulated from both primary and secondary windings.

With ring-type current-transformers, operational tests using the test-winding give accurate results, but if the current-transformer is of the high reactance type the use of a test-winding does not necessarily give a faithful reproduction of actual operational conditions because the secondary winding leakage reactance when the test-winding is being used to energise the core is not that obtained under actual working conditions.

One final point on test-windings: when not in use test-windings must be open-circuited *not* short-circuited. Very little thought should be necessary to confirm this because if the primary winding is energised and the secondary winding is connected to its burden, then a short-circuited test-winding on the same core would mean a complete breakdown of the normal relationship between the primary current and the secondary current; the current flowing through the burden in this condition would not be that given by the nominal ratio of the current-transformer.

CHAPTER 7

METHODS OF MODIFYING CURRENT-TRANSFORMER ERRORS

'Turns correction' or 'turns compensation' has already been mentioned and it has been shown how this simple technique of making the turns ratio slightly less than the nominal current ratio causes the percentage ratio error to become less negative by an amount constant over the whole operating range of the primary current, provided the overall power factor of the secondary circuit is unity or lagging. Furthermore, as long as the turns correction adopted is not too large or 'harsh' the phase errors are not affected.

Thus turns correction does not *invariably* assist in those current-transformers where a limitation is placed on the phase errors as well as on the ratio errors, as in all the Classes of Accuracy for measuring current-transformers in B.S. 3938 excepting Class D, or in those cases where there is a limitation placed on the variation of ratio errors over the primary current range as well as on their absolute values, as in the metering classes of accuracy in B.S. 3938. This comment does not mean that turns correction is not a useful technique to the current-transformer designer and it is frequently employed in practice, but where phase errors are specified it is these which almost always determine the design.

In fact this technique is so useful on occasions that the designer will adopt a slight modification—usually termed 'partial turns correction' in those cases where the number of secondary turns is so low that a correction of one full turn would be too harsh. This partial turns correction can only be carried out on certain types of construction and is not readily applicable, for instance, to those current-transformers in which the core is made up of a stack of laminations and where the secondary winding is wound on a former or a bobbin.

If the current-transformer is ring-type or similar with the secondary winding applied directly on the core then this partial turns correction is easily carried out by making the core of a number of separate sections and arranging the secondary winding in such a way that the last turn does not embrace the whole cross-sectional area of that core.

Let it be assumed that the core inside and outside diameters have been fixed and the axial length required is w inches. This core may be made up of x separate toroids so that the axial length of each is w/x inches. If then the number of secondary turns as determined by the nominal current ratio is N_s, but the last turn is arranged to embrace only $(x-1)$ core sections, then the percentage turns correction is given by $[N_s-(1/x)]/N_s \times 100\%$. If the last turn embraces only $(x-2)$ core sections the turns correction then becomes $[N_s-(2/x)]/N_s \times 100\%$, and so on. This technique frequently has some beneficial effect on the phase error as it introduces some leakage reactance into the secondary circuit.

A very similar technique sometimes used is to employ virtually two separate current-transformers, sharing a common primary winding, but where the secondary winding on each separate core is wound for half the rated secondary current and these secondary windings are then connected in parallel to supply the burden. A single turn correction on one of these secondary windings will effectively give an overall partial turns correction approximately one quarter of that obtained by a single turn correction on the corresponding 'single-core single-secondary winding' design. However, a full analysis of this technique demands a graphical method but it is of enough general interest to describe this rather fully.*

Let it be assumed that the nominal ratio of a current-transformer is K_n, but that this transformer consists of two cores of cross-sectional areas, A_a and A_b, which may or not be equal, and each having a secondary winding such that the nominal ratio of each section is $2K_n$. Let the turns of one section be N_{2a} and of the other, N_{2b}, all other quantities having these distinguishing suffixes a and b.

The vector diagram for these parallel connected secondaries is given in Fig. 43 for a lagging power factor burden, and although this diagram seems strange due to the manner in which the excitation triangles have been drawn, a brief examination will show that for each core there is no difference at all compared with the more orthodox method of presentation. Figure 43 has been drawn in the manner chosen simply for ease in the derivation of the final graphical approach.

If the total secondary current is I_s, then this is the vector sum of the currents in the two secondary windings, that is,

$$I_s = I_{2a} + I_{2b}. \tag{73}$$

* 'Current Transformers and their Operation', by Halacsy, *Electrical Times*, 26 June, 1952.

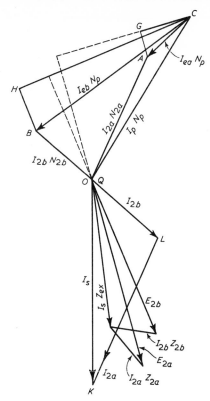

Fig. 43. Vector diagram for two
secondaries in parallel.

If Z_{ex} is the external secondary burden and Z_a and Z_b the internal impedances of these two secondary windings then, again, vectorially

$$E_{2a} = I_s Z_{ex} + I_{2a} Z_{2a} \tag{74}$$

and

$$E_{2b} = I_s Z_{ex} + I_{2b} Z_{2b}. \tag{75}$$

E_{2a} and E_{2b} are the induced e.m.f.s in each of the secondary windings.

If I_p = primary current,
    N_p = primary turns, and
I_{ea}, I_{eb} = exciting currents in the two cores, then vectorially

$$I_p N_p = I_{2a} N_{2a} + I_{ea} N_p = I_{2b} N_{2b} + I_{eb} N_p, \tag{76}$$

(I_{ea} and I_{eb} in primary amperes). Of these quantities only I_p, N_p, N_{2a}, N_{2b}, Z_{ex}, Z_{2a} and Z_{2b} are known in addition to the cross-sectional areas of the cores.

Because of the non-linear relationship between I_{ea} and E_{2a} (and between I_{eb} and E_{2b}) a full solution for the errors requires such a complex graphical approach that certain approximations must be adopted in order to obtain a practical method of solution.

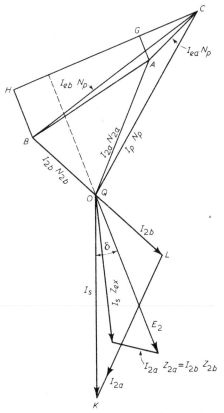

Fig. 44. Simplified vector diagram for
two secondaries in parallel.

The key approximation is the assumption that $E_{2a} = E_{2b} = E_2$, the vector diagram then simplifying to Fig. 44.

Now, E_2 is calculable and therefore from the well-known transformer equation (eq. (6) in chapter 2) the flux density in each core may be calculated and from the core material's magnetic characteristic curves I_{ea} and I_{eb} are found, together with their magnetising and watt-loss components. Thus the two excitation triangles in Fig. 44, *CGA* and *CHB,* may be constructed, although of course the position of these two triangles relative to the origin *O* has not yet been determined.

It must be remembered that the direction of the common base line of these two triangles, the line *HGC*, being parallel to the

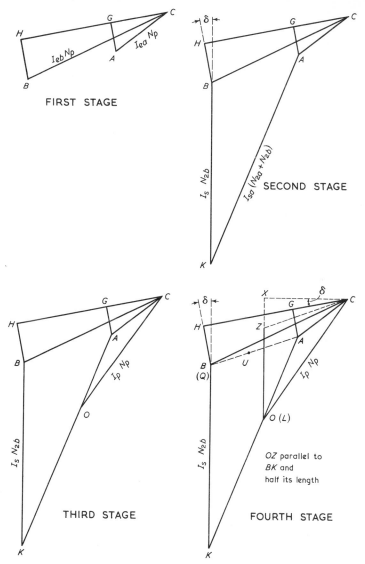

Fig. 45. Construction of error diagram for two secondaries in parallel.

flux vector is also known relative to the vector of the assumed common value of induced e.m.f. and hence also to the total secondary current I_s as the overall secondary power factor angle is known.

Now if eq. (73) is multiplied throughout by N_{2b} one obtains

$$I_s N_{2b} = I_{2a} N_{2b} + I_{2b} N_{2b},$$

and if the vectors in triangle QLK in Fig. 44 are increased N_{2b} times this ampere-turn triangle may be moved so that QL becomes coincident with BO, that is, Q and B, and L and O respectively become coincident.

In other words, starting from the two excitation triangles the vector $I_s N_{2b}$, that is BK, can be drawn to the correct scale through the point B at the known angle δ to HB as shown in Fig. 45. K may now be joined to A but again, while the origin O is along the vector KA, its actual position is not yet known. However,

$$KA = I_{sa}(N_{2a} + N_{2b})$$

and if KA is divided into two portions KO and OA and such that $KO/OA = N_{2b}/N_{2a}$, the position of the origin O is established and the vector diagram completed, thus giving both the direction and magnitude of the vector OC which is $N_p I_p$.

Now the nominal ampere-turns may be sensibly given by $\frac{1}{2}(I_s N_{2a})$ or $\frac{1}{2}(I_s N_{2b})$, which is shown as the vector OZ or LZ in Fig. 45. The overall error is then given by ZC and the dotted lines ZX and XC are proportional to the ratio error and phase error respectively. This vector diagram is, of course, grossly out of correct scale and a sensible and practical method depends on an easy way of determining the position of Z relative to the two excitation triangles and while there are two or three ways of doing this to reasonable accuracy, it can be shown that if U is the mid-point of the vector BA, then $ZU = \frac{1}{2}I_s(N_{2a} - N_{2b})$ and this is the basis of the suggested technique, remembering too that the angle between XC and the excitation base line is the same as the secondary circuit power factor angle.

Thus starting from two grid lines at right angles to each other and suitably scaled to give percentage ratio error and phase error as previously explained when discussing the M. & G. diagram, the excitation base line is drawn at the known secondary power factor angle δ to the phase error axis as shown in Fig. 46. Having calculated E_2 and obtained the flux densities in the two cores and from the material magnetic characteristic curves the magnetising and loss ampere-turns are found. Hence the two excitation triangles can be plotted on the base line, the points A and B are then joined and the mid-point U, obtained.

From this point U the line ZU of length $\frac{1}{2}I_s(N_{2a}-N_{2b})$ is then drawn parallel to the ratio error axis and as shown, once the point Z has been so determined, the ratio error and phase error can be immediately obtained. The same scales can be used for the ratio error axis and the phase error axis for various percentages of full-load current provided the scale for the excitation triangles is adjusted each time. The length of ZU, of course, remains constant.

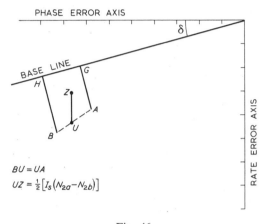

Fig. 46.

A similar technique to that just described is to again use two separate cores each with its own secondary winding, but with these secondaries connected in series and not in parallel. If the overall nominal ratio, that is, that of the set, is K_n, then one secondary winding would have the nominal turns decided by this K_n but the other would have turns correction applied. This effectively gives partial turns correction to the set as a whole but a full analysis of the problem can only be done graphically.

Use of shunts to modify errors

Examination of the vector diagram of the current-transformer, such as that shown in Fig. 2 in chapter 2, shows how important is the part played by the secondary circuit power factor in the determination of the performance of the current-transformer. This point has been mentioned elsewhere in this book, but for the present discussion it immediately indicates a number of ways in which the errors of the current-transformer may be modified by the use of primary and secondary shunts. Such shunts are either resistances or capacitances or a combination of these.

Taking the case of a secondary shunt, as shown in Fig. 47, such a shunt having a large resistance value compared with the burden, then from the vector diagram it is seen that the addition of the shunt increases the ratio error but decreases the phase error. The increase in ratio error can be easily overcome by the prior application of suitable turns correction, remembering that this increase in the ratio error is approximately $100R_b/R_{sh}\%$. The reduction in the phase error is approximately $\tan^{-1}X_b/R_{sh}$ radians.

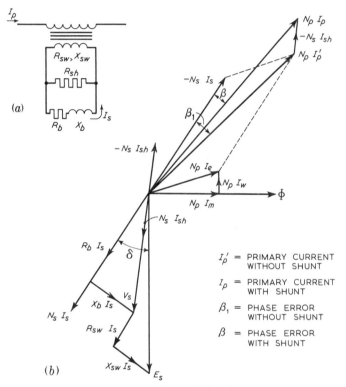

Fig. 47. Secondary resistive shunt.

As any impedance appearing on the secondary side of a current-transformer can always be replaced by one on the primary side, one obtains the same effect by using a resistance shunted across the primary terminals and with such a technique it may be shown that if the total resistance and total reactance of the current-transformer and its burden when referred to the primary side are given by R_p and X_p respectively, then the increase in ratio error is approximately $100R_p/R_{sh}\%$ and the decrease in phase error is $\tan^{-1}Z_p/R_{sh}$ radians.

Some advantage is gained from such a primary shunt in that it affords some protection to the current-transformer and the burden under transient conditions in the primary circuit.

The use of a secondary capacitive shunt leads to a reduction in both ratio error and phase error, in the former, approximately $200\pi f C X_b \%$ and in the latter $\tan^{-1} 2\pi f C R_s$ radians.

As before, a capacitive shunt may be used in the primary side, but here one must watch unwanted resonance effects. Alternative methods of error modification call for the use of an additional resistance or capacitance not connected as a shunt but to a tertiary winding on the core, the advantage of such a technique being due to the fact that the current taken by such a resistance or capacitance

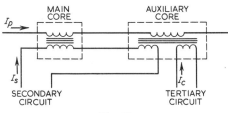

Fig. 48.

is proportional to the flux and hence to the secondary induced e.m.f. rather than to the secondary terminal voltage. The biggest advantage of the use of primary or secondary shunts or of the last-mentioned tertiary winding and additional resistance or capacitance is that all these methods offer a means whereby the effect on the errors varies with load current and is not constant in the same sense as when ordinary turns correction is employed.

It will be appreciated that such techniques as those described are only rarely employed and the same comment applies to the numerous methods developed over the years where what is termed 'two-stage transformation' is used.

The simplest two-stage current-transformer is shown diagrammatically in Fig. 48, the main core consisting of an electrical steel, while the auxiliary core is of a nickel-iron alloy, usually Mumetal. Both cores have a secondary winding of the same number of turns, while the auxiliary core has a tertiary winding also with this number of turns. As will be readily seen, the ampere-turns developed by this tertiary winding, when connected to an external burden, will be the difference between the primary and secondary ampere-turns on the auxiliary core and thus they will be substantially equal to the exciting ampere-turns (causing the errors) of the main core. Thus, provided the tertiary burden is small and by the use of

Mumetal the exciting ampere-turns required by the auxiliary core are made much lower than those for the main core, then the error introduced by these auxiliary ampere-turns will be much smaller than the main core errors and one obtains good compensation. Unfortunately, there is one serious drawback in that the associated instrument must have two independent current coils—one for the main secondary current, the other for the tertiary or corrective current.

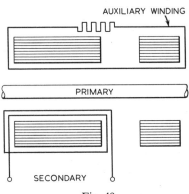

Fig. 49.

A similar technique leads to particularly advantageous correction of the phase error in that not only do the phase errors decrease but the variation of these over a range of primary load current also decreases. This technique is dependent on additional magnetisation from the primary side as shown in Fig. 49, from which it is seen that an auxiliary core operating at a high flux density energises a winding on the main core and it can be arranged by suitable design of this auxiliary core that the correction applied is greatest when the phase error is greatest, leading to a much 'flatter' phase-error characteristic. This technique was developed by Wellings and Mayo and one disadvantage in this current-transformer is the somewhat critical conditions associated with saturation of the auxiliary core.

Hobson* produced a somewhat similar current-transformer, as shown in Fig. 50, where again there are two cores, the main core and a compensator core—R_b is the main burden and the secondary current through this burden will be determined by the number of turns on the main core. With a compensating burden, R_c, connected as shown to one winding on the compensator core, then there will be an induced e.m.f. set up in this winding and the

* 'Instrument Transformers', by Hobson, *J.I.E.E.*, **91** (1944), part II, p. 182.

flux in the core will also induce a similar e.m.f. in the second winding on the core (the two compensator windings having the same number of turns). Thus the voltage across the main burden is shared between the two cores, or in other words, a reduced e.m.f. is required from the main secondary winding leading therefore to a reduction in both phase error and ratio error. Ideally, when $R_c = R_b$ (or to be precise, when $Z_c = Z_s$, where Z_s is the total secondary impedance), the main secondary induced e.m.f. is zero

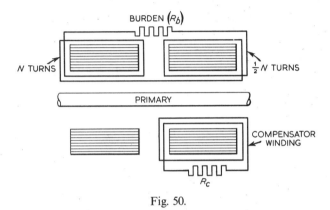

Fig. 50.

and the errors would disappear but, of course, there will be some watt-loss and magnetising ampere-turns required to maintain the compensator flux. Other factors cause some departure from the ideal, but this technique, employing normal design methods, give a current-transformer having exceptionally low errors.

There are numerous other methods suggested for the reduction of errors which depend on the technique of pre-magnetisation, that is, the use of additional a.c. magnetisation to pre-excite a core to a flux density in the maximum permeability region and to then superimpose the working flux on this. There are a number of ways of obtaining the additional a.c. magnetisation—from an external source, from an auxiliary core, and so on.

All these techniques offer the advantage that a basically ring-type construction may be adopted for quite low-rated primary current values and therefore are of interest in high-voltage circuits, for obvious reasons.

CHAPTER 8

TYPES OF CURRENT-TRANSFORMER CONSTRUCTION

As previously mentioned, current-transformers may be conveniently subdivided into those possessing a single-turn primary winding and those with a multi-turn primary winding. Such a subdivision is convenient from both the technical and commercial viewpoints as has been made clear by what has already been written, but it is worthwhile emphasising the advantages of the former over the latter type. These are that the current-transformer possessing a single-turn primary winding, whatever its detailed construction, gives the more robust design and, furthermore, one in which the performance over a wide range of primary current is easily predictable. As shown later, the use of a multi-turn primary winding in a protective current-transformer manufactured to B.S. 2046 put that current-transformer within the category of 'high-reactance' as defined in that standard and involved the manufacturer in additional testing to prove compliance with accuracy class requirements. B.S. 3938 preserves the categories 'low-reactance' and 'high-reactance' and keeps the requirement of special tests for current-transformers of the latter type, with some slight alteration.

There is one obvious comment that must be made; frequently a current-transformer may be given a name depending on its duty so that within the broad classification of current-transformers into 'measuring' and 'protective' current-transformers one frequently meets such terms as 'ammeter current-transformer', 'core-balance current-transformer', 'frame-leakage current-transformer', and so on. The use of these terms may sometimes confuse the uninitiated and thus it becomes important to emphasise that all these are, *fundamentally*, either of the single-turn or multi-turn primary type of construction.

The simplest form any current-transformer can take is the *ring-type* or *window-type*, examples of which are given in Fig. 51a, which shows three commonly used shapes, that is, rectangular, 'stadium' and circular core orifices. The core, if of a nickel-iron

Fig. 51a. Four varieties of ring-type current-transformers. (*The English Electric Co. Ltd.*)

Fig. 51b. Various stages in manufacture of a ring-type current-transformer. (*Foster Transformers Ltd.*)

Fig. 52. Typical resin-encapsulated ring-type current-transformer. (*The English Electric Co. Ltd.*)

alloy or an oriented electrical steel, is almost certainly of the continuously wound type, while in those current-transformers still using a hot-rolled electrical steel it will consist of a stack of ring-stampings. Before applying the secondary winding the core is insulated by means of end collars and circumferential wraps of pressboard such as 'Elephantide' or 'Presspahn', which, in addition to being the insulating medium, must also protect the secondary winding conductor from mechanical damage due to the sharp corners of the core, these steps in manufacture are shown in Fig. 51b.

In recent months these continuously wound cores have become available in encapsulated form, a variety of resins and other encapsulation materials being used, and applied either by a fluidised bed or electrostatic spraying technique, although in the U.S.A. encapsulated toroids have been used for several years.

The secondary winding conductor is then wound on the core, in many cases by means of a toroidal winding machine of which there are a number of makes available, although hand winding is still frequently adopted if the number of secondary turns to be wound is small.

Fig. 53. Range of low-voltage current-transformers in moulded cases. (*Dr.-Ing. Hans Ritz.*)

After the secondary winding has been placed on the core the ring-type transformer is completed by exterior taping, with or without first applying exterior end-rings and circumferential insulating wraps. Alternatively, the core and secondary winding assembly may be encapsulated.

Obviously there are numerous variations possible in the manufacturing techniques and materials one adopts, but with cores of nickel-iron alloy or oriented electrical steel, because of the strain-sensitive nature of these magnetic materials, care must be taken to avoid undue stresses and thus impregnation and encapsulation materials and methods must be carefully chosen. One point here is that while core encapsulation causes some degradation in magnetic performance it may well be worthwhile using a core so treated if the complete current-transformer is itself to be encapsulated, because no further degradation is then likely to be caused by the latter encapsulation. Figure 52 shows a typical encapsulated ring-type current-transformer, while Fig. 53 shows examples of ring-type current-transformers in moulded cases.

A near-relative to the ring-type current-transformer is the so-called *bushing-type* current-transformer; this is, in fact, indistinguishable from the ordinary ring-type but the term is used when the current-transformer fits over a fully insulated primary conductor such as over the oil-end of a terminal bushing of a power transformer or oil-circuit breaker. It is rather interesting to point

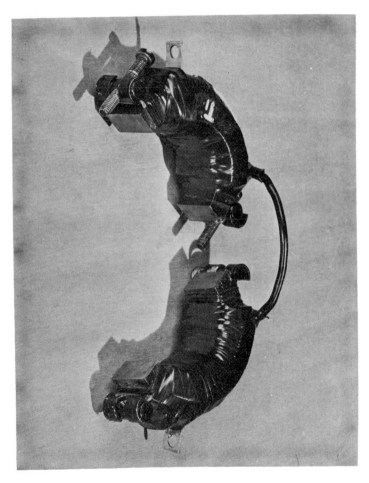

Fig. 54. Split-core current-transformer. (*The English Electric Co. Ltd.*)

out here that B.S. 3938 does not recognise ring-type and window-type current-transformers, both these types being called 'bushing current-transformers'.

Figure 54 shows a typical example of a *split-core* current-transformer manufactured in exactly the same way as the ring-type except that the core is split, each half having two finely ground or lapped gap faces. These current-transformers are assembled on to

Fig. 55. Laboratory type multi-ratio, high-accuracy current-transformers. (*Smith-Hobson Ltd.*)

the primary conductor 'on site' for either temporary or permanent duty. Changes in primary system operational conditions may demand the installation of additional current-transformers and the use of the split-core type enables this to be done without the inconvenient and possibly costly dismantling and then reassembly of primary bus-bars or cable runs. There are some disadvantages: before cutting the core it has to be resin-bonded causing some degradation in magnetic performance, there being some increase in both watts-loss and magnetising current as compared with the toroidal core, while the presence of the air-gaps, however small these may be made by careful machining, causes a further increase in magnetising current. Care must be taken to ensure the gap faces are perfectly clean and free from foreign matter. Clamping pressure must be held to the specified figure, too low a pressure may lead to increased errors while too high a pressure may cause deformation of the core and damage to the gap faces.

Fig. 56. Bar-primary current-transformer before assembly. The insulation of the primary bar incorporates a foil brought out to the clamps, improving impulse level by reducing 'edge effect' of the clamps. (*The English Electric Co. Ltd.*)

A typical laboratory type current-transformer is shown in Fig. 55. Responsibility for the provision of major insulation between the core and secondary winding assembly and the primary circuit is not in the hands of the manufacturer but is with the current-transformer user in all the types so far shown, although it is extremely unlikely that the laboratory type current-transformer is used in other than a low-voltage primary circuit.

The next type of current-transformer is that shown dissembled in Fig. 56, this being the *bar-primary* current-transformer, or, as it is sometimes termed, the *bar-type* current-transformer. Here the core and secondary winding are the same as in the ring-type and take up the same variety in form, but the fully insulated bar conductor constituting the single-turn primary winding is now an integral part of the current-transformer. The insulation on the primary conductor may be bakelised paper, either as a separate tube or wrapped directly on the bar, a porcelain tube or a resin moulded directly on the bar. The radial depth and axial length of this insulation will, of course, be determined by the specified power frequency and impulse-test voltages. Some bar-primary current-transformers are now fully resin-encapsulated, a technique finding increasing favour, particularly for current-transformers being used in 6·6 kV and 11 kV and similar primary systems.

Current-transformers having a multi-turn primary winding are normally termed *wound-primary* current-transformers in which, again, one naturally encounters a wide variety of mechanical assembly techniques and materials. They possess two major disadvantages, as already discussed; first, the number of primary turns one can use is determined by the ability of the mechanical structure to withstand the shock forces associated with primary short-circuit currents and the primary conductor cross-sectional area is frequently determined by this fault current and not the nominal full-load primary current. (Here, in all fairness, it must be pointed out that in many cases the orifice of a ring-type current-transformer may be required to accommodate a primary conductor capable of handling a continuous current in excess of the current-transformer's rated value, that is, a 150/5 current-transformer may be required to be mounted on a bus-bar capable of handling 800 A.) The second objection to many types of wound-primary current-transformers is that they possess secondary winding leakage reactance to such a degree that accurate estimation of performance at primary overcurrents is virtually impossible.

Figure 57 shows a wound-primary current-transformer typical of those used in low-voltage primary circuits. The secondary winding is wound on a bakelite former or bobbin and the heavy primary conductor either wound directly on top of the secondary, suitable

Fig. 57. Low-voltage wound-primary current-transformer. (*The English Electric Co. Ltd.*)

insulation being first applied over the secondary winding or the primary is wound entirely separately, taped with suitable insulating material and then assembled with the secondary winding on the core. While taping is still employed as major insulation for the primary winding in current-transformers for use in high-voltage primary circuits, one frequently encounters for this application a primary winding of flexible cable or strip wound into porcelain or bakelised paper tubes, as in the so-called 'trombone-type' current-transformer. Resin encapsulation is being increasingly used in the production of wound-primary current-transformers, one example being shown in Fig. 58, where this encapsulation has also been associated with a cruciform or stepped core section. This current-transformer is also of interest because it is an example of a 'double-secondary' current-transformer, that is, one in which there are two separate cores, each possessing its own secondary winding, one possibly for metering, the other for a protective duty. The use

Fig. 58. A double-secondary wound-primary current-transformer for 11 kV service using resin-cast coils. (*The English Electric Co. Ltd.*)

of the cruciform or stepped core section enables the designer, in the case of a single secondary current-transformer, to use the preferable circular form for the primary winding which, for maximum strength, is often of a rectangular sectioned conductor 'wound on edge'.

One other point of difference between the two wound-primary current-transformers shown is that the first uses the so-called shell-type transformer construction, the core consisting of 'E and I' or 'T and U' laminations or the equivalent while that shown in Fig. 59 uses the 'simple construction' where 'L' laminations, cut and punched rectangular laminations, or similar cores, are used.

In the manufacture of current-transformers the assembly of lamination stacks demands somewhat greater care than in ordinary transformers in order to keep the reluctance of the interleaved corners as low as possible and hence minimising the magnetising current. Sometimes the cut-wound core is used whether the

Fig. 59. Another 11 kV resin-cast wound-primary current-transformer.
(*Foster Transformers Ltd.*)

construction is 'shell' or 'simple' and here the precautions already
mentioned in connection with split-core current-transformers also
apply. Furthermore, the use of the strain sensitive magnetic alloys
either in lamination or wound-core form demand some care in
avoiding excessive pressure in clamping and the like, as this may
cause loss of performance.

Sometimes it is not apparent from the external appearance of a
current-transformer whether it has a multi-turn or single-turn
primary winding and in some cases the external constructional
arrangements may, in fact, be common to both types of primary
winding. Figure 60 shows such a current-transformer which is for
11 kV service but is also typical of the *post-type* current-transformer used for the highest primary system voltages. Figure 61
shows a very similar cast-resin current-transformer while Fig. 62
is a rather interesting special design of current-transformer.

There are some other points of interest: whenever possible
secondary windings in the case of ring-type current-transformers
should utilise the whole available winding length on the core, the
secondary turns being suitably spaced to accomplish this and the
insulation between secondary winding and core earth must be

Fig. 60. Outdoor current-transformer with porcelain insulation (both internal and external). (*Dr.-Ing. Hans Ritz.*)

Fig. 61. 10 kV cast-resin current-transformer for indoor service. (*Dr.-Ing. Hans Ritz.*)

Fig. 62. An interesting special current-transformer, cast ring-type with split-core. Used on overhead lines. Installed and removed by long pole. (*Foster Transformers Ltd.*)

capable of withstanding the high peak voltages caused if the secondary winding is open-circuited when primary current is flowing. In the case of a large number of secondary turns requiring more than one winding layer it is a frequently adopted technique to sectionalise this secondary winding to considerably reduce the peak voltage between layers.

With wound-primary current-transformers this particular problem is rarely met but it is of importance to try and obtain good relative positioning of the primary and secondary coils thus minimising the axial forces on both coils caused by primary short-circuit currents.

The choice of insulating material and other details of construction are frequently determined by whether the current-transformer is of the dry-type, that is, air insulated, or whether it is oil-immersed or compound filled, but there is little point in further discussion on this because, as pointed out earlier, the general insulation problems encountered in current-transformers are no different from those found in other electrical equipment. Neither is there any advantage gained by describing other types of current-transformers in addition to those already shown because this would merely result in a catalogue of types varying only in minor details from each other.

This present chapter is perhaps a good opportunity to make an appeal to users of current-transformers on behalf of the designer because it must be emphasised that he frequently finds himself without a completely free hand in design in that limiting dimensions or other requirements force him to adopt unsuitable proportions in his designs and an often-heard complaint from the designer is that space allocated for current-transformers in, for example, metal-clad switchgear, is too small or unsuitable for some reason. Certainly all too seldom is the instrument-transformer designer brought in at the earliest stages of the development of, for instance, a new range of switchgear. There is always some sacrifice of optimum design in a standardised range whether the product is a current-transformer or other equipment, but early appraisal of the space requirements for a logical range of current-transformers would considerably assist the designer in his task and sometimes lead to a simpler assembly, which in turn sometimes means greater robustness, of considerable interest in wound-primary current-transformers.

CHAPTER 9

CURRENT-TRANSFORMERS IN INDICATING AND METERING CIRCUITS

In the measurement of both energy and power the tested errors of the associated current-transformers to prove compliance with a specified class of accuracy are subject to possibly considerable modification in order to establish what may be termed the operational errors.

Taking, first of all, the measurement of power and considering the effect on the accuracy of measurement caused by the ratio error and phase error of any associated current-transformer, the effect of the ratio error is quite straightforward: a %R.E. of -1%, that is, a Ratio Correction Factor of $1\cdot01$, causes the instrument to read 1% low but the effect of the phase error is not so apparent. Consider the single-phase case; if the load power factor is $\cos\theta$, the primary current, I_p, and the primary voltage, V_p, then the true power W_p, is given by $V_p I_p \cos\theta$.

If the phase error of the current-transformer is β minutes the meter reading is $V_p I_p \cos(\theta-\beta)$ assuming this phase error is positive, thus giving a high reading.

To correct for the current-transformer phase error the meter reading has to be multiplied by the correction factor, K_β, given by

$$K_\beta = \frac{\cos\theta}{\cos(\theta-\beta)}$$

$$= \frac{1}{\cos\beta + \tan\theta\sin\beta}.$$

As β is a small angle $\cos\beta = 1$ and $\sin\beta = \beta$ radians so that

$$K_\beta = \frac{1}{1+\beta\tan\theta}, \ \beta \text{ in radians.}$$

or

$$K_\beta = \frac{1}{1+(\beta\tan\theta/3438)}, \beta \text{ in minutes,}$$

and when

$$\frac{\beta \tan \theta}{3438} < 0.05$$

$$K_\beta = 1 - \frac{\beta \tan \theta}{3438}. \tag{77}$$

Thus the error in measurement caused by the phase error of the current-transformer is also influenced by the primary load power factor and the higher this is the less the effect of any particular value of phase error as shown in Table 4.

Table 4. *Showing how any particular value of phase error has diminishing effect on wattmeter error as power factor of primary load increases*

Lagging power factor	Phase error to cause 0·1 % increase in instrument reading
0·5	2 minutes leading
0·6	2·6 minutes leading
0·7	3·4 minutes leading
0·8	4·5 minutes leading
0·9	7·0 minutes leading
0·95	9·5 minutes leading

For three-phase three-wire circuits in which the two-wattmeter method is adopted the true power, W_p, is given by

$$W_p = V_p I_p \cos(\theta + 30) + V_p I_p \cos(\theta - 30) \text{ watts,}$$

θ again being the power factor angle of the primary circuit.

Assuming that the phase error is again given by β minutes (for each of the two associated current-transformers), the meters read a total of $[V_p I_p \cos(\theta + 30 - \beta) + V_p I_p \cos(\theta - 30 - \beta)]$ watts and therefore the correction factor to be used to obtain the true power is now given by

$$K_\beta = \frac{\cos(\theta + 30) + \cos(\theta - 30)}{\cos(\theta + 30 - \beta) + \cos(\theta - 30 - \beta)},$$

which reduces to

$$K_\beta = \frac{1}{1 + \beta \tan \theta},$$

exactly the same as for the single-phase case.

When metering energy a further factor must be taken into account, namely, the load cycle of the circuit being metered.

Assume that the primary circuit nominal full-load current is the same as the rated primary current of the current-transformer and is given by I_p. Furthermore, let this analysis apply to a total time T_t which may be a day, a week or some other period. Then if it is assumed I_p is the full-load current for time T_f and for the remainder of the time, $T_t - T_f$, only xI_p load current is flowing, where x is some fraction of full-load, then the true kWh would be given by

$$\text{kWh} = \frac{V}{1000}[I_p T_f + xI_p(T_t - T_f)]$$

$$= \text{kW}_f[T_f + x(T_t - T_f)],$$

where kW_f = kilowatts at full-load.

If the error in registration at full-load is zero and at xI_p is $n\%$, then the error in registration during the period of light load is $\text{kW}_f x(T_t - T_f)n/100$ and the percentage error in registration over the whole unit period is

$$\frac{xn(T_t - T_f)}{T_f + x(T_t - T_f)}\%.$$

All the factors in this expression are known in any particular case and therefore this overall percentage error is easily calculable.

To assist in one's calculations—as I_p the full-load current flows for the fraction of the unit period T_f/T_t, then the percentage error in total registration is given by

$$\%\text{error} = \frac{xn(1 - T_f/T_t)}{T_f/T_t + x(1 - T_f/T_t)}\%, \qquad (78)$$

and one is therefore able to plot a family of curves of

$$\frac{x(1 - T_f/T_t)}{T_f/T_t + x(1 - T_f/T_t)}$$

against T_f/T_t, each curve corresponding to a particular value of x, as shown in Fig. 63, and once the value of this expression has been obtained from the appropriate curve the total error in registration is easily determined by multiplying by n.

It is instructive to take an example to indicate what may happen in practice: assume that over a certain period of time, full-load current is flowing for one-quarter of that period and for the remainder of the time only 10% full-load current exists.

Thus $T_f/T_t = 0.25$ and $x = 0.1$ and if at full-load the error in registration is zero and at 10% full-load is 1%, then the total error in registration for the whole period is given by

$$\frac{0.1 \times 1 \times (1-0.25)}{0.25+0.1(1-0.25)}\% = 0.231\%.$$

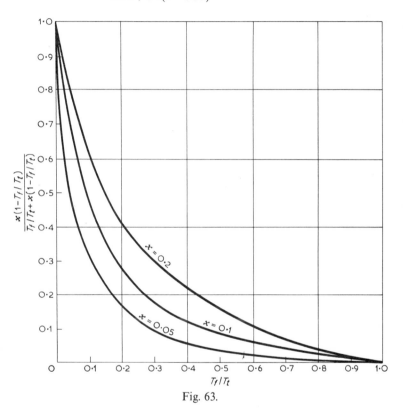

Fig. 63.

If the error at full-load is not zero but $n_1\%$ it can be shown that the total error in registration is then given by

$$\%\text{error} = \frac{xn(1-T_f/T_t)+n_1(T_f/T_t)}{T_f/T_t+x(1-T_f/T_t)}\% \tag{79}$$

Thus in the example chosen, if the error in registration at full-load had been 0.5% and not zero, then the total error over the whole period would have been approximately 0.61%.

It will be shown later that voltage-transformers also possess ratio and phase errors and invariably such transformers will be needed in the metering of both energy and power. The primary voltage is constant and the ratio error is also constant and can be easily compensated for in a watt-hour meter. On the other hand the ratio error in the associated current-transformer will not be constant and compensation for this is not so straightforward.

The phase errors of both the current and voltage-transformers are more important particularly at low power factors, as already indicated, and for this reason the variation of these errors with load should be kept as low as possible. This is why the metering classes in B.S. 3938 limit this variation in error as well as the absolute values.

It can be shown that the error in measurement caused by the phase error in a voltage-transformer is also dependent on the primary load power factor and if the correction factor is K_γ this is given by

$$K_\gamma = 1 + \frac{\gamma \tan \theta}{3438},\qquad(80)$$

γ being the phase error of the voltage-transformer, in minutes.

From eq. (80) it will be seen that the operational error due to a positive phase error in a voltage-transformer is opposite in sign to a similar phase error in the current-transformer because a voltage-transformer positive phase error (secondary voltage leading the primary voltage) gives an apparent primary power factor lower than the true value, thus causing the instrument to read lower than it should.

Combining eqs. (77) and (80) the correction factor to be applied for the total phase errors of both current and voltage-transformers is given by

$$K_t = 1 - \frac{(\beta - \gamma) \tan \theta}{3438}.\qquad(81)$$

If the ratio correction factors, as discussed on page 15, are K_c for the current-transformer and K_v for the voltage-transformer, the overall correction factor to be applied to the meter readings to compensate for all the errors of the associated instrument-transformers is quite simply given by $(K_c K_\beta K_v K_\gamma)$ or $(K_c K_v K_t)$.

As will be discussed later in the chapter dealing with other than British Standard Specifications, the products $(K_c K_\beta)$ and $(K_v K_\gamma)$ are known as the *Transformer Correction Factors* for the current and voltage-transformers respectively and the classes of accuracy are based on these transformer correction factors and not on the ratio errors and phase errors separately, as in the relevant British specification.

It has been shown that the operational errors obtained in the measurement of power are partly determined by the power factor of the primary circuit and in the measurement of energy also by the load cycle of the primary circuit, but examination of the pertinent equations shows that the greater the accuracy of measurement required the lower the errors of the associated current-transformer must be.

The choice of accuracy class will depend on the nature and relative importance of the measurements being taken—tariff metering, for instance, demands a higher accuracy than statistical metering. With current-transformers having a low-rated primary current necessitating the use of the wound-primary type of construction there may have to be some sacrifice of accuracy on occasions owing to the limitation placed on the number of primary turns one can use for a given short-circuit current rating determined by the mechanical strength of the assembly being used. In very general terms, for 11 kV 150 mVA (13·1 kA) short-circuit rating (for $\frac{1}{2}$ sec.) the minimum primary current *sensibly attainable* for class AM is 50 A and for class BM, 30 A, while for 6·6 kV 250 mVA (21·9 kA) and the same time rating these minimum primary current ratings are 80 A and 50 A respectively, all these assuming a burden of 5 VA. With present-day magnetic materials such as Mumetal 40 there is no great difficulty in attaining class AM or BM in the bar-primary or equivalent types of construction for a minimum primary current rating of 150 A, or 100 A for class CM.

A rated burden of 5 VA is usually sufficient for the current coils of the commonly adopted combination of commercial meters, such as a kWh main meter plus kWh check meter plus kVArh meter. Precision metering generally requires current-transformers having a higher rated burden—say 7·5 VA, as precision meters have a somewhat higher VA burden than commercial types.

Current-transformers for use with indicating ammeters and similar instruments are generally not limited in their phase errors and there is little comment one can make on these. Class D for ammeter service is frequently specified and, of course, one often encounters the case of a current-transformer fulfilling a dual role in that it supplies both a relay or trip coil and an ammeter. For greater accuracy it is not unusual to specify 'class C ratio error only' and certain manufacturers offer current-transformers specifically for ammeter service only, such transformers having their permissible ratio errors specified as percentages of the full load or rated current and not as in B.S. 3938, thus corresponding to the commonly adopted technique of specifying the instrument errors as percentages of the full-scale reading.

There is, however, one type of indicating duty which does deserve some attention and this is the case of a current-transformer supplying a rectifier-type instrument. The following remarks also apply in general to any burden consisting of a d.c. operating coil fed from a current transformer through a rectifier.

For a moving-coil instrument the rectifier is almost always of the copper-oxide type because this possesses the lowest losses, while for relays and machine excitation applications where the voltages encountered are higher the selenium type has been widely used. The germanium and silicon rectifiers of more recent introduction are generally used for even higher voltage conditions.

The usual connection one adopts is the well-known bridge arrangement both for single-phase and three-phase circuits, the active area of the rectifier being used is dependent on the burden current, and the number of elements in series depends on the burden voltage. For the single-phase bridge connection the following relationships exist between a.c. and d.c. voltages and between a.c. and d.c. currents:

If I_{ac} = r.m.s. secondary current in current-transformer,

I_{dc} = burden current (mean value),

V_{ac} = r.m.s. secondary winding terminal voltage,

V_{dc} = voltage drop in burden (= $I_{dc}R_b$, where R_b is the burden resistance),

a = number of series elements per bridge arm,

V = mean forward voltage per rectifier element (over complete cycle),

then for a resistive burden

$$I_{ac} = 1\cdot11 I_{dc} \text{ amperes} \tag{82}$$

and

$$V_{ac} = 1\cdot11(V_{dc}+4aV) \text{ volts.} \tag{83}$$

The internal voltage drop in the current-transformer is, of course, $I_{ac}(R_{sw}+jX_{sw})$ volts and this, added to V_{ac} gives the required secondary induced e.m.f.

Typical values of V for the various types of rectifier are:

Copper oxide	0·2 volts
Selenium	0·5 volts
Germanium	0·35 volts
Silicon	0·55 volts.

Precise information is, of course, readily available from the manufacturers of the rectifier one is contemplating using, but one important point to remember is that both copper oxide and selenium rectifiers are subject to ageing which causes an increase of up to 25% in the value of V.

V_{ac}, as determined by eq. (83), is the r.m.s. voltage across the bridge rectifier and it is this voltage which determines the number of elements in each arm of the bridge. Typical peak reverse voltages per element are:

Copper oxide	12 volts
Selenium	40 volts
Germanium	300 volts
Silicon	1000 volts.

There are a number of points to be remembered—should the d.c. burden become disconnected from the current-transformer and rectifier, current flowing in the primary winding will cause a high secondary voltage, almost certainly causing the rectifier to fail 'in reverse' unless it has been specially designed to meet their condition, or a ballast resistor having the same ohmic value as the burden is connected in parallel with the burden, this connection being made on the d.c. side of the rectifier. Thus if the d.c. burden current corresponding to full-load primary current is, say 200 mA, the current-transformer secondary current will be $2 \times 1 \cdot 11 \times 200$ mA, that is, 444 mA and it is this value which determines the number of secondary turns.

It is also important that the rectifier is protected against heavy primary over-load currents and in order to do this the flux density in the core at full-load primary current should be as high as possible commensurate with the accuracy requirements so that the secondary current under over-load conditions is severely limited. The third point to remember is that the performance of the current-transformer may often be determined by the rectifier characteristics rather than by the burden itself. A simple example of this is an instrument rectifier of the copper-oxide type which is often of the single-element type so that from eq. (83), although the burden voltage drop may be 0·1 volt, the rectifier component of the current-transformer secondary voltage will be eight times this (i.e., $4 \times 2 \times 0 \cdot 1$ volts). While the self-capacitance in all rectifiers must be taken into account in higher frequency applications there is no need to do this for most power-frequency work. However, it must be remembered that a rectifier has a non-linear resistance so that the burden the rectifier itself presents to the current-transformer is similarly non-linear and will have some effect on waveform.

In the single-phase case at present under discussion, if the d.c. burden contains inductance, as it frequently will, the current on the a.c. and d.c. sides of the rectifier are no longer identical as in the purely resistive burden case. In the first half-cycle of a.c. current the d.c. burden current is the same until just after the first peak. During this period the burden inductance stores energy and as the a.c. current decreases after the first peak this stored energy maintains the burden d.c. current at a higher value but decaying exponentially. In this so-called 'relaxation period' the burden current flows through all four arms of the rectifier and this continues until the a.c. equals the decaying d.c. current at which point the a.c. forces the circuit back to its original operation. Thus each cycle of a.c. current maintains two 'forcing' and two 'relaxation' periods, the ratio of a.c. to d.c. current depending on the time constant of the burden.

The presence of inductance in the d.c. burden also has its effect on the voltage relationships and leads to 'peakier' secondary voltage waveforms. The problem is further complicated if the primary current is itself non-sinusoidal and one must resort to graphical methods of solution, although some assistance may be gained by compensating for the burden inductance by the use of a parallel R.C. circuit which has the effect of making the burden appear purely resistive.

This general problem of employing a current-transformer to supply to a burden a d.c. current proportional to an a.c. primary current is not the same as that encountered if the current consists of unidirectional pulses, such as occurs in connection with protective current-transformers in some power-rectifier arrangements. Here the basic problem is that the whole of the dynamic hysteresis loop is not available for core excitation, only that portion between 'positive' remanence and 'positive' saturation being so. Thus in order to prevent saturation the only practical solution in almost all cases is the insertion of air-gaps into the magnetic circuit.

Finally in this section it seems pertinent to discuss briefly the d.c. *current-transformer*, this term being applied to a transductor being used to measure d.c.* The transductor is particularly useful for the measurement of very large direct currents having obvious advantages over shunts such as

(i) The instrument is isolated from the meter.

(ii) A shunt for very large direct currents is bulky and may have such a low required resistance that calibration is difficult. (This may well be the most important advantage, and in some cases a compelling reason to use a d.c. current-transformer.)

(iii) As with a.c. current-transformers the instrument can be protected from damage as the core can be designed to saturate at a given d.c. current.

* *Magnetic Amplifiers and Saturable Reactors*, consulting editor M. G. Say (George Newnes, 1954).

(iv) The resistance of the connecting leads from the meter to the transductor is not so critical as when a shunt is used so that the meter may be sited some distance away.

(v) If necessary a number of meters can be connected to the one unit.

One further advantage but certainly not the least, is that for large-scale installations the cost of the transductor is much less.

As with most other transductor applications the accuracy and linearity of the d.c. current-transformer depends on the core material, which should be an alloy offering a very high impedance up to saturation and thereafter the lowest possible impedance; this requirement is best met by the nickel-iron alloys, particularly H.C.R. alloy, although for some large equipments the oriented electrical steels may offer sufficient accuracy.

It is impossible in the space available to give other than a basic outline of the operation of the d.c. current-transformer. The simplest circuit is that shown in Fig. 64 and as with other transductors

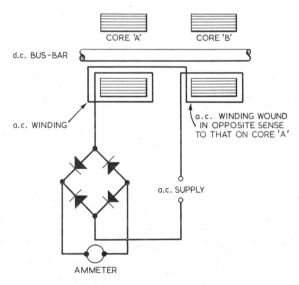

Fig. 64. d.c. current-transformer.

the object is the production of a variation in the impedance of the a.c. circuit such that the resulting variation in a.c. current is proportionate to the variation of the d.c. flowing in the primary bus-bar or, in other words, the production of a substantially linear relationship between a.c. ampere-turns and d.c. ampere-turns, and if the average rectified a.c. current is given by I_{ac}, then

$$I_{ac} = N_{dc}I_{dc}/N_{ac}.$$

(In the bus-bar d.c. current-transformer $N_{dc} = 1$.)

Because the a.c. voltage V_{ac} may be varied considerably without any alteration in I_{ac} (for a particular value of I_{dc}) the secondary circuit resistance is not a critical factor in the transformer operation.

It will of course be appreciated that the transductor or saturable reactor is more commonly used in circuits in which the 'power side' is a.c. and the d.c. is the deliberately varied control. Thus in many cases the a.c. windings consist of few turns of heavy conductor, while the d.c. winding has more turns of finer gauge conductor. Sometimes, therefore, one is confused by the d.c. current-transformer in that not only is the d.c. winding a single-turn bar-primary of possibly large cross-section, but also because the d.c. current is no longer the one which is deliberately varied. This confusion does not arise if one remembers that the relationship is not between a.c. and d.c. currents but is fundamentally between a.c. and d.c. ampere-turns and therefore the mode of operation of the d.c. current-transformer is the same for any other similar transductor.

Summation current-transformers*

In electrical supply practice it frequently happens that the currents in a number of feeders are not required to be individually metered or measured but are summated into one meter or instrument. One obvious reason for this is the considerable saving that is possible in the first cost of the metering equipment and in its installation.

There are a number of ways in which summation may be carried out, the simplest is to pass all the feeders concerned through a ring-type current-transformer, or if the currents are small, to use a common core with suitable multi-turn primary windings and a single secondary winding. This method, electromagnetically very straightforward, unfortunately has severe practical limitations, particularly if the voltage of the primary system feeders is other than low or if these feeders are mechanically spaced more than a few inches apart. A particular form of this technique is seen in the core-balance current-transformer, used for earth-fault protection.

The second method is to use a separate current-transformer in each feeder and connect the secondary windings of all these current-transformers in parallel to one meter or instrument. This

* 'Current Summations with Current Transformers', by Hobson, *Proc. I.E.E.* **102**A (1955), p. 581.

method has two objections to it in practice, the first is that unless special ratios, or to be more precise, unless special nominal secondary current ratings for the individual current-transformers are adopted, the meter or burden current may be large. The second objection is that all the current-transformers must have the same nominal ratio, although the full-load currents in the feeders may differ considerably.

Let a = number of transformers in parallel,

   K_n = nominal ratio of each transformer,

   Z_b = burden impedance, that is, the actual meter impedance.

Furthermore, let it be assumed that the primary current is the same in each current-transformer and is given by I_p. Also that the total secondary circuit impedance for each current-transformer is the same and is given by Z_t, or in other words, the secondary winding impedance plus the connecting lead impedance is the same throughout, that is, $Z_s = Z_t - Z_b$.

Finally, let

$$I_s = \text{secondary current in each transformer} = I_p/K_n$$

and

$$I_e = \text{exciting current in each transformer.}$$

Now the total current being measured = aI_p

and the total error current   = aI_e,

so that the overall summation error $= \dfrac{aI_e}{aI_p} = \dfrac{I_e}{I_p}$.

This is based on the fact that the exciting current, I_e, is representative of the total error of an individual transformer in that the vector sum of the ratio error and the phase error is directly proportional to it.

The burden current   = aI_s

and the burden voltage = $aZ_b I_s$,

so that the e.m.f. induced in each secondary winding, E_s, is given by

$$E_s = Z_s I_s + aZ_b I_s$$

$$= I_s(Z_s + aZ_b). \tag{84}$$

I_e corresponds to this value of induced e.m.f. and is found in the normal manner from the magnetic characteristic curves of the core material being used.

Consider now *that while the total primary current remains unchanged at 'aI_p'*, some of the feeders are idle, that is, not carrying current, and the number of loaded feeders is now b, the total primary current being shared equally among them.

Under this condition the burden current remains unchanged at its previous value aI_s but the current in each secondary winding is now aI_s/b.

The secondary induced e.m.f. in each loaded current-transformer, E_l, is now given by

$$E_l = aZ_bI_s + \frac{aZ_sI_s}{b} \text{ volts,}$$

or

$$E_l = I_s\left(aZ_b + \frac{aZ_s}{b}\right) \text{ volts.} \tag{85}$$

The secondary induced e.m.f., E_i, in each of the idle current-transformers is assumed to equal the voltage across the burden as the only current passing through the secondary winding of each is now a small exciting current with a corresponding negligible voltage drop, these exciting currents in the idle current-transformers being supplied by the secondaries of the loaded current-transformers.

Therefore

$$E_i = aZ_bI_s \text{ volts.} \tag{86}$$

Thus the induced e.m.f.s in the idle current-transformers have decreased while those in the loaded current-transformers have increased (compared with E_s) and as this change is not great it can be assumed that the exciting current changes linearly with the induced voltage.

Thus in each loaded current-transformer, the exciting current now becomes

$$aI_e\left(\frac{Z_b + Z_s/b}{Z_s + aZ_b}\right) \text{ amperes,}$$

so that the total exciting current for b loaded current-transformers is

$$aI_e\left(\frac{Z_s + bZ_b}{Z_s + aZ_b}\right) \text{ amperes,} \tag{87}$$

for $(a-b)$ idle transformers the total exciting current is

$$I_e\left(\frac{a^2Z_b - abZ_b}{Z_s + aZ_b}\right) \text{ amperes,} \tag{88}$$

so that the total exciting current for *all* the current-transformers is

$$I_e\left[\frac{a(Z_s+bZ_b)+a^2Z_b-abZ_b}{Z_s+aZ_b}\right] \text{ amperes} = aI_e \text{ amperes.} \quad (89)$$

Therefore the exciting current is the same as when all the feeders were equally loaded; neither has the total primary current been changed so that the overall summation error is also unchanged.

Therefore, when summating by paralleling secondary windings, the overall summation error, for any particular value of total primary current, is independent of the distribution of that current in the primary feeders, provided the individual errors of the current-transformers are similar and the impedances in the secondary circuits of these are also similar.

If the individual errors are not similar or the individual secondary impedances are not the same, then there will be some change in the overall summation error depending on the distribution of the primary current, but this change is always less than the difference in the individual errors, often much less and the change may then be ignored. However, if turns correction has been used on some of the current-transformers there is a more marked change in the overall summation error due to change of primary current distribution because the ratio error of a current-transformer in which turns correction has been used is no longer indicative of its exciting current.

When turns correction is not present it may be shown that the overall summation errors—both ratio and phase errors—are equal to the sum of the errors of the individual transformers, divided by the number of current-transformers, that is, they are equal to the average errors provided the errors of the individual current-transformers are those corresponding to the correct effective test burden.

Thus if a current-transformers are to be used in a summation circuit, the actual burden impedance being Z_b ohms, then the effective burden at which each current-transformer must be tested is (aZ_b + lead resistance) ohms for various percentages of its own rated full-load current. Then, when summated, they are tested at the actual burden Z_b, at the same percentages but now of the total rated full-load current (the sum of the individual full-load currents). As already indicated, the summation error will be the same as the average of the individual errors.

In practice there is no great difference in performance whether the paralleling is carried out at the current-transformers or at the burden, although if the burden is some distance away there is some slight advantage if the former location is adopted.

Again, there is a commonly used protective application for this technique of paralleling secondary windings and that is in the residual connection of current-transformers in three-phase systems for earth-fault protection, but this will be discussed later.

The third method and the most flexible one for the summation of currents in a number of feeders is to use a summation current-transformer in association with feeder current-transformers which need not have the same ratios. In this method each feeder has its own current-transformer, ring-type or wound-primary type depending on the ratio and its secondary winding connected to its appropriate summator primary winding as shown in Fig. 65. The summator or summation current-transformer has a single secondary winding which is connected to the burden.

If

K_{n1}, K_{n2}, K_{n3}, etc. = individual nominal ratios of the feeder current-transformers,

I_{p1}, I_{p2}, I_{p3}, etc. = rated primary currents of these,

I_{s1}, I_{s2}, I_{s3}, etc. = rated secondary currents of these,

N_1, N_2, N_3, etc. = corresponding number of turns of the summator primary windings,

N_s = summator secondary turns,

I_s = summator rated secondary current,

K_{ns} = overall ratio,

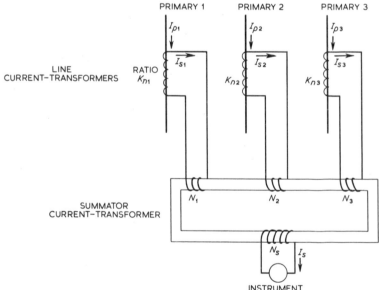

Fig. 65. Schematic diagram of summator current-transformer.

then

$$K_{ns} = \frac{\Sigma I_p}{I_s}$$

and

$$\frac{I_{s1} N_1}{I_{p1}} = \frac{I_{s2} N_2}{I_{p2}} = \frac{I_s N_s}{\Sigma I_p}. \tag{90}$$

If

$R_b + j X_b = Z_b =$ burden impedance,

$\qquad Z_s =$ resistance of summator secondary winding,

R_1, R_2, R_3, etc. = resistances of summator primaries,

then the induced e.m.f. in summator winding is E_s, given by

$$E_s = I_s [R_s + (R_b + j X_b)] \tag{91}$$

and the induced e.m.f. in first summator primary, E_{s1}, is therefore

$$E_{s1} = \frac{N_1 I_s}{N_s} [R_s + (R_b + j X_b)] \tag{92}$$

and the corresponding volt-ampere burden is

$$E_{s1} I_{s1} = \frac{N_1 I_{s1} I_s}{N_s} [R_s + (R_b + j X_b)], \tag{93}$$

substituting for $N_1 I_{s1}$ from eq. (90)

$$E_{s1} I_{s1} = \frac{I_{p1}}{\Sigma I_p} I_s{}^2 [R_s + (R_b + j X_b)]. \tag{94}$$

Equation (94) therefore gives that part of the total burden imposed on the first line current-transformer by the resistance of the summator secondary winding and the impedance of the burden itself. In addition, due account must be taken of the losses in the summator primary windings, and with the assumption that the current densities and mean lengths of the coils are the same for all these primary windings, then if P is the total loss in all the summator primaries, then the loss in the first primary P_1, is given by

$$P_1 = \frac{I_{p1}}{\Sigma I_p} P \text{ watts.} \tag{95}$$

Adding this to the right-hand side of eq. (94) gives the total burden on the first line current-transformer VA_1, whence

$$VA_1 = \frac{I_{p1}}{\Sigma I_p} [(P + I_s{}^2 R_s) + I_s{}^2 (R_b + j X_b)], \tag{96}$$

and similarly for all the line current-transformers. Equation (96) does not take into account the loss in the leads connecting the line current-transformers to the corresponding summator primary windings and obviously these must be added if of any significant magnitude.

The overall errors of the complete summation equipment consists of two parts. (i) The errors of the line current-transformers tested at the correct effective burden values but converted into what are termed 'combined' errors, and (ii) the errors of the summation current-transformer itself.

The combined errors need some explanation. The ampere-turns supplied to each of the summator primary windings and therefore the vector sum of all these ampere-turns to all the primary windings are not the correct value due to the errors of the line current-transformers and there is a combined ratio error and a combined phase error.

If the ratio errors for the line current-transformers are given by r_1, r_2, r_3, etc., and the phase errors by β_1, β_2, β_3, etc., it may be shown that

$$\text{Combined ratio error} = \frac{I_{p1}}{\Sigma p}r_1 + \frac{I_{p2}}{\Sigma p}r_2 + \frac{I_{p3}}{\Sigma p}r_3, \text{ etc.}, \qquad (97)$$

and

$$\text{Combined ratio error} = \frac{I_{p1}}{\Sigma p}\beta_1 + \frac{I_{p2}}{\Sigma p}\beta_2 + \frac{I_{p3}}{\Sigma p}\beta_3, \text{ etc.} \qquad (98)$$

If the line current-transformers all have the same nominal ratio then the combined error is the average error (both for ratio and phase error).

Thus the practical procedure is as follows: the line current-transformer primary currents, I_{p1}, I_{p2}, I_{p3}, etc., must be known, as is the summator secondary current I_s. Having assumed a value for N_s, the summator secondary turns, then the summator primary turns are determined from eq. (90) as the summator primary currents I_{s1}, I_{s2}, etc., will be known.

The burden impedance is known and the summation transformer's losses calculable once a core area has been adopted and therefore VA_1, VA_2, VA_3 are determined from eq. (96). If the lead resistance loss is not negligible it has to be added to each of these to determine the burden at which each of the line current-transformers must be tested or at which the errors are to be calculated. Thus r_1, r_2, r_3, β_1, β_2, β_3, etc., are now known and the combined ratio error and phase error calculated from eqs. (97) and (98), respectively.

These combined errors added to those of the summation current-transformer give the desired overall errors.

As with the summation of current by use of paralleled secondaries, the overall errors of a summation current-transformer are not affected by the distribution of the total current in the primary feeders, but for other reasons it is obviously necessary not to exceed the rated full-load primary current in any individual feeder.

Two final points that must be mentioned is that summation of currents, whichever method is adopted, is usually carried out for the purpose of energy or power measurement and therefore all these methods are only applicable if the voltages of the feeders are the same, both in magnitude and phase. The other point concerns the designation of summation current-transformers on their rating plates and unfortunately there is no standard method. One common method is to give the currents ratings of the summator windings, such as $5 + 5 + 5/5$ A and state 'equal primary windings' or if these are not equal, the ratio of the appropriate line current-transformer is given for each summator primary winding.

CHAPTER 10

INTRODUCTION TO PROTECTIVE CURRENT-TRANSFORMERS

Throughout this book mention has been made of the fact that there are considerable differences between the operational requirements of measuring current-transformers and those of protective current-transformers and, as expected, the design approach is therefore different for each type. These differences are so considerable that it is advisable to segregate the two types for detailed discussion and this course has been adopted in this book.

Some of these differences have already been mentioned: as a general rule one is interested only in the ratio error of a protective current-transformer and no limit is placed on the phase error, one exception being current-transformers in certain phase-comparison systems. Another difference is that in the measuring current-transformer one is concerned about the errors only for a limited range of primary current, the usual ranges being 5% to 125% or 20% to 125% of the rated full-load value, whereas in many protective current-transformers it is essential to have some knowledge of the performance over a much wider primary current range, frequently up to many times the rated full-load value.

Both these differences apply to steady-state conditions in the primary circuit and there is no real point in considering the performance of measuring current-transformers at other than these steady-state conditions, where as in the case of protective current-transformers their performance during transient conditions in the primary circuit may well be of prime importance.

There is another important difference between measuring and protective current-transformers. The former are frequently employed as separate units and their performance gauged in like manner, one of the very few exceptions being current-transformers used in summation circuits, but with protective current-transformers one is frequently interested not in the performance of individual current-transformers as such but in the overall performance of a protective system employing a number of current-transformers which are interconnected in some manner. Or again, in some types of protective circuit, the fact that the individual current-transformers have low errors may not necessarily result in the protective circuit having a high performance.

There is, of course, no difference in the mechanical construction of protective current-transformers compared with those used in metering and other applications and they use the same magnetic materials and core forms except that the nickel-iron alloy, Mumetal, is infrequently employed in protective current-transformers. The reason for using oriented electrical steel as opposed to one of the hot-rolled grades may, however, be a different one to that applicable when measuring current-transformers are concerned, where the main advantage of the oriented electrical steels are their much lower iron losses and higher permeabilities at the lower flux density levels. In many protective current-transformers the higher saturation flux density (i.e. the greater available flux density range) of the oriented electrical steels is the main reason for their adoption. Of course there are also protective applications where the operating flux density is of necessity low and here the advantages of the oriented electrical steels are the same as when used for measuring current-transformers.

All these points will be discussed in the following chapters but it is necessary first of all to briefly recapitulate some facets of the basic theory applicable to any type of current-transformer in order to understand the general approach one adopts in the study of protective current-transformers.

It has been shown that the ratio error of any current-transformer is determined by, amongst other factors, the overall power factor of the secondary circuit. If one limits discussion to other than capacitative burdens and, for the moment, to those cases where the turns ratio is equal to the nominal current ratio, that is where no turns correction has been used, then the ratio error is always negative. Remembering these limitations, for any particular level of flux density the minimum ratio error occurs when the overall power factor of the secondary circuit is unity while the maximum ratio error occurs when this power factor is the same as the core power factor (that is, the ratio of the core watt-loss current to the total exciting current). This core power factor or loss angle varies with the flux density and is partly determined by the type of core construction being used.

In an earlier chapter error curves have been shown (Figs. 19–22 in chapter 4) for various magnetic materials in the continuously wound core form and from these it will be seen that as the flux density increases the unity power factor ratio error more closely approaches the maximum ratio error until, at the knee-point flux density, there is little difference and beyond this point the ratio error becomes independent of the overall secondary power factor as it is then determined by the total exciting current.

If turns correction is used, then the ratio error corresponding to the condition of equality of the secondary circuit and core power factors is simply more negative, or, put another way, less positive, than that at the unity power factor condition and depending on the degree of correction used the unity power factor error could *numerically* be the maximum at any particular flux density. However, there is still the convergence of error curves at flux densities above the knee-point and again beyond this point the ratio error becomes independent of the overall secondary power factor.

Reverting to the case where turns correction has not been adopted the foregoing remarks may be summarised by commenting that at low-flux densities the ratio error is correctly given by

$$\%\text{R.E. at } xI_{pn} = -100\left(\frac{I_m \sin\delta + I_w \cos\delta}{xI_{sn}}\right)\% \qquad [(29)]$$

and having a maximum value given by

$$\%\text{R.E. at } xI_{pn} = \frac{-100I_e}{xI_{sn}}\%. \qquad [(33)]$$

(See Chapter 4.)

While at the higher flux densities eq. (33) is the only practical equation that is applicable, irrespective of the secondary circuit power factor, this may be used even for the lower flux densities if the secondary power factor angle is approximately the same as the core material's power factor angle, without causing a great deal of practical inaccuracy in one's calculations. There is one further aspect to consider. If the current-transformer is a ring-type or of such other type that the secondary winding leakage reactance is negligible then for any specified burden power factor the actual overall secondary circuit power factor will be greater, the difference being determined by the magnitude of the secondary winding resistance and connecting lead resistance. On the other hand, if a wound-primary current-transformer is used and the secondary winding leakage reactance is not negligible then the overall secondary circuit power factor may be lesser than, or greater than, the specified burden power factor, depending on the relative values of the constituent resistances and reactances.

So much for the current-transformer, but what about the relay? Many relays have a reactive power factor and furthermore both this and the impedance change with the magnitude of the current flowing through the operating coil. Figure 66, for instance, shows how the impedance of a typical inverse-definite-minimum time (I.D.M.T.L.) relay falls with increase of current and this diagram also indicates the change in its power factor.

Thus the performance of a current-transformer supplying such a relay is not readily calculable in precise or detailed terms and if one is going to introduce a general specification for such applications then obviously some simplification is essential.

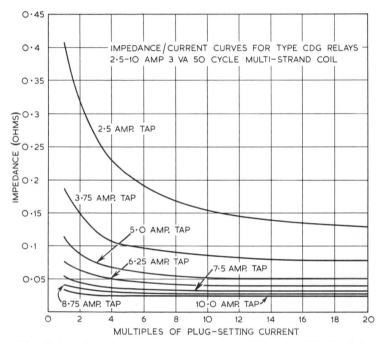

Fig. 66. Impedance/current curves for an I.D.M.T.L. relay. (*The English Electric Co. Ltd.*)

This has been done in that section of B.S. 3938 covering certain types of protective current-transformers in that the burdens are specified at a power factor of 0·7 lagging and not at unity power factor as for measuring current-transformers in the same Standard. The assumption of maximum ratio error condition is also applied and the total exciting current is therefore adopted as the basis for the calculation of the percentage ratio error, as in eq. (33).

B.S. 3938 repeats the very useful information given in B.S. 2046 concerning the correct burden values and other design parameters to specify for various protective duties, but the greatest advantage of these two standards is that they eliminated the often chaotic situation prior to their introduction when the user employed B.S. 81 classes of accuracy for protective current-transformers sometimes with dire results in that the current-transformer he eventually obtained was totally unsuitable for its required duty.

Before discussing protective current-transformers in detail it is necessary to indicate how protection systems are most suitably classified for the purpose of that discussion.

Classification of protection circuits

Protection circuits are conveniently classified into four main groups:

A. Non-balance circuits and where transient stability is of no importance.

B. Balance circuits such as 'Merz-Price', 'Solkor' and the like.

C. Restricted earth-fault schemes using instantaneous relays.

D. Other protective schemes not included in these three categories.

In greater detail the first group covers direct-acting trip coils for overcurrent and earth-fault protection; overcurrent protection with induction, thermal- or instantaneous-type relays and earth-fault protection with induction-type relays. It is the current-transformers for these forms of protection that are covered by B.S. 3938 and as they represent the vast majority of protective current-transformers they will form a major part of the discussion in this book.

The second group covering balance schemes of protection requires current-transformers having a high degree of similarity in their characteristics which are not catered for in B.S. 3938 and such current-transformers are therefore the subject of specific agreement between manufacturer and user. But see note at end of chapter 13 on the Accuracy Class 'X' in B.S. 3938.

Restricted earth-fault schemes using instantaneous relays are again not covered by B.S. 3938 and the transient stability is of major importance.

The final group covers various types of protection circuits where the desired characteristics of the associated current-transformers may or not be covered by the accuracy classes in B.S. 3938.

When discussing protective current-transformers one must inevitably encounter terms used in association with a.c. protection circuits and particularly in the context of the operational desiderata of such circuits. It seems advisable briefly to discuss some of the more important of these for the benefit of readers not having previous experience of them.

Operational conditions in an electrical power system may be broadly classified, for the purpose of the present discussion, into two main categories—'steady-state' and 'transient'. The former requires no further explanation, while the latter is a current possessing an initial peak value possibly many times that of the system's final steady-state value, the period of decay from the one to the other often being a matter of minutes. One common cause of transients is the switching-in of a power-transformer into a system, such a transient being its magnetising in-rush current. While the total decay time may be measured in minutes, the very high and damaging peaks of current are those over the first few cycles but as will be seen later the main problem as far as current-transformers are concerned is that transients possess a d.c. component which cause inevitable core saturation in many cases.

Now the 'stability' of a protective circuit may be defined as the maximum value of primary current that circuit can withstand without incorrectly operating, and this term is prefaced by 'steady-state' or 'transient' whichever is the pertinent one. Returning to the case of the transient in-rush currents caused when switching-in a power-transformer—this is a 'healthy' primary circuit condition but current-transformers on the primary side of that power-transformer will not be able to distinguish between this condition and a heavy primary fault current and mal-operation of the associated relay could occur. Thus the protective circuit must possess a reasonable level of 'transient stability'.

To take just one further case: one may have a protective circuit using a number of current-transformers interconnected in some manner for earth-fault protection. Such a circuit must possess reasonable 'phase-fault' stability so that phase faults do not cause mal-operation of the associated relay.

The 'sensitivity' of a protective circuit may be defined as the lowest value of the appropriate primary fault current that will cause relay operation and later on it will be seen that frequently the designer must compromise in his designs between the requirements for sensitivity and stability.

CHAPTER 11

PROTECTIVE CURRENT-TRANSFORMERS TO B.S. 3938

B.S. 2046 introduced a number of new terms and it is advisable to discuss these before proceeding. It still preserved the over-current factor (O.C.F.) as defined in B.S. 81 which indicated the capability of the current-transformer to withstand the thermal and dynamic stresses due to a heavy overcurrent in the primary winding. This factor was not to be confused with the one introduced in B.S. 2046 termed the *rated saturation factor*, defined as 'the ratio of the rated primary saturation current to the rated primary current', the *rated primary saturation current*, in turn, being defined as 'the value of current assigned by the manufacturer as the maximum primary current at which the transformer will comply with the relevant accuracy clauses of the specification'.

Thus if the rated saturation factor was 20, the current-transformer had to maintain its specified accuracy up to 20 times the full-load primary current.

Another important term introduced by B.S. 2046 was the *rated secondary saturation e.m.f.* defined as 'with rated burden connected the product, in volts, of the rated secondary saturation current, in amperes, and the total impedance of the secondary circuit, including the impedance of the secondary winding in ohms'. It is of interest to point out here that for testing purposes these impedances were added arithmetically and not vectorially. The *rated secondary saturation current*, as one would expect, was defined as 'the secondary current equal to the rated primary saturation current divided by the transformation ratio'.

Thus two aspects of current-transformer operation had undergone some simplification in the preparation of this standard: (i) the arithmetic addition of impedances instead of the correct vectorial one, leading to the calculated flux density and exciting current being pessimistically high, and (ii) the use of the maximum ratio error condition, that is, the use of eq. (33) in the calculation of the ratio error as shown in Table 5, which gives the classes of accuracy in B.S. 2046.

In chapter 4 there was some discussion of the fact that eq. (33) and allied equations were fundamentally incorrect and that they ignored the presence of the very 'quality' they were being used to calculate, namely the ratio error. It was pointed out that no great practical inaccuracy was caused by using these equations for calculation mainly because of the practical uncertainties involved such as the spread or scatter of the core material's characteristics, which, in the case of measuring current-transformers covered by B.S. 3938 is greater than the inherent inaccuracy of the method.

With the type of current-transformer now being discussed it should be even more apparent that eq. (33) is fundamentally incorrect and furthermore that because of the ratio error, the rated secondary saturation e.m.f. would in any case never be attained in practice with rated primary saturation current flowing and with the rated burden connected to the secondary terminals. As this point was of some importance to the better understanding of B.S. 2046 it is felt that some explanation should be given and this is best done by taking a simple example:

Table 5. *B.S. 2046 Classes of accuracy*

Class	Ratio error at rated primary current (%)	Ratio error above rated primary current up to rated primary saturation current (%)	Exciting current expressed as a percentage of rated secondary saturation current, measured at rated secondary saturation e.m.f.
S	±3	± 3	3
T	±5	±10	10
U	±7·5	±15	15

Table 6. *Limits of error for protective current-transformers to B.S. 3938*

Class	Current error at rated primary current (%)	Limits of composite error at accuracy limit primary current (%)
S	±3	5
T	±5	10
X	This class covers current-transformers for special-purpose applications. Limits of error specified by knee-point e.m.f., exciting current at this e.m.f. and by secondary winding resistance	

Suppose that one wanted to find the %R.E. for a current-transformer having a ratio of 50/5 A and a secondary winding resistance of 0·1 ohms when this is supplying a burden of 0·4 ohms and at a primary current of 1000 A, that is, at a saturation factor of 20, the only other information that is available being the excitation curve, as shown in Fig. 67.

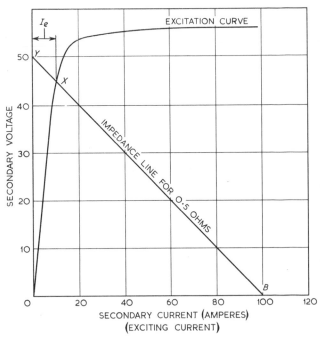

Fig. 67. Current-transformer excitation curve with impedance line.

The basic problem here is that the actual secondary current corresponding to this primary current of 1000 A is not known but for any particular case, total secondary impedance = secondary induced e.m.f. ÷ secondary current = a constant, and one can draw, as shown in Fig. 67, an impedance line BXY having a slope equal to the burden impedance, that is, a slope of 0·5, the point B on the current axis corresponding to a secondary current equal to the primary current of 1000 A divided by the transformation ratio, K_n, which in the case being considered equals 10, so that the nominal secondary current is 100 A. The intersection of this impedance line with the excitation curve then gives the operating point and by inspection it is found that the exciting current I_e, is 10 A, in secondary values. The secondary induced e.m.f., E_s, is 45 volts and using the assumption that the condition of maximum ratio error applies, that is, that the secondary and exciting currents are in direct anti-phase with each other, the actual secondary current is

$$(100-10)\,\text{A}, \quad \text{that is,} \quad 90\,\text{A}.$$

Now, by definition, and as already given in chapter 2

$$\text{R.E. at } I_p = 100\left(\frac{K_n I_s - I_p}{I_p}\right)\%,$$

where I_s and I_p are the actual secondary and primary currents respectively.

Thus

$$\%\text{R.E. at } 1000\,\text{A} = \frac{100(900-1000)\%}{1000} = -10\%.$$

However, if this current-transformer was to be manufactured to B.S. 2046 and remembering that the saturation factor was 20, the rated secondary saturation e.m.f., that is, the voltage at which the current-transformer must be tested to prove compliance with its class of accuracy requirements, would have been

$$20 \times 5 \times (0.4+0.1)\,\text{volts}, \quad \text{that is,} \quad 50\,\text{volts}.$$

From Fig. 67 the exciting current at this value of the secondary e.m.f. is found to be 13 A and from the method suggested in B.S. 2046 (but also commonly used elsewhere) the $\%$R.E. at the rated primary saturation current would be given by

$$\%\text{R.E.} = \frac{-100 I_e}{F I_{sn}}\%,$$

where

$$F = \text{saturation factor},$$
$$I_{sn} = \text{rated or nominal secondary current}.$$

Thus, in the case being considered

$$\%\text{R.E. at } 1000 \text{ primary amperes} = \frac{-100 \times 13}{20 \times 5}\% = -13\%.$$

But a strict interpretation of the fundamental ratio error equation, still using the maximum ratio error condition, means that $I_p = K_n(I_s + I_e)$, I_p and I_s again being actual values, so that with

$E_s = 50$ volts, $Z_s = 0.5$ ohms, I_s is still 100 A and $I_p = 10(100+13)$A $= 1130$ A, therefore

$$100 \left(\frac{K_n I_s - I_p}{I_p} \right) \% = \frac{-130}{1130} \% = \% \text{R.E. at 1130 A} = -11.5\%.$$

Thus enough has now been said to show that in B.S. 2046 one used a secondary saturation e.m.f. that in practice the current-transformer would never require to attain with the rated burden connected and the rated primary saturation current flowing. Furthermore, the error equation adopted by B.S. 2046 gave a pessimistic figure for the $\%$R.E. compared with the 'true' $\%$R.E., that is, that calculated from the definitive ratio error equation.

It can be argued that the example chosen exaggerates the problem and there is some justification in this because it was found in practice that for many designs the core cross-sectional area to be used was determined solely by the rated secondary saturation e.m.f. and the actual errors were so low that although the lowest class of accuracy may have been specified the current-transformer more than comfortably met the requirements of a better class. This was particularly true when the core material was one of the oriented electrical steels and the primary ampere-turns available were reasonable in magnitude. Nevertheless, the designer was forced to be more liberal in his design when using the B.S. 2046 method than when he used the basic graphical method already described and the liberality of his design increased the poorer the class of accuracy specified, but this was a small price to pay for the considerable advantages of B.S. 2046.

A good economic design of a protective current-transformer to B.S. 2046 was one in which the secondary saturation e.m.f. corresponded to the knee-point of that current-transformer's excitation curve and in these circumstances the customer was able to utilise what was possibly the main advantage of B.S. 2046, because the rating plate immediately gave him the minimum terminal voltage under primary fault conditions he could expect to obtain without saturating the core and thereby causing the secondary current waveform to depart from the sine-wave which, in the case of induction-type relays, causes greater inaccuracy in the overall protection system than an inherently high $\%$R.E.

Thus, if rated saturation factor $= F$ and rated burden at 0.7 p.f. lagging $= P$ volt-amperes and rated secondary current $= I_{sn}$, then the current-transformer would give $P \times F/I_{sn}$ terminal volts at a secondary current of $I_{sn} \times F$ amperes without saturating.

For this reason it was somewhat unfortunate that the word 'saturation' appeared in these definitive terms in B.S. 2046 as none of them was concerned with the true saturation region of the core material. On occasions, particularly with protective current-transformers in a standard range of designs, the flux density corresponding to the secondary saturation e.m.f. may be considerably below the knee-point value and care must be taken that the maximum possible secondary current during primary fault conditions does not then exceed the safe short-time rating of the associated relay.

Now it has already been pointed out elsewhere in this book* that the new standard, B.S. 3938, replaces the terms 'overcurrent' and 'overcurrent factor' with 'short-time current' and 'short-time factor' respectively when defining the maximum primary current the current-transformer can withstand dynamically and thermally. The term 'overcurrent' is now used for any fault current in excess of the relevant rated value of primary current.

However, at this stage of the present discussion the most important change made in B.S. 3938 in the nomenclature used in B.S. 2046 is the abolition of the word 'saturation' in defining the maximum current at which the specified accuracy of transformation has to be maintained, being replaced by 'accuracy limit'.

Thus the rated secondary saturation e.m.f. of B.S. 2046 becomes the 'secondary limiting e.m.f.', the saturation factor becomes the 'accuracy limit factor' and similarly the rated primary and secondary saturation currents become the 'accuracy limit primary and secondary currents' respectively. The important point to remember is that in the discussion earlier in this chapter on the merits of using the expression $100I_e/FI_{sn}$ to calculate the percentage ratio error the comments made apply equally to B.S. 3938 as to B.S. 2046, the only difference being that of nomenclature, that is, one has to make the substitution of 'accuracy limit' for 'saturation' where necessary. One other point of difference between B.S. 2046 and B.S. 3938 is that in the latter, one has now to use vectorial addition of the rated burden and the secondary winding resistance in calculating the secondary limiting e.m.f.

A protective current-transformer to B.S. 3938 is, in the context of its transformation performance, specified by three factors (i) the class of accuracy, (ii) its rated accuracy limit factor, and (iii) its VA rating. Its full manufacturing specification will of course, include all those factors previously discussed in chapter 1 but it is only necessary here to limit discussion to the correct choice of (i) (ii) and (iii) above, and in order to do this the various applications covered by B.S. 3938 must be segregated. From Table 6 it will be seen that there have been changes in the classes of accuracy compared with B.S. 2046, the principal change being the abolition of class U and the introduction of a class 'X', of which more later.

* See page 104.

Overcurrent protection

In this application the most important requirement is that the current-transformer must be capable of developing a sufficiently high value of secondary induced e.m.f. in order to give the secondary current corresponding to the maximum primary fault current at which the protection device must operate, that is, there must be no premature loss of ratio due to core saturation.

The ratio error will be determined by the type of relay or device being used and will depend on the necessity or otherwise for the close preservation of the current-transformer ratio in order to maintain accurate relay current-time characteristics. Thus a direct-acting overcurrent trip coil will demand only class T and a relatively low accuracy limit factor not generally exceeding five, the VA rating of the current-transformer being selected according to the trip-coil consumption. This class of accuracy is also applicable to any overcurrent protection employing instantaneous or time-delayed relays with the accuracy limit factor being determined by the level of the fault current up to which the relay is required to operate.

For overcurrent protection using I.D.M.T.L. relays the same class of accuracy, class T, is required and the accuracy limit factor is determined by the maximum primary fault current at which the relay current-time characteristics are to apply.

Figure 66 has already shown how the impedance of an I.D.M.T.L. relay falls with increase of current and therefore the performance of a current-transformer supplying such a relay may well be ultimately determined by the resistance in the secondary circuit external to the relay, including the current-transformer secondary winding resistance and the resistive component of any other burden in the same circuit, such an an ammeter. Figure 68 gives the terminal voltage of the current-transformer required to pass 20 times the plug setting for a typical I.D.M.T.L. relay for the various plug settings and for various values of additional resistance but excluding the current-transformer secondary winding resistance. This terminal voltage is the working equivalent of the rated secondary limiting e.m.f. less the secondary winding resistance drop (at the rated secondary saturation current) and is therefore equivalent to the product of the rated burden and the accuracy limit factor divided by the rated secondary current. For example, from Fig. 68 it is seen that this produce will have to have a value of 150 in order to give the 30 volts terminal voltage required for a rated secondary current of 5 A when the 'additional resistance' in the secondary circuit is of the order of 0·13 ohms. This product value of 150 is commonly specified for this application and can be

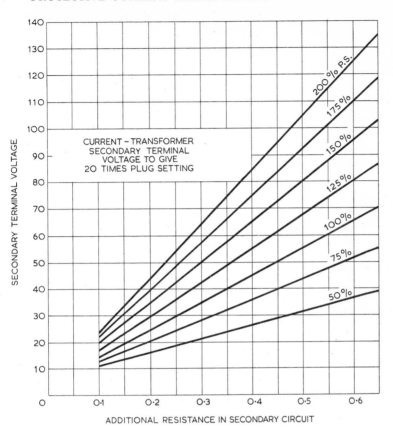

Fig. 68.

Table 7. *Details of VA ratings, etc., for typical* I.D.M.T.L. *relay* (50–200% *plug settings for overcurrent protection*)

Setting (%)	Current (A)	Resistance (ohms)	Reactance (ohms)	Consumption (VA)
50	2·5	0·22	0·342	2·54
75	3·75	0·113	0·152	2·66
100	5	0·07	0·082	2·71
125	6·25	0·052	0·056	2·95
150	7·5	0·04	0·038	3·08
175	8·75	0·031	0·027	3·16
200	10	0·027	0·021	3·38

attained without much difficulty except for low-rated primary currents but it is still very important to reduce as much as possible the resistance external to the relay as considerable saving can then be made in the required core size or it may frequently enable the designer to retain the ring-type construction, avoiding the need to adopt the less-attractive wound-primary construction.

If there is an ammeter or other instrument in the same circuit there is another reason why it is sound practice to supply it from another core because its operational requirements are completely different from those of the relay in the context of both range of primary current and of errors. Furthermore a relatively low saturation is of assistance in limiting the secondary current the ammeter must withstand when primary fault current is flowing.

While the required product of rated burden and accuracy limit factor is found in this manner it is still necessary to determine the required burden because the current-transformer must preserve its ratio error down to the rated full-load primary circuit, or in the case of the associated relay having a number of plug settings, down to the minimum plug-setting current. In the case of a 50–200% I.D.M.T.L. relay for overcurrent protection this means that the current-transformer must have a reasonable ratio error down to 50% of its nominal secondary current. In order to calculate the %R.E. in such a case one must first calculate the effective burden and this applies to any relay or device which has a number of plug settings or tappings.

If P_r = actual burden at the plug setting in VA,

P_e = effective burden in VA,

I_{sn} = rated or nominal secondary current,

I_r = plug-setting current,

then $P_e = P_r(I_{sn}/I_r)^2$ volt-amperes.

The VA ratings of a typical I.D.M.T.L. relay at the various plug settings are given in Table 7 from which it will be seen that because these VA ratings are sensibly constant the maximum *effective* burden at rated secondary current occurs at the minimum plug setting, that is, the 50% plug setting, and is therefore four times the actual burden at the plug-setting current so that the maximum effective burden on the current-transformer is approximately 12 VA. Thus a protective current-transformer supplying an overcurrent I.D.M.T.L. relay is frequently specified, according to B.S. 3938 nomenclature, by 15S10 or 15T10 depending on whether class S or class T accuracy limits are chosen, the former being preferred where the primary system discrimination is obtained by grading the time-settings. The rated burden is therefore usually 15 VA and the rated accuracy limit factor 10. It may be that some confusion is experienced by the uninitiated who finds he has to specify an accuracy limit factor of ten for a protective current-transformer supplying an I.D.M.T.L. relay where that current-transformer may well have to deliver twenty times the maximum plug-setting current so that in the case of a 50–200% relay this will be forty times its rated secondary current.

It must be remembered that the impedance of such a relay, as shown in Fig. 66 and Table 7, decreases as the plug setting itself and the number of times plug setting both increase and the real criterion is whether or not a current-transformer with the specified VA rating and accuracy limit factor will satisfactorily develop a *working* secondary saturation e.m.f. of sufficient magnitude to deliver the desired maximum values of secondary current on any plug setting necessary for correct relay operation: it can be shown that by adopting the B.S. 3938 method this is so, provided the actual resistive voltage drop in the current-transformer secondary winding during primary fault conditions does not exceed a certain figure— hence there is a limit placed on the resistance of the secondary winding and this may be best explained as follows:

Let it be assumed the rated burden $Z_b = 0.6$ ohms, the accuracy limit factor $F = 10$, the rated secondary current $I_{sn} = 5$ A and, the resistance of the secondary winding is R_{sw}. Let the working burden on the 200% (10 A) plug setting have a saturation value of Z_{bs} and for these I.D.M.T.L. relays a typical value of this is 0.022 ohms (for a 5 A relay).

The current-transformer is tested at its rated secondary limiting e.m.f., E_{ss}, given by

$$E_{ss} = I_{sn} \times F(Z_b + R_{sw}) \text{ volts}$$
$$= 50(0.6 + R_{sw}) \text{ volts} \tag{99}$$

(using arithmetic addition for simplicity)

the maximum secondary induced e.m.f. this current-transformer will be required to develop at twenty times the 200% plug-setting current is E_w, given by

$$E_w = 2 \times I_{sn} \times 20(Z_{bs} + R_{sw}) \text{ volts}$$
$$= 200(0.022 + R_{sw}) \text{ volts} \tag{100}$$

and E_w must be less than E_{ss} to ensure that premature saturation of the current-transformer does not occur. This means that the resistance of the secondary winding should not exceed the following value:

$$R_{sw} \ngtr \frac{25.6}{150} \text{ ohms,}$$

or in general terms

$$R_{sw} \ngtr \left(\frac{FZ_b - 40Z_{bs}}{40 - F} \right) \text{ohms.}$$

The need for this check is obvious because the actual working voltage drop in the current-transformer secondary winding is, in the case chosen, four times that used to compute the rated secondary limiting e.m.f. at which the current-transformer is tested and which, as already indicated, corresponds to the knee-point flux density in a good economic design. Should R_{sw} exceed the figure given then true saturation could occur and the current-transformer would not be capable of developing the correct secondary current levels during severe primary fault conditions when the relay is on its 200% plug setting. Obviously some assistance has been gained by specifying a rated burden of 15 VA when the effective working burden is only 12 VA but one must not be over generous in this manner because this would again possibly lead to excessively large cores remembering that in these protective current-transformers the factor principally determining core size is the rated secondary limiting e.m.f.

It is extremely important, when one is considering current-transformer performance in association with multi-setting relays such as I.D.M.T.L. type, that the correct approach is being used or the correct comparisons are being made, commensurate with normal operating conditions. For instance, for any particular value of number of times plug setting it is obvious that the induced secondary e.m.f. requirements are most onerous when the 200% plug setting is used, but this does not necessarily mean that this plug setting corresponds to the poorest ratio errors. For twenty times the 200% plug setting the secondary induced e.m.f. will be greater than for twenty times the 50% plug setting and the flux density and hence the exciting ampere-turns will also be greater for the former, but as the available primary ampere-turns will also be greater for the 200% plug setting the poorer ratio error will be determined by the corresponding flux densities and the core characteristics. If the flux density for the 200% plug setting is below the saturation level then the ratio errors will generally be least at this plug setting.

While this approach may provide interesting information it may not be directly of much use in practice because one is merely comparing performances at two entirely different values of primary current, whereas what one may normally require to know is how the performance of a relay and its associated current-transformer for some particular value of primary current is influenced by the choice of plug setting. In these circumstances, again with an I.D.M.T.L relay, for overcurrent protection, the maximum induced secondary e.m.f. occurs on the minimum plug setting and as the primary ampere-turns are held constant the worst ratio errors must also occur at the minimum plug-setting.

It must be emphasised that the introduction of B.S. 2046 and the correct selection of rated burden, saturation factor and class of accuracy as defined in that specification and perpetuated in the later standard B.S. 3938, means that it is no longer necessary, in many relevant applications, to carry out such detailed examination of the performance of the current-transformer concerned. When a detailed examination is required the user of the current-transformer will almost invariably prefer to establish *primary operating currents* for various relay operating conditions rather than calculate ratio error as such.

Evaluation of primary operating current

The problem usually facing the current-transformer user is quite easily stated: the operating characteristics of a certain relay are known as are the details of any additional burden and connecting leads. For a particular value of relay current he wishes to determine the primary operating current, that is, the corresponding current flowing in the primary circuit required to cause relay operation, the only other information in his possession being the resistance of the secondary winding of the associated current-transformer, its excitation characteristic and, for precise calculation, the core power factor.

Thus, for a particular relay current I_r which is now I_s, the actual secondary current, the secondary induced e.m.f. is given by

$$E_s = Z_s I_s \text{ volts,}$$

Z_s being the total impedance of the secondary circuit.

Then from the current-transformer excitation curve the corresponding exciting current, I_e, is found, and if the core power factor angle ϕ is also given, then the exciting current may be resolved into its watt-loss and magnetising components. The primary operating current, I_{poc}, which has precisely the same identity as the 'actual primary current' in chapter 2, which dealt with the elementary theory of current-transformers, is then found from

$$I_{poc} = K_t(I_s + I_m \sin \delta + I_w \cos \delta) \text{ amperes,} \qquad (101)$$

δ, as before, being the overall power-factor angle of the secondary circuit, K_t is the turns ratio and I_m and I_w are given in secondary amperes.

If the operating flux density is high enough or there is sufficient similarity between the secondary circuit and core power factors that the assumption of maximum ratio error conditions may be adopted, then

$$I_{poc} = K_t(I_s + I_e) \text{ amperes.} \tag{102}$$

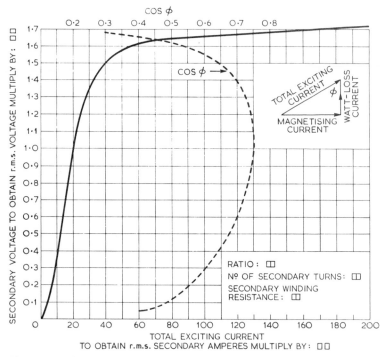

Fig. 69. Typical excitation curve of the 'calculated type'. (*Note.* Scale multipliers required for both secondary voltage and secondary current—for secondary current scale multiplier is l/N_s, where l = mean length of magnetic circuit in metres, N_s = secondary turns; for secondary voltage scale multiplier is $4·44\,fAN_s$, where f = frequency, A = nett core cross-sectional area in sq. metres.)

From this discussion it is therefore plain that the excitation curve of a current-transformer, as shown in Fig. 69, should include the core power factor, the resistance of the secondary winding (so that the total secondary impedance and overall secondary power factor may be established) and the turns ratio.

The manufacturer may supply the actual excitation curve for the current-transformer and is frequently requested to do so by the customer or he may supply a calculated or typical excitation curve of which Fig. 69 is an example, in which case the user must not expect complete agreement with the excitation curve he obtains should he carry out an excitation test because of the unavoidable variations in core material characteristics mentioned elsewhere.

There are two dangers to be guarded against if one adopts this technique of using the current-transformer excitation curve in order to determine primary operating current, the first of these is so immediately apparent that objections to the use of the technique because of it are hardly valid. This objection is due to the fact that the first assumption one has to make is that the secondary current used as the basis of one's calculations is actually attainable by the current-transformer, but this may be immediately checked in many applications. Should this secondary current be such that the calculated corresponding secondary induced e.m.f. is in excess of the 'saturation voltage' given by the excitation curve, then obviously the current-transformer is not capable of delivering the value of secondary current concerned.

Should the required secondary induced e.m.f. correspond to the knee-point voltage or a little above this, then the secondary current will be in the region where the current-transformer is beginning to lose ratio and the calculated primary operating current will be of somewhat uncertain accuracy.

The second objection is limited to those current-transformers in which the secondary winding leakage reactance is not negligible. These have already been dealt with in chapter 5 and for this present discussion all that needs to be added is that with such current-transformers the primary exciting current is influenced by the leakage flux set up by the primary load current and is not therefore the same as the secondary exciting current (obtained by the usual test in which the primary winding is open-circuited) multiplied by the turns ratio. In these cases the excitation characteristic cannot be used to predetermine the current-transformer's performance during primary fault conditions.

For this reason B.S. 2046 distinguished between 'high-reactance' and 'low-reactance' current-transformers, the demarcation between these two types being of necessity, an arbitrary one. 'High-reactance' current-transformers were defined in B.S. 2046 as those in which the ratio error actually measured in a primary current test at the rated primary saturation current at rated burden exceeded that given by $1 \cdot 2(I_e/I_{ps}) \times 100\%$, where I_e was the exciting current at the rated secondary saturation e.m.f. (from the usual excitation characteristic) and I_{ps} was the rated primary saturation current.

If the current-transformer design was such that it fell into the high-reactance category one sample had to undergo a type-test with primary saturation current at the rated burden together with a secondary exciting current test at the secondary saturation e.m.f.

Other current-transformers of the same design, in order to prove compliance or otherwise with the accuracy requirements, needed only to undergo the latter test and their *derived errors* established, these derived errors being defined in B.S. 2046 in the following manner. Thus if

A = %R.E. of type-tested current-transformer determined by primary current test.

B = secondary exciting current of this current-transformer as a percentage of the rated secondary saturation current measured at the rated secondary saturation e.m.f.

C = exciting current of identical design of current-transformer, expressed in same manner as B

the derived error was given as $A + 2(B - C)\%$ and this was not to be greater than the specified error at primary saturation current. It must be emphasised that this derived error was to be used only in this manner and for no other purpose.

Ring-type and bar-primary current-transformers with a centrally placed primary and evenly distributed secondary winding it should be noted, were deemed to be low-reactance current-transformers without any further proof and so one of the advantages gained by employing these types was that one does not require to carry out primary saturation current type tests.

Here the second major difference between B.S. 2046 and the new standard B.S. 3938 occurs in that there are some changes in respect of these two classifications 'low-reactance' and 'high-reactance'.

There is no change in what constitutes a low-reactance current-transformer or in the manner in which one may use a measurement of exciting current at the secondary limiting e.m.f. to determine compliance with the limits of composite error (replacing derived error and given in Table 6), but the previously discussed demarcation between the two types used in B.S. 2046 is modified and more detailed information given on testing high-reactance types.

This is done in B.S. 3938 by stating that all protective current-transformers other than those known to be of the low-reactance type must be tested for composite error against a reference current-transformer whose own composite error, it is recommended, does not exceed 0.2%. The test-circuit is a simple one: the secondary windings of both current-transformers are connected 'to circulate' with a low-impedance ammeter measuring the 'spill' current. The secondary of the reference-transformer also has an ammeter in circuit and that of the current-transformer has its rated burden connected. If when the reference-transformer's ammeter shows a current corresponding to the rated accuracy limit current (call this I_s), the spill current is I_c amperes, then the composite error of the current-transformer under test is given by $(I_c/I_s) \times 100\%$. One must of course be careful not to overheat the current-transformers as one is using the nominal currents multiplied by the accuracy limit factor and therefore the duration these currents are allowed to be maintained for is limited.

One very important point is that this composite error is not necessarily identical with the so-called vectorial error, that is, that calculated from a measurement of exciting current, because in many protective current-transformers the secondary limiting e.m.f. corresponds to a flux density approaching saturation level and the exciting current will possess harmonics. Thus while the composite error is determined from an exciting current test if the current-transformer is of the low-reactance type, it must be determined from the test described for other current-transformers and it will be found that the composite error is greater than the vectorial error.

B.S. 3938 gives an alternative test circuit employing two reference current-transformers and if a number of current-transformers of identical design are to be tested only one need be tested as indicated, the composite errors of the others being determined by an indirect test.

Thus in all the previous and following discussions in which the current-transformer excitation curve is used to predetermine primary operating currents it must be remembered that this technique is strictly applicable only to low-reactance current-transformers.

Earth-fault protective schemes covered by B.S. 3938

As already mentioned B.S. 3938 covers only those types of protection where transient stability is not one of the operational requirements and is therefore generally limited to current-transformers used in association with I.D.M.T.L. earth-fault relays and direct-acting trip coils as shown in Fig. 70. For combined earth-fault and overcurrent protection the latter determines the product of accuracy limit factor and burden while the former determines the accuracy class.

For those cases where phase-fault stability and accurate time grading are not needed it is recommended that class 'T' is adopted, but where either or both of these requirements are present the better accuracy, that is, class 'S' should be used. In both cases it is recommended that the product of the accuracy limit factor and rated burden should approach 150 and when class 'C' is used one generally obtains phase-fault stability up to ten times the rated primary current without any difficulty.

In addition to phase-fault stability which denotes the ability of the protective system to prevent mal-operation of the earth-fault relay or element during a phase-fault, the user is also interested in the earth-fault sensitivity of the system, or in other words, in what is the minimum earth-fault current required to cause operation and at which plug setting this may be obtained. These two points must be discussed at some length because not only are they important in their own right but certain facets of these problems apply to many other forms of protection.

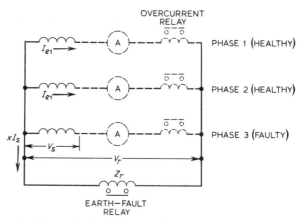

Fig. 70. Residual connection of current-transformers for unrestricted earth-fault protection.

First, consider the question of sensitivity. From Fig. 70 it is seen that an earth-fault on one phase energises the current-transformer in that phase which must now provide not only the relay current but also the exciting currents of the current-transformers in the healthy phases.

Let x be the percentage plug setting,

I_s = current-transformer rated secondary current,
Z_r = impedance of earth-fault relay including lead resistance to points A and B in the figure,
$\left.\begin{array}{l} Z_{b1} \\ Z_{b2} \\ Z_{b3} \end{array}\right\}$ = total impedances of overcurrent relays, ammeters or other devices in the individual phases. These may or may not be similar.
n = total number of current-transformers residually connected.

The voltage across the relay and therefore across the residual connection is

$$V_r = \frac{xI_sZ_r}{100} \text{ volts.} \tag{103}$$

In each healthy phase, ignoring the voltage drop associated with the exciting current flowing in an ammeter or overcurrent relay, the excitation characteristic of the current-transformer gives the exciting current corresponding to V_r, now assumed to be the terminal voltage of each healthy phase current-transformer. Let this exciting current per transformer be I_{e1}; then V_s, the terminal voltage of the current-transformer in the faulty phase (phase 3 in Fig. 70), is given by

$$V_s = V_r + Z_{b3}\left[\left(\frac{xI_s}{100}\right) + (n-1)I_{e1}\right] \text{ volts.} \tag{104}$$

From the current-transformer excitation curve the exciting current corresponding to this voltage V_s is then found—let it be I_{e3}, then the primary operating current I_{poc} is given by

$$I_{poc} = K_t\left[\frac{xI_s}{100} + (n-1)I_{e1} + I_{e3}\right] \text{ amperes.} \tag{105}$$

It will be noted that the assumption of maximum ratio error condition has again been adopted and impedances added arithmetically. For more accurate determination of I_{poc} one should use the more correct eq. (101), and vectorial addition of the impedance as the basis of one's calculations, but in many cases a further simplification may be used by assuming that V_r is the reference voltage for all the current-transformers concerned, this gives a common value of exciting current, I_e, and I_{poc} is then given by

$$I_{poc} = K_t\left[\frac{xI_s}{100} + nI_e\right] \text{ amperes.} \tag{106}$$

If this technique is repeated for all the available plug settings on the earth-fault relay and the various calculated values of primary operating current plotted against plug settings than one obtains the 'Vee' curve shown in Fig. 71, which immediately shows that the minimum primary operating current does not necessarily correspond to the minimum relay setting. This diagram also shows that, although the operating flux density in the current-transformer may be quite low, it is possible to set a relay to such a low value that the current-transformer will never be capable of operating that relay, because at low settings the increase in the effective burden impedance is such that the shunt impedances of the current-transformers take a greater portion of the available primary ampere-turns. Too low a setting will, of course, also impair the current time characteristic of the relay because the actual current taken by the relay with a heavy earth-fault current flowing in the primary may be much lower than its corresponding nominal value, perhaps only a half of it so that the relay will be slow in its operation and not give its correct operating time relative to other relays in the primary system.

The performance of residually connected current-transformers for earth-fault protection is adversely affected if they are additionally burdened by overcurrent relays and ammeters and although combined earth-fault and overcurrent protection using the one set of current-transformers is common practice it is not a good one.

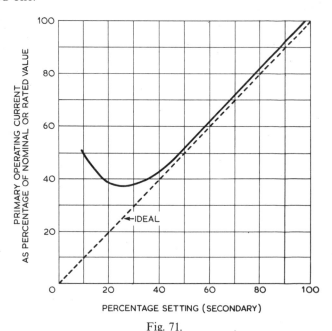

Fig. 71.

The 'Vee' curve shown in Fig. 71 is not limited to residually connected current-transformers and a further analysis of the condition shown is worthwhile.

If

I_s = relay setting current,
I_e = current-transformer exciting current,
I_{poc} = primary operating current,

then, as before

$$\frac{I_{poc}}{K_t} = (I_s + I_e),$$

furthermore, if

W_r = relay volt-ampere rating at the setting current I_s,
Z_m = core impedance, that is, exciting impedance,

then

$$I_e = \frac{W_r}{Z_m I_s},$$

so that

$$\frac{I_{poc}}{K_t} = I_s = \frac{W_r}{Z_m I_s} = I_{so}, \qquad (107)$$

(putting $I_{poc}/K_t = I_{so}$),

$$\frac{dI_{so}}{dI_s} = 1 - \frac{W_r}{Z_m I_s{}^2},$$

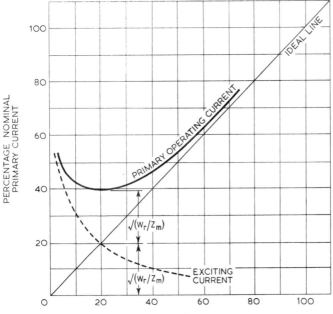

Fig. 72. Typical current-transformer 'Vee' curve. (This curve is of particular interest in ring-type core-balance current-transformers where matching of the external impedance with the internal impedance is important.)

and the *minimum* primary operating current therefore occurs when $W_r/Z_m I_s^2 = 1$, that is, when $I_s = \sqrt{(W_r/Z_m)}$, and this minimum primary operating current referred to the secondary side equals $2\sqrt{(W_r/Z_m)}$ or, in other words, the primary operating current is at its minimum when the exciting current equals the relay setting current or when the current-transformer exciting impedance

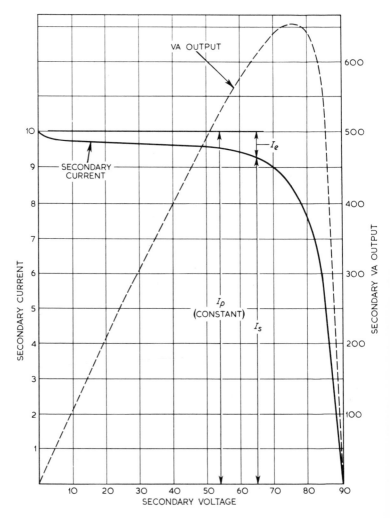

Fig. 73. Output curve of a current-transformer. (*Note.* If the excitation curve is a universal one subject to scale multipliers as shown in Fig. 69, then the multiplier for the output curve would be $l/N_s \times 4{\cdot}44\,fAN_s$, that is, $4{\cdot}44\,fAl$.)

matches the relay impedance. This is shown graphically in Fig. 72*
and it is easily proved that at the point of minimum primary
operating current the slope of the exciting current curve is equal
and opposite to the ideal line.

It is sometimes useful to know the maximum output a current-
transformer is capable of delivering for a particular value of primary current. Using again the assumption that $I_p/K_t = I_s + I_e$,
that is, that the secondary overall power factor is such that the
exciting current is in anti-phase to the secondary current, the
excitation curve can be used immediately to indicate the relationship between the secondary current and the secondary induced
e.m.f. when the total secondary impedance varies but the primary
current remains constant as shown in Fig. 73. The VA curve
follows immediately by multiplying the secondary current and its
corresponding secondary induced voltage, arriving at a curve
similar to that also shown in Fig. 73. For greater accuracy the
internal burden due to the secondary winding resistance must, of
course, be subtracted from the VA curve, but this is usually an
unnecessary refinement. If the core used is of ring-stampings or of
the continuously wound type a universal output curve for any
particular alloy may be drawn from which the output is immediately
obtainable by the use of a suitable multiplier as shown in Fig. 73.
It will be found that the maximum output of a current-transformer corresponds closely to the knee-point or maximum permeability flux density.

* See Mathews, *Protective Current Transformers and Circuits* (Chapman and Hall).

CHAPTER 12

INTRODUCTION TO CURRENT-TRANSFORMERS IN BALANCE SYSTEMS OF PROTECTION

Only the broadest outline of the current-transformer requirements encountered in the numerous balance systems of protection is offered here; therefore emphasis is laid on certain aspects that are common to many of these systems. Detailed information on the individual systems is readily available from the relay manufacturers and numerous articles on these systems have also appeared in the technical journals. Neither is any attempt made to offer the highly mathematical treatment necessary for a complete understanding and knowledge of all aspects and the reader wishing to examine the subject in such detail must look elsewhere.

It has already been pointed out that B.S. 3938 is limited to current-transformers in protective systems in which transient instability is of no importance because of the relatively slow time response of relays such as the induction type. Similarly, transient instability need not be considered in low-speed balance systems.

Now, the basic circuit for any balance system of protection is shown in Fig. 74a and ideally no matter what the magnitude or waveform the primary current has, for a fault outside the protected

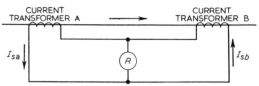

Fig. 74a. Basic circuit for balance forms of protection.

zone the relay should not operate. The ability of the system to do this is termed its stability, this being prefaced by either 'steady state' or 'transient' depending on the type of through-fault being considered. However, the suitability of a balance system depends, not only on its stability factor, that is, the ratio of its maximum through-fault current at which it is stable to its nominal full-load current, but also on its sensitivity which is given by the lowest value of primary current occurring with a fault inside the protected zone that will correctly operate the relay. This is an extremely important point because, unfortunately, in many balance systems the requirements for stability and sensitivity are opposing each

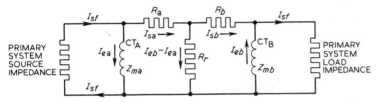

Fig. 74b. Equivalent circuit when R_r is small. R_a = resistance of secondary winding of current-transformer A plus resistance of pilot leads to relay; R_b = similar to R_a but for current-transformer B; I_{sf} = secondary current corresponding to through-fault primary current; Z_{ma} and Z_{mb} exciting impedances of the current-transformers.

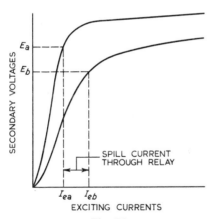

Fig. 74c.

other in respect of the design of the associated current-transformers. Nevertheless a sufficiently low minimum relay setting is essential in order to give reasonable protection if, for instance, the equipment being protected is a power transformer. It can be shown that if a delta/star transformer, with resistance earthing of the neutral point of the star winding, is protected by a balance system having a 20% minimum setting it has 59% of its star winding unprotected (measured from the neutral point). Here though, a further factor comes into the picture because although protection of 80% of the star winding would require a fault setting of $2\frac{1}{2}$% or thereabouts, if the power transformer range of tappings was 10% one would obtain mal-operation of the protective system simply by the normal healthy out-of-balance caused by tap-changing. In such a case there would have to be some additional protection applied—probably in the form of restricted earth-leakage protection of the star winding.

It is emphasised that throughout the next two chapters 'resistances' rather than 'impedances' have been used. This has been done purely for the sake of clarity—most relays possess inductance and therefore their impedances should be used. As far as current-transformers are concerned if they are of the low-reactance type then the secondary winding resistance is used in the calculations. If on the other hand wound-primary type current-transformers are concerned then the secondary winding impedance should be used, but owing to the approximate nature of the equations developed arithmetic addition of impedances may be used in all cases.

Now consider the equivalent diagram for the balance system of Fig. 74a, as shown in Fig. 74b, which also includes the excitation characteristics of the two current-transformers, then if

I_p = rated primary current,
I_s = rated secondary current,
I_r = nominal relay setting current = $x I_s/100$, where x is the percentage setting of the relay,
n = number of times rated primary current up to which stability is required,
I_{sa} and I_{sb} = actual secondary currents during through-fault conditions.

Using the resistance symbols given in Fig. 74b, then

$$E_a = I_{sa}R_a + R_r(I_{sa} - I_{sb}), \qquad (108)$$

$$E_b = I_{sb}R_b + R_r(I_{sb} - I_{sa}). \qquad (109)$$

Taking the case of a zero relay resistance the latter terms on the right-hand side of both these equations are eliminated and

$$E_a = I_{sa}R_a \quad \text{and} \quad E_b = I_{sb}R_b.$$

From the two excitation curves (Fig. 74c) the corresponding exciting currents I_{ea} and I_{eb} are found and

$$\frac{nI_p}{K_t} = I_{sa} + I_{ea} = I_{sb} + I_{eb} \qquad (110)$$

(K_t = turns ratio),

so that the current tending to operate the relay I_{ro}, is given by

$$I_{ro} = I_{sa} - I_{sb}$$

$$= \left(\frac{nI_p}{K_t} - I_{ea}\right) - \left(\frac{nI_p}{K_t} - I_{eb}\right)$$

$$= I_{eb} - I_{ea}. \tag{111}$$

Thus to obtain the desired stability $I_{ro} < I_r$ so that $I_{eb} - I_{ea} < I_r$.

This is the technique applied to balance systems using low-impedance relays, as in practical cases no relay may have true zero impedance.

For internal faults—assuming primary fault current in current-transformer A, the minimum primary operating current, I_{poc} is given by

$$\frac{I_{poc}}{K_t} = I_r + I_{ea}' + I_{eb}', \tag{112}$$

I_{ea}' now being the exciting current corresponding to

$$E_a' = I_r(R_a + R_r) \text{ volts}$$

and I_{eb}' corresponding to $I_r R_b$ volts.

In many cases it will be found that these exciting currents will play an insignificant part in determining I_{poc}. Thus, provided the fault current at which stability is required is not high enough to cause saturation and that $I_{eb} - I_{ea} < I_r$, is met, there is no absolute necessity for perfect matching of the excitation curves, neither does the relay have to be connected across equipotential points on the pilot wires, that is, R_a need not equal R_b. Of course, if closer matching of excitation characteristics and greater equality between R_a and R_b can be attained, then for a given relay-setting current one would obtain higher stability. Equalising resistances are sometimes inserted into a particular system to improve stability, but such an action decreases sensitivity, that is, increases E_a' and hence the exciting currents I_{ea}' and I_{eb}'. In some cases, instead of trying to obtain matching of excitation characteristics, the individual exciting currents are themselves made less than the relay-setting current.

Returning to the case where the protected equipment is a power-transformer, matching of characteristics of the current-transformers often presents considerable difficulties because they may be of widely different current and voltage ratings. In other cases where the current-transformers are of the same ratio they may well be situated in different types of switchgear with inevitably different available space so that again identical designs cannot be used.

One example worth discussing is that of an induction-type relay being used for restricted or balanced earth-fault protection on a power-transformer winding, as shown in Fig. 75a. (Here, incidentally, is a case where the neutral current-transformer, Fig. 75b, often has different dimensions to those in the phases.) Faults within the power-transformer winding will cause only the neutral current-transformer to be energised by fault current and the primary operating current for any particular relay setting is determined in exactly the same way as shown in chapter 11 for unrestricted earth-fault protection, remembering only that there are now three 'idle' current-transformers and not two.

For faults outside the protected zone it is assumed that the neutral current-transformer supplies the voltage drop caused by its own resistance and that of the pilot leads back to the line current-transformers and relay (these last named are usually relatively close together), while the line current-transformer energised by fault current has only its internal resistive drop to supply. From the excitation curves the exciting currents for these two e.m.f.s, E_n and E_l, respectively, are found and the difference between them is the maximum spill current into the relay. Provided this is a reasonably low percentage of the relay setting current (say 25%) the arrangement is then considered stable, remembering that steady-state conditions only are under discussion.

Consider now the case of a relay having a high impedance in the balance circuit shown in Fig. 74a. The limiting case is when the impedance of the relay is infinite corresponding to open-circuiting the relay connection. Thus the secondary currents I_{sa} and I_{sb} must

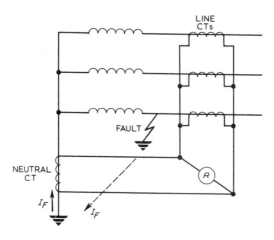

Fig. 75a.

Fig. 75b. Typical neutral current-transformer. (*Smith-Hobson Ltd.*)

now share the same identity, that is, $I_{sa} = I_{sb} = I_s$ and as the primary fault current is common to both current-transformers their exciting currents must also be equal, that is, $I_{ea} = I_{eb}$ and this is shown in Fig. 76a.

Assuming the excitation characteristics are of the same shape and furthermore for the sake of simplicity that they may be taken as linear, that is, of the form $y = mx$, then

$$E_a = m_a I_{ea}$$

and

$$E_b = m_b I_{eb},$$

so that as

$$I_{ea} = I_{eb}$$

$$\frac{E_a}{m_a} = \frac{E_b}{m_b}.$$

I_{sf} the secondary current corresponding to the primary fault current at which stability is required, is equal to nI_p/K_t, and the loop equation is given by

$$I_{sf}(R_a + R_b) = E_a + E_b$$

$$= E_a\left(1 + \frac{m_b}{m_a}\right) \tag{113}$$

and

$$E_a = \frac{I_{sf}(R_a + R_b)m_a}{m_a + m_b}. \tag{114}$$

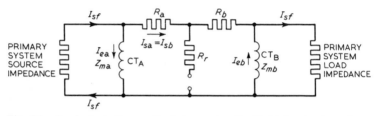

Fig. 76a. Equivalent diagram for balance circuit with high-relay impedance (in diagram R_r infinite). (*Note.* R_a includes secondary winding resistance of CT_A; R_b includes secondary winding resistance of CT_B.)

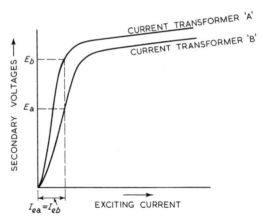

Fig. 76b. Excitation curves for Fig. 76a.

The maximum voltage appearing across the relay is $(E_a - I_{sf}R_a)$ and this equals

$$\frac{I_{sf}(R_b m_a - R_a m_b)}{m_a + m_b}.$$

Putting $m_b/m_a = K$ this maximum relay voltage E_{rf} then becomes

$$E_{rf} = \frac{I_{sf}(R_b - KR_a)}{1+K}. \tag{115}$$

Thus with a knowledge of the current-transformer excitation curves, when a high-impedance relay is used in a balance circuit (such a relay frequently has its settings given in terms of voltage), provided E_{rf} as determined from eq. (115) does not exceed the voltage setting being used, then stability will be maintained on through-fault currents up to nI_p amperes, or the relative values of R_b and R_a, as before, may be suitably adjusted to give the desired stability. When calculating the internal fault current to cause operation of the relay at the setting chosen it will be found that as the relay current consumption is negligible it may frequently be ignored. Thus if the setting voltage is V_r volts, the exciting currents for the two current-transformers (again call them I_{ea}' and I_{eb}') are then found from the characteristic curves and the primary operating current is then taken as $K_t(I_{ea}' + I_{eb}')$.

Again it will be seen that closer similarity between exciting characteristics and between R_a and R_b can have only a beneficial result both from the stability and sensitivity aspects, but also in some cases the relay manufacturers recommend the use of 1 A or even 0·5 A secondaries in order to reduce the burden on the current-transformers by their internal resistances and those of the pilot wires.

CHAPTER 13

FURTHER NOTES ON BALANCE SYSTEMS OF PROTECTION

Consider first what happens in a current-transformer which is partially magnetised by d.c. upon which is superimposed an a.c. component. From Fig. 77a it is seen that the higher the d.c. component and hence the higher up the excitation curve is the operating point, the greater is the exciting current required for the same alternating voltage until with d.c. saturation the exciting current would equal the input current, and the a.c. exciting impedance

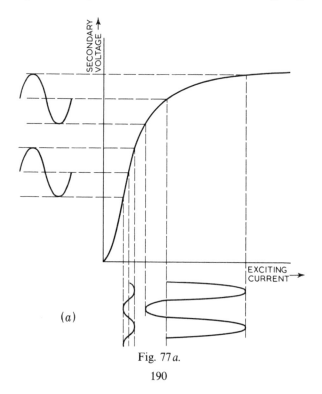

(a)

Fig. 77a.

becomes zero. Such a condition in a current-transformer in a balance system means that there would be no development of e.m.f. by that current-transformer into the balance circuit and as far as the other unsaturated current-transformer is concerned it may be treated as a resistor—its value being that of the secondary winding resistance.

Many faults are of a transient nature, possessing some degree of asymmetry and therefore a d.c. component. A balance system of protection used on a power-transformer is unable to distinguish between an asymmetrical internal fault and the possibly heavy inrush primary magnetising current that can occur when the power-transformer is switched-in, mentioned in chapter 10, and the balance system of protection, must have a reasonably high level of transient stability.

Now Fig. 77b shows the flux density in the core of a current-transformer excited by a fully asymmetrical current and as shown, the peak flux density is approximately given by X_p/R_p times that

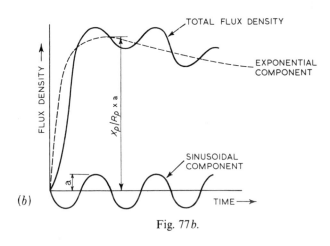

Fig. 77b.

due to its sinusoidal component, X_p/R_p being the reactance/resistance ratio of the primary system. The change in flux required to transform the d.c. component of a fully asymmetrical wave is X_p/R_p times that required for a similar symmetrical a.c. wave. As the X_p/R_p ratio may have a value up to 25–30, any current-transformer, in order to avoid saturation under asymmetrical fault conditions, must operate on the linear part of its excitation characteristic for a secondary voltage 25–30 times that determined for the maximum symmetrical steady-state fault condition so that at this fault current the flux density in the core must not exceed

0·06 webers/sq. metre, or thereabouts, if the core material is oriented electrical steel.*

Put another way

If B_1 = peak flux density corresponding to rated full-load current,

B_k = knee-point flux density,

and

$$x = \frac{\text{maximum fault current (asymmetrical value)}}{\text{rated primary current}},$$

then

$$B_1 < \frac{B_k}{x[1+(X_p/R_p)]}. \tag{116}$$

Such a requirement frequently leads to extremely large current-transformers, sometimes impracticably large. Should the relay possess inductance, as it frequently does, eq. (116) is modified to

$$B_1 < \frac{B_k}{xP}, \tag{117}$$

where P is a function both of the X_p/R_p ratio and of $\cos \delta$, the power factor of the secondary circuit, as shown in Fig. 78.

Equations (116) and (117) ignore the possibility that the current-transformer concerned, at the incidence of a fully asymmetrical fault current in the primary circuit, may possess some residual magnetism. The worst possible condition is when the fault current and residual flux are both acting in the same direction and then

$$B_1 < \frac{B_k - B_r}{xP}, \tag{118}$$

B_r being the remanent flux density.

To meet this requirement demands even larger cores and is usually impracticable except for very small burdens. This condition with residual magnetism present can occur in high-speed auto-reclose systems with a fault following rapidly after another and it is sometimes recommended that current-transformers used in such applications should have cores of hot-rolled electrical steel rather than of oriented material because in the former type, although the knee-point flux density is lower, the difference between knee-point and remanent flux densities is somewhat greater than for the oriented electrical steels which possess a more sharply defined knee-region.

---

* 'Voltage Transformers and Current-transformers associated with Switchgear', by Gray and Wright, *Proc. I.E.E.*, **100** (1953), part II, p. 223.

Many modern high-speed balance systems of protection and similar types, therefore, are based on the principle that current-transformer saturation under through-fault conditions is inevitable and to avoid extremely large current-transformers or special types such as those possessing air-gaps, it becomes necessary to incorporate features in the relay itself or in the overall protective system which allows for this saturation of current-transformers.

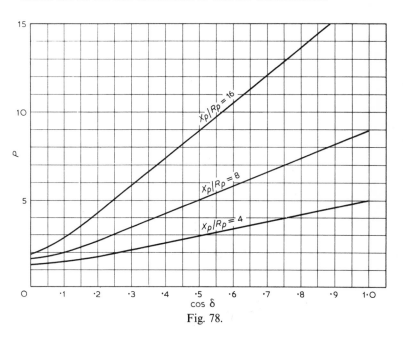

Fig. 78.

A simple example of the latter is the use of stabilising resistances and considering the restricted (balance) earth-fault scheme using an instantaneous relay shown in Fig. 75a it is assumed that with an asymmetrical through-fault current the neutral current-transformer becomes fully saturated, this current-transformer then supplies no e.m.f. in the balance circuit and may be represented by its secondary winding resistance as shown in Fig. 79, but the line current-transformers are assumed not to saturate and to have infinite exciting impedance.

If the maximum asymmetrical primary through-fault current up to which stability is required is given by I_{pf} and the corresponding secondary current is I_{sf}, that is, $I_{sf} = I_{pf}/K_t$, then the maximum voltage appearing across the relay is now $I_{sf}(R_a + R_n)$, R_n being the secondary winding resistance of the neutral current-transformer.

If, as before, the relay setting current is I_r, then the stabilising resistance required, R_{st}, is given by

$$R_{st} \geq \frac{I_{sf}(R_a+R_n)}{I_r}.\tag{119}$$

The presence of this stabilising resistor will, of course, affect the sensitivity of the system and a further limitation is placed on the value of R_{st} because for speedy operation of the relay under internal fault conditions the e.m.f. required to pass operating current

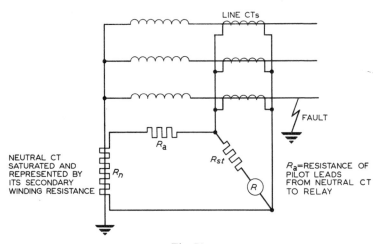

Fig. 79.

through the relay and stabiliser should be approximately 50% of the current-transformer saturation voltage. Put another way, saturation on internal faults should not occur at less than approximately twice the fault setting. Any e.m.f. developed by the saturated current-transformer will improve the stability.

Returning also to the high-impedance relay case, assuming that current-transformer B is the one saturating the equivalent diagram of Fig. 76a becomes that given in Fig. 80. E_b is assumed to be zero as in the previous case and also the exciting impedance of the unsaturated current-transformer is assumed infinite so that the maximum voltage appearing across the relay is given by

$$E_r = I_{sf}R_b \text{ volts.}\tag{120}$$

This then becomes the minimum relay setting to ensure transient stability for a fully asymmetrical through-fault current of $K_t I_{sf}$ amperes.

With these voltage-operated high-impedance relays the maximum peak voltage across the relay assuming full asymmetry would be $2\sqrt{2}I_{sf}R_b$ volts, but in practice most relays operate on r.m.s. voltage and a blocking condenser or rectifier-operated coil nullifies the factor 2 so that relay operation is normally based on eq. (120). Again, any e.m.f. developed by the saturated current-transformer will improve the stability.

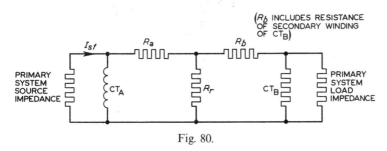

Fig. 80.

Another common method adopted to overcome this problem of inevitable current-transformer saturation, when considering power-transformer protective circuits, is to use a biased relay. The out-of-balance current tending to cause mal-operation increases with the magnitude of the through-fault current so that the stability increases if some restraint or bias is put on the relay, such restraint being itself proportional to the through-fault current. Therefore the ratio of the turns on the operating coil to those on the bias coil may be adjusted so that the relay will operate only when the out-of-balance current exceeds a certain proportion of the through-fault current, that is, of the bias current. The use of such a relay gives rise to the term percentage differential protection—if

$$N_b = \text{total bias coil turns,}$$

$$N_r = \text{operating coil turns,}$$

$$B = \text{bias ratio} = \frac{N_r}{N_b} = \frac{\% \text{bias}}{100},$$

then, at the maximum through-fault current for which stability is required

$$N_r I_r = N_b I_{sf},$$

and it can be shown very easily that for both centre-tapped bias coils or rectifier-fed bias, to a pessimistic approximation,

$$\frac{\text{setting voltage unbiased}}{\text{setting voltage biased}} = \frac{I_{sf}}{I_r}B.$$

For internal faults

$$I_{sf} = \frac{I_r(BZ_m + R_r)}{(BZ_m - B^2 Z_m - BR_r)},$$

where Z_m is the exciting impedance of the current-transformer fed by the fault current and it can be shown for fault currents greater than five times rated full-load current

$$Z_m \geq \frac{2R_s}{B} \text{ ohms,} \tag{121}$$

where R_s = resistance of secondary winding and for n current-transformers in parallel (as in bus-bar protection circuits)

$$Z_m \geq \frac{2R_s n}{B} \text{ ohms} \tag{122}$$

and this determines the maximum permissible exciting current I_e at a maximum secondary voltage V_s of

$$\frac{I_{sf} R_s}{B} \text{ volts} \quad I_e \leq \frac{V_s}{Z_m} \text{ amperes.}$$

Considerable help is given to the current-transformer designer as many relays used in the various protection schemes have undergone considerable testing by the manufacturers under all possible conditions from which they have established the minimum exciting characteristics for the associated current-transformers. Examples of these are given in Tables 8, 9 and 10.

Both the 'Translay' and 'Solkor' systems of balance protection are good examples of the technique, previously mentioned, where the requirements for the associated current-transformers with respect to stability are made as simple as possible by the incorporation of suitable features in the relay itself, although the method adopted for 'Translay' is not the same as for 'Solkor'.

The former uses a relay which is of the induction type and therefore inoperative under transient conditions, while pilot-wire capacitance currents and disimilarity between associated current-transformers are compensated for by the use of a bias coil.

Solkor systems, on the other hand, employ static summation transformers and tuned relays.

The manufacturers of relays have published excellent pamphlets giving details of their operation and they are recommended to the reader of this book who wishes to have more information.

Table 8. *Current-transformer requirements for English Electric relays*

Relay type	Application	Minimum knee-point voltage (E_k)	Maximum exciting current	
CAG 14	Restricted earth fault (3 current-transformers)	$2I_f(R_{sw}+R_p)$	$\dfrac{I_s-I_r}{3}$ at	$\dfrac{E_k}{2}$ volts
CAG 14	Restricted earth fault (4 current-transformers)	$2I_f(R_{sw}+R_p)$	$\dfrac{I_s-I_r}{4}$ at	$\dfrac{E_k}{2}$ volts
CAG 14	Bus-bar differential	$2I_f(R_{sw}+R_p)$	$\dfrac{I_s-I_r}{n}$ at	$\dfrac{E_k}{2}$ volts
CAG 14	Residual check	$2I_f(R_{sw}+R_c)$	$\dfrac{I_s-I_r}{3q}$ at	$\dfrac{E_k}{2}$ volts
CAG 14	Machine differential	$2I_f(R_{sw}+R_p)$	$\dfrac{I_s-I_r}{2}$ at	$\dfrac{E_k}{2}$ volts
DDG 5% bias	Machine differential	$2\cdot4I_f(R_{sw}+R_b+R_r)$	$\dfrac{I_s-I_r}{2}$ at relay	operating voltage
DDG 10% bias	Machine differential	$2I_f(R_s+R_b+R_r)$	$\dfrac{I_s-I_r}{2}$ at relay	operating voltage
DDT and DDGT	Transformer and generator/transformer differential	With star CTs. $2I_f(R_s+R_b+R_r)$ With delta CTs. $\dfrac{2}{\sqrt{3}}I_f(R_s+R_b+R_r)$		

I_f = secondary current equivalent to max. fault current;
I_s = effective fault setting;
I_r = relay operating current;
n = no. of CT groups forming protected zone;
q = no. of incoming circuits;
R_{sw} = current-transformer secondary winding resistance;
R_p = maximum lead-resistance between relay and any CT;
R_b = lead resistance between CTs concerned and relay;
R_c = total lead resistance per phase;
R_r = impedance of one half of bias winding.

Table 9. *Current-transformer requirements for Translay and other A.E.I. relays to give good settings and high stability*

Relay type	Minimum secondary knee-point voltage (V)	Maximum allowable CT exciting current at the stated voltage
DG 2	$0{\cdot}25IR_s$	——
DGT 2 and DGTA 2	$3{\cdot}0IR_s$ (star) $5{\cdot}2IR_s$ (delta)	——
DS 4	$30I\left(\dfrac{6}{I^2}+R_L\right)$ If pilot-wire capacitance >1 microfarad, knee-point voltage is multiplied by $(1+0{\cdot}3C)$, C being the pilot-wire capacitance	$0{\cdot}05I$ amp. at $\dfrac{30}{I}$ volts
DSB 5	$30I\left(\dfrac{12}{I^2}+R_L\right)$	$0{\cdot}01I$ amp. at $\dfrac{5}{I}$ volts
DSC 4	$30I\left(\dfrac{9}{I^2}+R_L\right)$	$0{\cdot}05I$ amp. at $\dfrac{30}{I}$ volts
DT 2 and DTA 2	$12I\left(\dfrac{3}{I^2}+R_L\right)$ (star) $12I\left(\dfrac{6}{I^2}+R_L\right)$ (delta)	$0{\cdot}015I$ amp. at $0{\cdot}013V$ volt $0{\cdot}02I$ amp. at $0{\cdot}013V$ volt
DY 2	$I_F\left(\dfrac{15}{I^2}+R_L\right)$	——
DZ	$I_F\left(\dfrac{26-0{\cdot}5M}{I^2}+R_L\right)$ (For standard 6-element scheme)	——
FOS	$10I\left(\dfrac{7}{I^2}+R_L\right)$	$0{\cdot}05I$ amp. at $0{\cdot}1V$ volt
HM 2	$I_F\left(\dfrac{12}{I^2}+R_L\right)$ and not less than $\dfrac{120}{I}$ volts	$0{\cdot}02I$ amp. at $\dfrac{9}{I}+I(R_{CT}+R_w)$ volt

Table 9—continued.

Relay type	Minimum secondary knee-point voltage (V)	Maximum allowable CT exciting current at the stated voltage
HMB 2	$I_F\left(\dfrac{14}{I^2}+R_L\right)$ and not less than $\dfrac{120}{I}$ volt	$0.02I$ amp.
HHTA 3	$\dfrac{120}{I}+I_F R_L$ (star)	* $0.016I$ amps. at $\dfrac{10}{I}+I(R_{CT}+R_w)$ volt and $0.1I$ amp. at $\dfrac{40}{I}+IR_L$ volt
	$\dfrac{175}{I}+I_F(R_{CT}+3R_w)$ (delta)	* $0.016I$ amp. at $\dfrac{10}{I}+0.3I(R_{CT}+3R_w)$ volt and $0.06I$ amp. at $\dfrac{40}{I}+0.5771I(R_{CT}+3R_w)$ volt
HO 2 and HT 2	$\dfrac{120}{I}+I_F R_L$	* $0.016I$ amp. at $\dfrac{10}{I}+I(R_{CT}+R_w)$ volt and $0.1I$ amp. at $\dfrac{40}{I}+IR_L$ volt
PBD 2	$6I\left(\dfrac{6}{I^2}+R_L\right)$ (star) $6I\left(\dfrac{12}{I^2}+R_L\right)$ (delta)	——
PBG 2 generator protection	$0.4I\left(\dfrac{600}{I^2}+R_L\right)$	——

Table 9—continued.

Relay type	Minimum secondary knee-point voltage (V)	Maximum allowable CT exciting current at the stated voltage
PBG 2 generator/ transformer protection	$2 \cdot 5I\left(\dfrac{24}{I^2} + R_L\right)$ (star) $2 \cdot 5I\left(\dfrac{48}{I^2} + R_L\right)$ (delta)	——

I = relay 100% current;

R_{CT} = resistance of secondary winding of current-transformer;

R_w = resistance per lead from CT, to relay panel;

M = I_F/I, I_F being maximum through-fault current (secondary);

R_s = resistance of stabilising resistor = R_L/B, where $R_L = R_{CT} + 2R_w$ and B is the per unit bias. (This is approx. equation for R_s.) Also impedance of other devices such as instruments must be taken into account when calculating R_L. Where two sets of current-transformers are connected in parallel the permissible exciting currents must be halved.

* This requirement applies where the system minimum internal fault level is less than three times the CT rated primary current. When fault level exceeds this, permissible exciting currents can be increased.

Table 10. *Current-transformer requirements for Reyrolle Solkor protection schemes*

For plain-feeder protection

Knee-point voltage must not be less than

$$\frac{50}{I} + I_F(R_{CT} + 2R_L),$$

where I = rated secondary current,

I_F = maximum secondary current under through-fault connections,

R_{CT} = secondary resistance of current-transformer,

R_L = lead resistance between the current-transformer and the Solkor-box.

In addition, exciting currents of the current-transformers at opposite ends of the feeder must not differ by more than 0·25 amp. up to 10 volts (5 A secondaries).

For teed-feeder protection

Similar to above but knee-point voltage must not be less than

$$\frac{4I_F}{I^2} + I_F(R_{CT} + 2R_L).$$

For Solkor-B, plain-feeder protection

Exactly as for plain-feeder protection.

For Solkor-R feeder protection
  Similar to that previously given: Knee-point voltage

$$\not< \frac{50}{I} + \frac{I_F}{N}(R_{CT} + 2R_L),$$

I_F now being the maximum primary current under through-fault conditions,
N is the current-transformer ratio,
R_L is the lead resistance between the current-transformers and relay, per phase.

  It is recommended that no other burdens are included in the circuit, but if this is unavoidable the additional burden must be taken into account when determining knee-point voltage.

Returning to Tables 8, 9 and 10 it is immediately seen that in many cases a current-transformer for use in a balance scheme of protection is specified by
  (i) a knee-point e.m.f. which must be exceeded, and
  (ii) an exciting current not to be greater than a particular value at the specified knee-point e.m.f.
This is done in class X in B.S. 3938 with the addition of two further points, namely
  (iii) the turns ratio which must be maintained within $\pm 0.25\%$ of its specified value and
  (iv) the resistance of the secondary winding.
Thus B.S. 3938 can be used in a wider sphere than B.S. 2046 because it can be used for many current-transformers for balance forms of protection once the user and manufacturer have between them determined the desiderata already detailed here.

CHAPTER 14

THE TESTING OF CURRENT-TRANSFORMERS

The insulation problems met in the design of current-transformers and the test procedures to prove the insulation level attained by a current-transformer are exactly the same as for other equipments and consist of insulation resistance measurements, power frequency and impulse over-voltage tests and the like. This chapter does not discuss these tests but limits discussion to some of the techniques used to determine the ratio and phase errors of a current-transformer. This in itself is a subject upon which one could write a book and all that is attempted here is a broad outline of some of the basic circuits that are in use.*

There is a method of classification of test techniques which is a reasonably obvious one:

(i) Techniques in which the primary current is itself precisely measured and the corresponding secondary current equally precisely measured for both magnitude and its phase relationship with the primary current, and

(ii) test techniques in which the current-transformer being tested is compared against a standard or master current-transformer, the errors of which are already known.

Further subdivision of test techniques may be made, dependent on the detailed circuitry and the instruments that are used, but it is felt the major division adopted is sufficient for this present discussion, those test methods falling with category (i) being termed 'absolute methods' and those in category (ii) 'relative methods'.

The choice of method finally adopted may well depend on whether the testing is being carried out in a well-equipped measurements laboratory, in a production testing department handling large numbers of current-transformers or 'on site'. For the second named, some precision may be sacrificed for a more rapid test method, while for the last named two important requirements of

---

* For a description of numerous test circuits for determining instrument-transformer errors, see Hague, *Instrument Transformers* (Pitman).

the test equipment are that it should be both portable and robust.

Probably the most obvious way of testing a current-transformer for its ratio error is the circuit shown in Fig. 81, this being an example of the absolute method of testing. There is a direct-reading ammeter inserted in the primary circuit and a second ammeter connected in series with the burden in the secondary circuit.

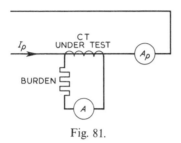

Fig. 81.

There are obvious disadvantages in this method such as the difficulty in taking accurate simultaneous readings from the two instruments and the non-uniform nature of the ammeter scales offers a further hazard at low currents. Another disadvantage is the upper limit placed on the primary current by the non-availability of direct-reading ammeters above 500 A. This last disadvantage is easily overcome by the insertion in the primary circuit of a current-transformer of known errors to supply the primary circuit ammeter. This method of ratio error test is probably of most use in the field testing of ammeter current-transformers and other low-accuracy types, including some protective current-transformers.

Consider next the case where again only the ratio error is to be measured and that a standard or master current-transformer is available having the same nominal ratio as the current-transformer being tested, together with two ammeters. The test-circuit being as shown in Fig. 82. S is the standard current-transformer, B_m the burden at which its errors are known, while X is the current-transformer under test and B_x the burden at which its errors are required to be found.

The circuit is completed by the two ammeters A_1 and A_2 and two changeover switches so connected that either ammeter may be inserted into either current-transformer secondary circuit at will.

With these switches such that the ammeter A_1 is in the standard current-transformer circuit, then with a primary current of I_p flowing through the series-connected primary windings the current in A_1 is I_s and if the corresponding ammeter reading is

I_1 and the correction or calibration factor C_1 then

$$I_s = C_1 I_1.$$

Similarly, the current in the unknown current-transformer is I_x, the ammeter reading in A_2 is I_2 and if this ammeter's correction or calibration factor is C_2, then

$$I_x = C_2 I_2.$$

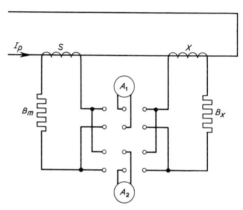

Fig. 82.

With the same primary current the switches are now changed so that A_2 is in the standard current-transformer circuit and now

$$I_s = C_2 I_{21},$$

while A_1 in the unknown current-transformer secondary circuit shows a new reading I_{11}, so that

$$I_x = c_1 I_{11}.$$

Thus

$$I_s^2 = c_1 c_2 I_1 I_2$$

and

$$I_x^2 = c_1 c_2 I_{11} I_{21}.$$

Now K_c is the current ratio of the standard current-transformer and K_{cx} that of the unknown current-transformer.

$$K_c = \frac{I_p}{I_s} \quad \text{and} \quad K_{cx} = \frac{I_p}{I_x},$$

so that

$$K_{cx} = \frac{K_c I_s}{I_x}$$

and

$$K_{cx} = \left(\frac{I_1 I_2}{I_{11} I_{21}}\right)^{\frac{1}{2}} K_c. \tag{123}$$

From eq. (123) it will be seen that the instrument correction factors have been eliminated but the accuracy of this test method falls off at low loads.

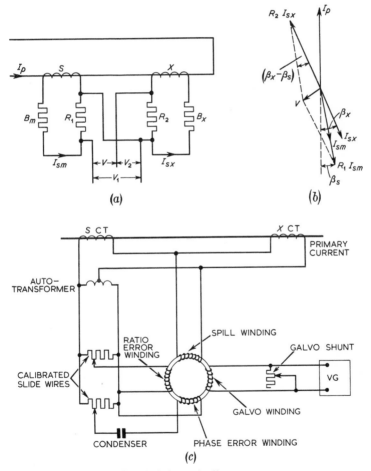

Fig. 83. Schematic diagram.

It will be appreciated that this two-ammeter method, with suitable instruments, is also useful for the checking of the ratio errors of some protective current-transformers at their specified saturation factors.

Numerous methods, in both the suggested main categories, exist for the testing of current-transformers for both ratio and phase errors, one of the simpler methods using a.c. potentiometers being shown in Fig. 83a. Here again a common primary current is passed through a standard current-transformer and the current-transformer under test, the latter having its rated burden and a suitable four-terminal resistance in its secondary circuit while the standard current-transformer also has a similar resistance and the burden at which its own errors are known. The method is quite simply the measurement of the voltages V_1 and V_2 across the two resistances and their vector difference by means of an a.c. potentiometer and of the phase displacement between V_1 and V.

If K_c is again the actual current ratio of the standard current-transformer and K_{cx} that of the transformer under test then

$$K_{cx} = \frac{R_2 V_1}{R_1 V_2} K_c$$

and from this the ratio error is calculable. Similarly, as shown in Fig. 83b if β_s is the known phase error of the master current-transformer, β_x the required phase error of the unknown current-transformer and ϕ is the measured phase difference between V and V_1 then

$$V_2 \sin(\beta_x - \beta_s) = V \sin \phi$$

from which

$$(\beta_x - \beta_s) = \frac{V}{V_2} \sin \phi,$$

to a sufficiently accurate degree for even precision testing.

There are a number of specially designed test equipments available, probably the most popular one in this country being the Petch-Elliott current-transformer test-set shown in Fig. 84b. As seen from the basic circuit diagram the secondary windings of the current-transformer under test and a standard current-transformer are connected to circulate and the resulting 'spill' current which is the vector difference of the secondary currents of these two current-transformers is then used to energise a toroidal core. Also wound on this toroidal core is a winding fed through a variable resistance, the object of this winding is to nullify that component of these 'spill' energising ampere-turns caused by the difference in the ratio errors of the two current-transformers, while

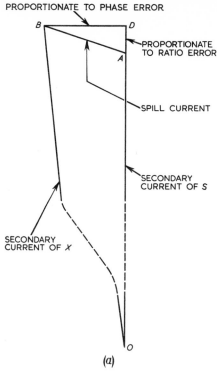

(a)

Fig. 84a.

a third winding on this core is supplied through a second variable resistance in series with a condenser, the ampere-turns on this winding nullifying that component of the spill energising current due to the difference in the phase errors of the two current-transformers. When, by suitable adjustment of the two variable resistances, the spill energising ampere-turns are completely counterbalanced the flux in the toroidal core is zero and no deflection occurs in the vibration galvanometer supplied from a fourth winding on the core. The differences between the ratio errors and phase errors of the master and unknown current-transformers are then immediately read from the calibrated adjusting knobs of the two variable resistances. The set also includes a selector switch enabling one to test 5 A, 1 A or 0·5 A current-transformers, reversing switches in association with the two variable resistances so that positive and negative errors are measurable and an ammeter to indicate primary current calibrated in percentages of its full-load value. Terminals are provided to enable burdens to be inserted in

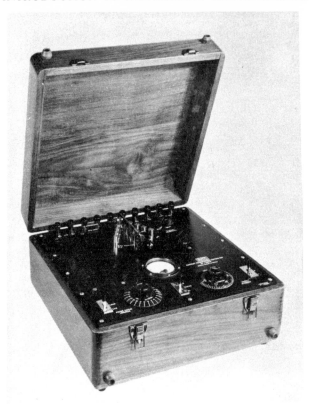

Fig. 84b. Petch-Elliott current-transformer testing set.
(*Elliott Bros. (London) Ltd.*)

the master and unknown current-transformer secondary circuits and when balance is achieved, the additional burden placed on the unknown current-transformer by the bridge is very small and may be neglected. This bridge therefore enables one to check the current-transformer for its errors very quickly and is ideally suited for production testing. It is also portable and thus of interest to those engineers more concerned with field testing.

The only other test-circuit that must be mentioned is that developed by Arnold, originally for the National Physical Laboratory but, like the Petch-Elliott test-set, is now in common use. Arnold's method also employs the relative bridge technique as shown in Fig. 85, where the difference or spill current passes through the resistance R, called the 'common resistor', which in practice consists of three resistances in series of 0·01, 0·1 and 1 ohm, any two of which may be short-circuited thus altering the range of the test-circuit. The voltage drop across this common resistor is balanced on a potentiometer which, as shown, consists of a continuously variable mutual inductance and non-inductive slide-wire supplied through a 5/5 isolating transformer from the master current-transformer secondary. Indication of balance is again given by a vibration galvanometer and again B_x is the rated burden of the current-transformer under test.

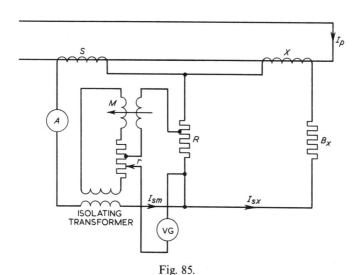

Fig. 85.

It can be shown that if

$$F_m = \frac{\text{true ratio}}{\text{nominal ratio}} \text{ for master current-transformer}$$

and

$$F_x = \frac{\text{true ratio}}{\text{nominal ratio}} \text{ for current-transformer under test,}$$

then

$$F_x - F_m = \frac{r}{R},$$

and if

β_m = phase error of standard current-transformer,
β_x = phase error of current-transformer under test,

then

$$\beta_x - \beta_m = \frac{2\pi f M}{R}.$$

In the commercially manufactured test-equipment based on Arnold's circuit the non-inductive slide-wire is calibrated in percentage ratio error and the variable mutual inductance in minutes of phase angle error. Two different sets are available— one, for instance, is capable of only testing 5 A secondaries, another is capable of testing both 5 A and 1 A secondaries, while either set is obtainable in a self-contained transportable unit. As with the Petch-Elliott, the master current-transformer and the common primary supply are separate.

From what has been written it will be obvious that the equipment needed for a good test-room for current-transformers will consist of many separate items, some of which will be relatively expensive.

The first item required is a supply transformer capable of delivering the largest rated primary current concerned. This transformer must incorporate some means of variation and should be of ample capacity.

A standard, multi-ratio current-transformer for each rated secondary current in which one is interested is required, that is,

Fig. 86. Test-room supply transformer and control unit. (*Smith-Hobson Ltd.*)

for 5 A, 1 A and 0·5 A, although one current-transformer may be so designed to cater for all values of secondary current. The errors of all standard current-transformers at all ratios must be known and this 'calibration' can be quite expensive.

A complete range of burden resistances (or in some cases burden impedances) are required and even when the Petch-Elliott or similar testing set is used one must also have available suitable ammeters for the testing of low-accuracy current-transformers.

Some engineers prefer to keep all test components separate, thus preserving a reasonable degree of portability. On the other hand if one is concerned with the production testing of a large number of current-transformers it is advisable to incorporate all components into one test-bench using links and suitable switches to alter ratios, burdens and so on.

Figure 55 showed a typical multi-ratio standard current-transformer and Fig. 86 shows one example of a commercially available primary supply transformer and control unit for use in a current-transformer test-room.

Testing of protective current-transformers

From the chapters dealing with the various categories of protective current-transformers it is obvious that these require quite different techniques of testing than those applied for instance to measuring current-transformers manufactured in accordance with B.S. 3938.

The testing of low-reactance protective current-transformers to B.S. 3938 presents no difficulty, while those coming outside this category require a test for composite error demanding a primary supply capable of delivering possibly many thousands of amperes.

The testing of current-transformers being used in balance forms of protection also demands a similar source of primary test current, but also one in which the pertinent fault levels of primary current can be applied suddenly in the same manner that an actual through-fault current happens. This means too that the test equipment must be such that one can obtain the correct degree of asymmetry. This demands a generator of high capacity and some means of varying the X/R ratio of the primary test-circuit in order to do this, or alternatively the primary circuit must have a sufficiently low power factor to give asymmetry closely akin to the maximum obtained in actual service.

Such stability testing is not done as a routine test and, in fact, many small manufacturers do not possess suitable equipment.

Sensitivity testing does not present so many difficulties but like the test-plant used for stability testing it must be possible to supply three-phase, phase-to-phase and phase-to-earth currents.

CHAPTER 15

SOME NOTES ON OTHER NATIONAL SPECIFICATIONS

When comparing British specifications with those of other countries one expects to find differences in insulation tests, permissible temperature rises, rated frequency and so on, but as this book is principally concerned with the transforming function of instrument-transformers, comparisons here are limited to classes of accuracy and the manner in which they are specified.

With reference to current-transformers the American Standards Association specification for instrument-transformers, C.57.13–1954 is particularly interesting in the approach it adopts. For measuring current-transformers three burden values are specified, designated by B–0·1, B–0·2 and B–0·5, each having a certain value of resistance and inductance such that at 60 cycles and 5 A rated secondary current the impedance in ohms is given by the burden designation number, the power factor being 0·9. As reactance is determined by the frequency, then for 25 cycles the burden impedances differ from these 60-cycle figures because the inductances remain the same, and the power factor becomes 0·98.

Similarly, there are a further four standard burdens for protection applications: B–1, B–2, B–4 and B–8, where again these designation numbers give the impedance in ohms at 60 cycles and 5 A, the power factor being 0·5, while at 25 cycles and 5 A the power factor becomes 0·81, accompanied as before, by a lowering of the burden impedance.

While this method of specifying burdens is somewhat different to that employed in the British specifications the method of specifying accuracy classes is even more dissimilar from the British one. For metering applications, four accuracy classes are specified for current-transformers designated by 1·2, 0·6, 0·3 and 0·5 with corresponding limits of the *transformer correction factor* at both 100% and 10% rated primary current.

This transformer correction factor (T.C.F) is defined as that factor by which the meter readings must be multiplied to correct for the error introduced by the current-transformer through the combined effect of the ratio and phase errors. The relationship between what may be termed the 'combined error' and the T.C.F. is a simple one:

$$\text{Percentage combined error} = 100(\text{T.C.F.} - 1).$$

The accuracy class designation figures are in fact the percentage combined errors at 100% full-load primary current so that:
The limits of T.C.F. at 100% rated current

$$= 1 \pm \frac{\text{percentage combined error}}{100}$$

$$= 1 \pm \frac{\text{accuracy class designation}}{100}.$$

For accuracy classes 1·2, 0·6 and 0·3 the limits of T.C.F. at 10% rated current

$$= 1 \pm \frac{\text{accuracy class designation}}{50},$$

or in other words the permissible percentage combined error at 10% rated current is twice that allowed at 100% rated current.

For the fourth class, 0·5, the limits of the T.C.F. are the same for both 100% and 10% rated current and are given by

$$1 \pm \frac{\text{accuracy class designation}}{100}.$$

In this accuracy class the T.C.F. specified also applies to 150% full-load current.

It has already been shown elsewhere in this book that the errors introduced in meter readings by the phase error of the associated current-transformer is also dependent on the power factor of the *primary* load and for this reason the T.C.F.s are also related to a range of primary power factor of unity to 0·6 lagging.

At 0·6 p.f. lagging in the primary circuit a 2·6 minutes leading phase error gives an instrument reading 0·1% too high and this power factor is the basis of the A.S.A. standard. As the primary circuit power factor increases so does this instrument error decrease. At unity power factor in the primary circuit the current-transformer phase error has a negligible effect on the reading.

Now the T.C.F. is the product of the *ratio correction factor* [previously mentioned in chapter 2 and which is given by $100(\text{R.C.F.} - 1)$ = %R.E.*] and the correction factor for phase error. When the primary power factor is unity the limits of the R.C.F. are the same

* Note particularly this difference compared with British practice where if the R.C.F. > 1 the %R.E. is negative.

as for the T.C.F. Another way of expressing this is that the percentage combined error is the algebraic sum of the percentage ratio error and the phase error (when also expressed as a percentage).

Thus for a particular specified T.C.F., these American standards allow a larger phase error if the ratio error is such that this larger phase error compensates for it. Put another way, if the total error is limited to $\pm0.5\%$, the phase error can be $\pm1.0\%$ if the ratio

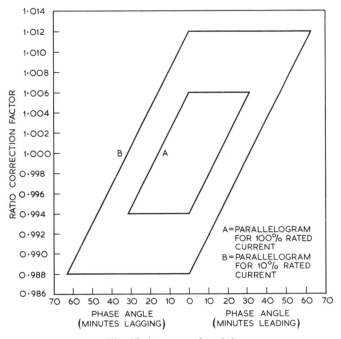

Fig. 87. Accuracy class 0·6.

error is $\pm0.5\%$ provided the relative signs are such that the algebraic sum does not exceed the specified $\pm0.5\%$, but if the ratio error is zero the phase error is then also limited to $\pm0.5\%$. This is best shown graphically by the control parallelograms actually used in the American standard, one example being given in Fig. 87 for the 0·6 class of accuracy. To meet this class of accuracy the ratio and phase errors at the rated burden must fall within the parallelogram related to the percentage full-load current concerned, and this means that the T.C.F. will not then exceed 1 ± 0.006 at 100% full-load current or 1 ± 0.012 at 10% full-load current at primary load power factors from unity down to 0·6 lagging.

This American standard, as far as protective current-transformers are concerned, uses a very similar approach to that in B.S. 3938 in that the basis of the accuracy classes is the secondary terminal voltage which the current-transformer delivers at twenty times rated secondary current without exceeding its specified ratio error of which there are two, 10% and $2\frac{1}{2}\%$. It also distinguishes between current-transformers having a 'low' secondary winding leakage reactance, designated by the letter 'L' and those having a 'high' value of this reactance, designated by the letter 'H'.

Thus for 'L-class' protective current-transformers, for each of the seven standard burdens, the three lowest having a power factor of 0·9 lagging the remaining four, 0·5 lagging, as already mentioned (at 60 cycles and 5 A), there are two standard accuracies. For example, with a standard burden B–0·5, one may have either 10L50 or 2·5L50—the 10 and 2·5 being the percentage ratio error and the 50 is the secondary terminal voltage at twenty times rated secondary current $(20 \times 5 \times 0·5 \text{ volts})$ up to which the current-transformer must preserve its specified ratio error, so that as in B.S. 3938 this ratio error must not be exceeded for the secondary current range of rated to twenty times rated value.

For high-reactance current-transformers, that is, those in the 'H-class', these requirements are repeated except that the secondary current range is from five times to twenty times rated value *and in addition* the current-transformer must not exceed its specified ratio error with a burden impedance four times the standard burden for a secondary current range from rated to five times rated value.

It must be remembered that should the frequency of excitation be other than 60 cycles or the rated secondary current be other than 5 A, then there will be commensurate changes in the burden impedance and the limiting secondary terminal voltage.

The German specification covering instrument-transformers is VDE 0414/12.62, issued by the Verband Deutscher Elektrotechniker (VDE) e. V. (Association of German Electrical Engineers) and while this differs from the British specification B.S. 3938 in some important points the dissimilarity is not so great as between the British and American specifications.

For current-transformers VDE 0414/12.62 gives ten accuracy classes as shown in Table 11 and it will be noticed that this specification adopts $\%$R.E. (here termed the current error) and phase difference in minutes as in the British specification. These ten accuracy classes are in two main categories: the first limits the current error and phase error over the same range as in B.S. 81, that is, 120% to 10% nominal or rated primary current except for class 3, which specifies ratio error only and then only between 100% and 50% rated primary current. The second category

Table 11. Classes of accuracy for current-transformer in VDE 0414/12.62

Accuracy class	Plus or minus percentage ratio error (at percentages of nominal primary current)							Plus or minus phase error in minutes (at percentages of nominal primary current)						
	200	120	100	50	20	10	5	200	120	100	50	20	10	5
0·1	—	0·1	0·1	—	0·2	0·25	—	—	5	5	—	8	10	—
0·2	—	0·2	0·2	—	0·35	0·5	—	—	10	10	—	15	20	—
0·5	—	0·5	0·5	—	0·75	1·0	—	—	30	30	—	40	60	—
1	—	1·0	1·0	—	1·5	2·0	—	—	60	60	—	80	120	—
3	—	—	3·0	3·0	—	—	—	—	—	—	—	—	—	—
0·1 G	0·1	—	0·1	—	0·2	0·25	0·4	5	—	5	—	8	10	15
0·2 G	0·2	—	0·2	—	0·35	0·5	0·75	10	—	10	—	15	20	30
0·5 G	0·5	—	0·5	—	0·75	1·0	1·5	30	—	30	—	40	60	90
1 G	1·0	—	1·0	—	1·5	2·0	—	60	—	60	—	80	120	—
3 G	—	—	3·0	3·0	—	—	—	—	—	—	—	—	—	—

(excepting class 3 G) specifies the errors over a much wider range of primary current, 200% to 5% rated value, and current-transformers in these classes, 0·1 G to 3 G, are intended for duty in association with watt-hour meters and like equipment of wide operational range. It is important to note that the current-transformers are required to be capable of continuous operation at 200% rated current, while those in the first category must be able to operate continuously at 120% rated current, unlike the British requirements. The specified limits of error are also applicable to burden values between the rated value and one quarter of this, the range of burdens being somewhat greater than the British one—5 VA to 60 VA for some classes of accuracy—the secondary power factor being specified as 0·8 lagging. Current-transformers in classes 3 and 3 G are required not to exceed the specified ratio error between rated and one-half rated burden, again with a power factor of 0·8 lagging. Under certain circumstances the burden power factor is changed to a unity one, in the case of 1 A or 5 A rated secondary current this is when the burden at which the test is to be made corresponds at rated current to a lower output than 3·75 VA. For example, if the current-transformer is specified as class 0·5 and the rated burden is 10 VA, then the tests at one quarter the rated burden, that is, 2·5 VA, will be carried out at this burden value as a unity power factor and not 0·8 lagging power factor one.

In addition to the class of accuracy a current-transformer manufactured to this German specification is also defined by a *rated overcurrent figure* which is not the same as the British overcurrent factor. This rated overcurrent figure is defined as 'that multiple of primary rated current at which the current error equals -10% at rated burden' and is given in the form '$n < \ldots$' or '$n > \ldots$'. When the current-transformer is for metering or a similar application this rated overcurrent figure has to be less than the specified value, that is, $n < 5$, $n < 10$ or $n < 20$, the first two being applicable to accuracy classes 0·2, 0·5 and 1·0, the latter two to accuracy classes 0·2 G, 0·5 G and 1 G. In this way some limitation is placed on the maximum secondary current the current-transformer will develop with primary fault current flowing, thus affording some protection to the associated meter or instrument.

On the other hand, for current-transformers for protection applications which only have accuracy classes 1, 3, 1 G or 3 G this rated overcurrent figure is given by $n > 10$ or $n > 5$, thus indicating the minimum secondary terminal voltage the current-transformer will develop before saturating.

Instead of the British short-time factor, the German specification uses the 'primary maximum thermal current', usually given on the rating plate as 'KA therm', which is the r.m.s. primary current, the thermal effect of which the primary winding can withstand for 1 second without damage and the 'dynamic maximum current', which is the first peak of the primary current, the dynamic effect of which the current-transformer can withstand without damage, the secondary winding being short-circuited, this dynamic maximum current being given on the rating plate as 'KA dyn'.

VDE 0414/12.62 also lays down some relationship between KA therm and KA dyn. The primary conductor cross-sectional area in sq. mm. must not be less than

$$\frac{\text{KA therm}}{0.180} \quad \text{for copper or} \quad \frac{\text{KA therm}}{0.118} \quad \text{for aluminium}$$

and if KA dyn. is at least 2·5 times KA therm it need not be given on the rating plate.

Also, the permanent short-circuit current, to repeat the term given in this specification, should not exceed

$$\frac{\text{KA therm}}{[t+0.05(50/f)]},$$

where t is the current 'cut-off' time in seconds and f is the frequency in c.p.s., this equation allowing for the thermal effect of the decaying d.c. component, but if this short-circuit current exceeds this figure when t is less than 1 second then it must also be less than or equal to 0·4 KA dyn. in order not to exceed the dynamic strength of the current-transformer.

The minimum cross-sectional area of the secondary winding conductor to be used is also given in the specification but to return to the rated overcurrent figure n—three test-methods are given which may be used to determine whether or not the current-transformer complies with its specified n. One is the 'overcurrent method' in which the primary current at which the current error equals -10% is directly measured so that this method is obviously limited to those current-transformers having both a low-rated primary current and a low overcurrent figure. The other two methods are approximate, one based on the excitation curve of the current-transformer concerned, while the other is termed the 'overcurrent' method in which, as its name suggests, the induction corresponding to the overcurrent figure is obtained at less current than in normal operation by employing a higher burden than that specified. There is no point here in elaborating further on these two methods except to point out that one assumption made in the latter technique is that the secondary winding leakage reactance is assumed to be 0·75 times the secondary winding resistance (in wound-primary current-transformers).

VOLTAGE-TRANSFORMERS

CHAPTER 16

INTRODUCTION TO VOLTAGE-TRANSFORMERS

In the introductory chapter to the subject of the current-transformer the comment was made that comparison between this and the ordinary power-transformer could lead to some confusion to the newcomer and therefore it was far better to consider the current-transformer on its own merits. On the other hand, when considering the voltage-transformer, or, as it is sometimes still called, the potential-transformer, such comparison with the ordinary power-transformer is inevitable for the simple reason that the voltage-transformer is nothing more than an ordinary power-transformer in which care has been taken to minimise the unavoidable errors of transformation. This comment, of course, applies only to the electromagnetic type of voltage-transformer and does not apply to the capacitor voltage-transformer. Even with the electromagnetic type there are only one or two applications which demand special treatment for, in the main, the voltage-transformer may be looked upon as a power-transformer being used for a particular duty.

Thus a considerable part of the subject-matter in this section of this book will be familiar to any reader having some knowledge of 'ordinary transformer theory'. However, as in the case of the current-transformer, the main part of the discussion will deal with the electromagnetic circuit and there is no attempt made to discuss the insulation problems encountered in voltage-transformer design because these are precisely the same as those found in ordinary transformers.

It is sometimes argued that the theory of operation of the ordinary power-transformer and hence of the voltage-transformer is considerably simpler than that of the current-transformer, the reason normally advanced in favour of this argument being that the voltage-transformer, as will be seen, frequently is required to operate at only one voltage and hence at one value of flux density and never has to undergo the wide variation in operating flux density encountered in the current-transformer. While this is true it does not mean there is intrinsically more difficulty in the theory and operation of the current-transformer compared with that of the voltage-transformer.

Definition and functions of the voltage-transformer

The voltage-transformer is probably most simply defined as 'an instrument-transformer for the transformation of voltage from one value to another, usually a lower one'.

Certain standard secondary voltage ratings are adopted and these enable one to use standard coil voltages in associated instruments and relays, offering the obvious technical and commercial advantages of such standardisation. The use of auto-wound transformers for voltage-transformer duties is not precluded, but again for obvious reasons the use of such transformers is limited to low-voltage circuits. B.S. 3941 gives numerous values of rated primary voltage but only four rated secondary voltages: 110, $110/\sqrt{3}$, 220 and $220/\sqrt{3}$ volts.

There is no point in discussing at this stage the primary and secondary windings and the magnetic circuit as in the case of the introductory chapter on the current-transformer. The relay, instrument or other device connected to the secondary winding of a voltage-transformer is termed the burden as in the current-transformer, but this is now synonymous with the load of an ordinary power-transformer. Burdens are always specified (in this country) in volt-amperes at the rated secondary voltage and at some particular power factor.

Thus if the rated burden $= P$ volt amperes and the rated secondary voltage $= V_s$ volts, then the ohmic impedance of the burden Z_b is given by

$$Z_b = \frac{V_s^2}{P} \text{ ohms.} \tag{124}$$

If the burden power factor is $\cos \delta$, then its ohmic resistance is $R_b = Z_b \cos \delta$ ohms and its ohmic reactance is $X_b = Z_b \sin \delta$, that is, $Z_b = (R_b^2 + X_b^2)^{\frac{1}{2}}$ ohms.

As in most applications one is concerned with a constant primary voltage and hence with a constant secondary voltage there is no confusion likely to be caused by the use of volt-amperes in specifying the magnitude of a voltage-transformer burden, unlike the case with current-transformers.

Specification data required by the voltage-transformer designer

There is a certain amount of information required by the designer before he can proceed with the design of any voltage-transformer.

(1) Rated primary voltage.
(2) Rated secondary voltage.
(3) Rated burden.

(4) Supply frequency.

(5) Number of phases.

(6) The required performance specified either in the form of a 'class of accuracy' or in some other way.

(7) Desired insulation level, both power frequency and impulse requirements. (See Note below.)

(8) Any other requirement not covered by the relevant specificacation such as limiting dimensions.

Note. B.S. 3941 specifies only one insulation level (power frequency and impulse test voltages) for rated primary voltages of 66 kV and below. For higher primary voltages two insulation levels are given, one for both effectively and non-effectively earthed systems and a second lower level for effectively earthed systems only.

CHAPTER 17

BASIC VOLTAGE-TRANSFORMER THEORY

While it must not be forgotten that the ultimate fundamental relationship between the primary side and the secondary side of the voltage-transformer is that between their respective ampere-turns, for the purpose of this present discussion one may define the *ideal* voltage-transformer as one in which, with the rated burden connected across the secondary terminals, the secondary terminal voltage bears *exactly* the same relationship to the voltage applied across the primary terminals as the secondary turns do to the primary turns and furthermore these two terminal voltages are in precise phase opposition to each other.

Thus, ideally,

$$V_p I_p = V_s I_s; \quad N_p I_p = N_s I_s \quad \text{and} \quad \frac{V_p}{V_s} = \frac{N_p}{N_s}. \tag{125}$$

Consider now the practical case: with the secondary winding connected to its burden and an alternating voltage applied to the primary terminals, an alternating flux Φ is induced in the core, linking both primary and secondary turns, of just sufficient magnitude to induce in the secondary winding an e.m.f., E_s, which will cause a secondary current I_s to flow in the secondary winding and burden, the magnitude and phase of this current with respect to the secondary induced e.m.f. being determined by the total impedance of the secondary circuit.

As shown in Fig. 88

if R_b = resistance of burden in ohms,
      X_b = reactance of burden in ohms,
   R_{sw} = resistance of secondary winding in ohms,
   X_{sw} = leakage reactance of secondary winding in ohms,

then the total secondary impedance Z_s is given by

$$\mathbf{Z}_s = (R_{sw} + R_b) + j(X_{sw} + X_b) \text{ ohms},$$

the burden impedance, Z_b, is given by

$$Z_b = R_b + {}_j X_b \text{ ohms}.$$

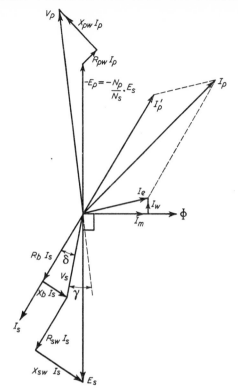

Fig. 88. Vector diagram for single-phase
voltage-transformers. (*Note.* Voltage drops
considerably exaggerated.)

The secondary induced e.m.f. E_s is given by $E_s = Z_s I_s$ volts and
the secondary terminal voltage by $V_s = Z_b I_s$ volts.

The relationship between E_s and the flux that induced it is
the well-known transformer equation

$$E_s = 4 \cdot 44 f B_m s A N_s \text{ volts,} \qquad (126)$$

where

f = frequency in c.p.s.,
B_m = peak flux density in webers/sq. metre,
A = gross cross-sectional area of core in sq. metres,
N_s = number of secondary turns,
s = core stacking or space factor, that is, ratio of nett area
to gross area.

Now if

N_p = number of primary turns and
K_t = turns ratio = N_p/N_s,

the secondary ampere-turns $N_s I_s$ must be counterbalanced by primary ampere-turns $N_p I_p'$ of the same magnitude and in precise phase opposition to them, but in addition the maintenance of the induced flux demands the expenditure of some primary ampere-turns as magnetising ampere-turns $N_p I_m$ and watts-loss ampere-turns $N_p I_w$, so that the *total* primary ampere-turns $N_p I_p$ are the vector sum of the load ampere-turns $N_p I_p'$, $N_p I_m$ and $N_p I_w$ as shown.

Now the flux induces an e.m.f. in the primary winding of E_p volts *in-phase with E_s* and such that

$$\frac{E_p}{E_s} = \frac{N_p}{N_s}$$

so that in opposition to this induced e.m.f. the primary applied voltage V_p must not only possess a component $(-E_p)$, but also another component to overcome the voltage drop in the primary winding itself. As shown in the diagram, the primary winding impedance consists of X_{pw}—its leakage reactance and R_{pw}, its resistance.

As before, the vector sum of the magnetising and watts-loss ampere-turns is termed the exciting ampere-turns, given by $N_p I_e$.

Now, if V_p, the actual primary voltage, is deliberately made equal to the nominal or rated voltage V_{pn}, then V_s, the actual secondary voltage, can no longer be equal to the corresponding nominal or rated value V_{sn} where

$$V_{sn} = \frac{V_{pn}}{K_n},$$

K_n being the nominal ratio. Thus there is a *ratio error* and, as shown in the diagram, there is also a *phase difference or phase error*, given by the angle γ in Fig. 88.

The ratio error is usually given in the form of a *percentage ratio error*, sometimes called the *percentage voltage error*, where

$$\%\text{R.E.} = 100\left(\frac{K_n V_s - V_p}{V_p}\right). \tag{127}$$

An alternative method is the use of a *voltage ratio factor* (V.R.F.), where

$$\text{V.R.F.} = \frac{K_v}{K_n}, \tag{128}$$

K_v being the actual voltage ratio, V_p/V_s. (This is also termed R.C.F. or *ratio correction factor*.)

So that

$$\%\text{R.E.} = 100\left(\frac{1}{\text{V.R.F.}} - 1\right) \tag{129}$$

and

$$\text{V.R.F.} \simeq 1 - \frac{\%\text{R.E.}}{100}, \tag{130}$$

The %R.E. is deemed to be positive if the actual secondary voltage V_s is greater than its corresponding nominal value V_{sn} for a given primary voltage.

Thus putting $V_p = V_{pn}$, then if V_s is greater than V_{pn}/K_n, the %R.E. is positive. Or put another way, the %R.E. is positive if the nominal ratio exceeds the actual ratio.

By convention the phase error is deemed to be positive if the actual secondary voltage vector V_s, when reversed, leads the primary voltage V_p.

Now it will be remembered that in the current-transformer the primary resistive and reactive voltage drops, although present, could be completely ignored in the determination of performance because they play no part in such a determination. In the voltage-transformer, on the other hand, as inspection of Fig. 88 immediately shows, all voltage drops, both on the primary side and secondary side, play their part in the determination of the errors.

Here, in order to develop suitable equations, it becomes necessary to use the well-known technique of referring all resistances and leakage reactances to either the primary or secondary side. If reference to the primary side is adopted, then the equivalent total resistance R_p and equivalent total reactance X_p are given by eqs. (131) and (132) respectively

$$R_p = R_{pw} + K_t^2 R_{sw}, \tag{131}$$

and

$$X_p = X_{pw} + K_t^2 X_{sw}. \tag{132}$$

The vector diagram given in Fig. 88 may now be revised to the equivalent primary vector shown in Fig. 89 and the corresponding vector equation is

$$V_p = -K_t V_s + (R_p + jX_p)I_p' + (R_{pw} + jX_{pw})I_e, \tag{133}$$

where I_e is the exciting current and is given by

$$I_e = I_m + jI_w.$$

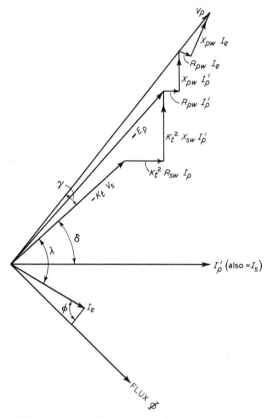

Fig. 89. Vector diagram for primary equivalent
circuit of voltage-transformer.

Thus the actual primary voltage consists of three components,
the first is the referred secondary terminal voltage, the second is
the total voltage drop (primary and secondary) due to the load
current referred to the primary side and the last is the voltage drop
due to the exciting current in the primary winding only. This is
shown in the equivalent circuit of Fig. 90, where the exciting current
is shown passing through the exciting impedance Z_m of the voltage-
transformer.

Using the angle symbols given in Fig. 89, where λ is the angle
between the exciting current and the secondary terminal voltage
reversed and δ is the burden power factor angle, then

$$V_p \cos \gamma = K_t V_s + I_p{}'(R_p \cos \delta + X_p \sin \delta) + I_e(R_{pw} \cos \lambda + X_{pw} \sin \lambda)$$
$$(134)$$

and

$$V_p \sin \gamma = I_p'(R_p \sin \delta - X_p \cos \delta) + I_e(R_{pw} \sin \lambda - X_{pw} \cos \lambda)$$
(135)

As γ is usually very small, $\cos \gamma = 1$, so that

$$\frac{V_p}{V_s} = K_v = K_t + \frac{I_p'(R_p \cos \delta + X_p \sin \delta) + I_e(R_{pw} \cos \lambda + X_{pw} \sin \lambda)}{V_s},$$
(136)

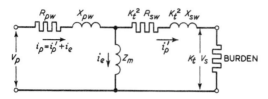

Fig. 90. Primary equivalent circuit of voltage-transformer.

Now, it is obvious from the diagram that because γ is small, $\lambda \simeq \phi$, where ϕ is the core power factor angle, that is,

$$\phi = \cos^{-1}\frac{I_w}{I_e},$$

so that

$$I_e \cos \lambda = I_e \cos \phi = I_w,$$
$$I_e \sin \lambda = I_e \sin \phi = I_m,$$

and eq. (136) becomes

$$\frac{V_p}{V_s} = K_v = K_t + \frac{I_p'(R_p \cos \delta + X_p \sin \delta) + (R_{pw}I_w + X_{pw}I_m)}{V_s}.$$
(137)

Similarly, by dividing eq. (134) by eq. (135), using the same assumption that $\lambda = \phi$ and furthermore neglecting all voltages appearing in the resulting denominator as negligible compared with $K_t V_s$, then the phase error γ may be given as

$$\gamma = \frac{I_p'(R_p \sin \delta - X_p \cos \delta) + (R_{pw}I_m - X_{pw}I_w)}{K_t V_s} \text{ radians.}$$
(138)

Equations (137) and (138) are the two basic ones used for the determination of the ratio error and the phase error, respectively, although, as with the basic current-transformer error equations, there is some modification to these for design purposes. For the present it is sufficient simply to comment that inspection of these two equations shows that the errors, both ratio and phase, of a voltage-transformer are due to two distinct voltage drops: (i) that due to the exciting current flowing in the primary winding only, and (ii) that due to the load current flowing in both windings, this latter voltage drop also being affected by the burden power factor.

There are two special cases to be considered.

(1) When on 'no-load', that is, with the secondary open-circuited, I_p' becomes zero and

$$K_v = K_t + \left(\frac{R_{pw} I_w + X_{pw} I_m}{V_s} \right), \tag{139}$$

also

$$\gamma = \frac{R_{pw} I_m - X_{pw} I_w}{K_t V_s} \text{ radians.} \tag{140}$$

(2) The second special case is when the burden power factor is unity, that is, when $\cos \delta = 1$ and $\sin \delta = 0$, then

$$K_v = K_t + \frac{I_p' R_p + (R_{pw} I_w + X_{pw} I_m)}{V_s}, \tag{141}$$

and

$$\gamma = \frac{-I_p' X_p + (R_{pw} I_m - X_{pw} I_w)}{K_t V_s} \text{ radians.} \tag{142}$$

It is of interest here to point out that the American standard for instrument-transformers which uses the previously mentioned R.C.F. technique gives the following equations which may be readily deduced from those already given.

If the R.C.F. at zero burden is denoted by R.C.F.$_0$, then

$$\text{R.C.F.}_0 = \frac{K_t}{K_n} + \left(\frac{R_{pw} I_w + X_{pw} I_m}{V_{pn}} \right), \tag{143}$$

V_{pn} again being the nominal rated primary voltage.

Similarly if the R.C.F. at rated burden is denoted by R.C.F.$_b$, then

$$\text{R.C.F.}_b = \text{R.C.F.}_0 + \frac{I_s}{K_t V_{pn}} (R_p \cos \delta + X_p \sin \delta). \tag{144}$$

If the phase error at zero burden is denoted by γ_0 in radians

$$\gamma_0 = \frac{R_{pw} I_m - X_{pw} I_w}{V_{pn}} \text{ radians,} \tag{145}$$

the phase error at rated burden is then given by

$$\gamma_b = \gamma_0 + \frac{I_s}{K_t V_{pn}}(R_p \sin \delta - X_p \cos \delta). \tag{146}$$

It will be noted that these equations must have been derived in much the same way as those previously given except that $K_n V_s$ has been taken as being equal to V_{pn}.

Finally, while radians have been used as the unit for phase error and are in fact the more logical, most specifications give phase errors in minutes of arc. The conversion is quite simple:

1 radian = 3438 minutes.

CHAPTER 18

DERIVATION OF DESIGN FORMULAE AND TECHNIQUE

It will be remembered that in the current-transformer the errors are specified on the basis of nominal primary current, but the direct application of the basic error equations led to an unnecessarily severe method of determining the errors and, largely due to the practical uncertainties in forecasting some of the factors concerned, it was possible to evolve a simpler set of error equations enabling the designer to work from the secondary side with a sufficient degree of precision.

A similar technique is used in the case of voltage-transformers and although the resulting equations are, in the strict sense, incorrect, they offer a realistic means of estimating the error.

For the moment let it be assumed that the core size has been chosen as have the number of primary and secondary turns, the primary and secondary winding conductors and furthermore that the dimensions of the coils have been decided.

The errors must then be calculated on the basis that the turns ratio is made equal to the nominal ratio, that is, $K_t = K_n$ and after the errors have been calculated turns correction may then be applied.

As

$$\frac{V_p}{V_s} = K_v,$$

eq. (127) may be rewritten as

$$\%\text{R.E.} = 100 \left(\frac{K_n - K_v}{K_v} \right) \%$$

and as K_t has been made equal to K_n, substitution in eq. (137) for K_t gives

$$K_n - K_v = - \left[\frac{I_p'(R_p \cos \delta + X_p \sin \delta) + (R_{pw}I_w + X_{pw}I_m)}{V_s} \right],$$

232

so that %R.E. on load is given by

$$\%\text{R.E.} = -100\left[\frac{I_p'(R_p\cos\delta + X_p\sin\delta)+(R_{pw}I_w + X_{pw}I_m)}{V_p}\right]\%. \quad (147)$$

It is sometimes argued that as there is usually only one standard value of nominal secondary voltage against many values of nominal primary voltage it is therefore advantageous to work from the secondary side. As the translation of eq. (147) into secondary values is so straightforward it is felt that this and subsequent equations are quite satisfactorily left 'on the primary side', for the present.

As V_p is only marginally different from its nominal value V_{pn}, no great practical inaccuracy is caused if one uses for calculation purposes

$$\%\text{R.E.}_{\text{on load}} = -100$$

$$\left[\frac{I_{pn}(R_p\cos\delta + X_p\sin\delta)+(R_{pw}I_w + X_{pw}I_m)}{V_{pn}}\right]\%, \quad (148)$$

where

$$I_{pn} = \left(\frac{\text{rated burden in VA}}{V_{pn}}\right)\text{ amperes.}$$

Similarly the phase error on load is given by

$$\gamma_{\text{on load}} = 3438\left[\frac{I_{pn}(R_p\sin\delta - X_p\cos\delta)+(R_{pw}I_m - X_{pw}I_w)}{V_{pn}}\right]\text{ minutes.}$$

$$(149)$$

When the burden is a unity power factor one

$$\%\text{R.E.}_{\text{u.p.f.}} = -100\left(\frac{I_{pn}R_p + R_{pw}I_w + X_{pw}I_m}{V_{pn}}\right)\% \quad (150)$$

and

$$\gamma_{\text{u.p.f.}} = 3438\left(\frac{-I_{pn}X_p + R_{pw}I_m - X_{pw}I_w}{V_{pn}}\right)\text{ minutes.} \quad (151)$$

The %R.E. on no-load is then

$$\%\text{R.E.}_{\text{no-load}} = -100\left(\frac{R_{pw}I_w + X_{pw}I_m}{V_{pn}}\right)\% \quad (152)$$

and

$$\gamma_{\text{no-load}} = 3438\left(\frac{R_{pw}I_m - X_{pw}I_w}{V_{pn}}\right)\text{ minutes.} \quad (153)$$

Now the flux density, B_m, is sensibly independent of load current and is given by

$$\frac{V_{pn}}{N_p} = \frac{V_{sn}}{N_s} = 4{\cdot}44\,fsB_mA. \tag{154}$$

Once B_m has been determined I_m and I_w are found from the usual watt-loss and magnetisation characteristic curves of the core material being used and these values are used in the series of equations just evolved.

R_p, the sum of the secondary winding resistance referred to the primary and the resistance of the primary winding itself is easily calculated.

X_p, the leakage reactance of the secondary winding referred to the primary side plus the leakage reactance of the primary winding itself is calculated from the basic equations given in chapter 5 when there was some discussion on the secondary winding leakage reactance of current-transformers. Equation (63) in that chapter gave the total leakage reactance referred to the secondary, but simple substitution in that equation of primary values gives, X_p, that is,

$$X_p = \frac{4{\cdot}44\,f N_p \Phi_t}{I_p}\ \text{ohms}, \tag{155}$$

where, as before, Φ_t = peak total leakage flux. Similar reduction to that employed in chapter 5 finally gives, for concentric coils

$$X_p = \frac{7{\cdot}9}{10^6}f\frac{N_p^{\,2}}{L}\left(b_d M_d + \frac{b_i M_i}{3} + \frac{b_o M_o}{3}\right)\ \text{ohms}, \tag{156}$$

the symbols having the same significance as before.

The calculation of X_{pw}, the leakage reactance of the primary winding, has, of course, the same problems as those encountered in the calculation of X_{sw}, the secondary winding leakage reactance when current-transformers were being considered and detailed in chapter 5. Numerous methods are employed, from assuming that $X_{pw} = \frac{1}{2}X_p$ to one in which the assumption used is that $X_{pw} = X_p$. Certainly with high-rated values of primary voltage the radial depth of the primary winding is considerably greater than that of the secondary winding so that there is some justification in using the pessimistic $X_{pw} = X_p$. Others seem to take the view that the centre of the interwinding duct is the boundary line of the leakage fluxes and use

$$X_{pw} = \frac{7{\cdot}9}{10^6}f\frac{N_p^{\,2}}{L}\left(\frac{b_d M_d}{2} + \frac{b_o M_o}{3}\right)\ \text{ohms}.$$

One design method is to segregate the core into two portions—the limbs which are assumed to carry no leakage flux and the yokes assumed to have leakage flux.

Thus if Φ is used to denote the limb flux, Φ_y the yoke flux and Φ_l the total leakage flux, then

$$\Phi_y = \Phi + \Phi_l.$$

It is common practice in many core designs (although not with oriented steels) to employ a yoke iron cross-section slightly greater than that in the limb section, but knowing these one is able to calculate the assumed flux densities in both sections of the core and from the usual magnetic characteristic curves one is able to obtain the corresponding watt-loss and magnetising currents.

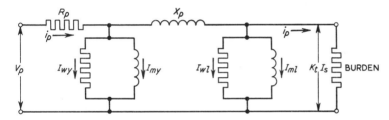

Fig. 91. Modified primary equivalent diagram for a voltage-transformer.

Thus if,

$$I_{wl} = \text{watts-loss current for the limbs,}$$
$$I_{wy} = \text{watts-loss current for the yokes,}$$
$$I_{ml} = \text{magnetising current for the limbs,}$$
$$I_{my} = \text{magnetising current for the yokes,}$$

then the equivalent circuit is assumed to be as shown in Fig. 91 and there is commensurate revision of the previously deduced error equations so that

%R.E. at no-load

$$= \frac{-100}{V_{pn}}[R_{pw}(I_{wl}+I_{wy})+X_p I_{ml}]\%, \qquad (157)$$

phase error at no-load

$$= \frac{3438}{V_{pn}}[R_{pw}(I_{ml}+I_{my})-X_p I_{wl}] \text{ minutes}, \qquad (158)$$

%R.E. on load

$$= \frac{-100}{V_{pn}}[R_{pw}(I_{wl}+I_{wy})+I_{pw}(R_p \cos \delta + X_p \sin \delta)+X_p I_{ml}]\%, \quad (159)$$

and phase error on load

$$= \frac{3438}{V_{pn}}[R_{pw}(I_{ml}+I_{my})+I_{pn}(R_p \sin \delta - X_p \cos \delta)-X_p I_{wl}] \text{ minutes.} \quad (160)$$

While the comment was made when introducing the voltage-transformer that it was merely a power-transformer in which care was taken to minimise the inevitable errors of transformer, it will be appreciated that this comment was being used to spotlight the operational similarities between these two types of transformer and hence their dissimilarity with the current-transformer. There are, of course, considerable differences between the power-transformer and the voltage-transformer. While there are exceptions, power-transformers of low VA ratings generally have low-rated voltages, while those of higher VA ratings also have higher operating voltages. The larger volume required for the higher VA rating means there is comparatively little difficulty in also accommodating the greater amount of insulation required for the higher voltage.

Thus in a range of transformer designs, say from 100 kVA to 1000 kVA, for any particular kVA rating there is comparatively little difference in the core dimensions for either 11 kV or 33 kV rated primary voltages. Frequently the same core section is used and for the higher voltage the window dimensions are only slightly larger than for the lower voltage. Therefore in general terms it may be said that the 'size' of a power-transformer is determined by its kVA rating, that is, its output.

The output of a voltage-transformer, on the other hand, is very low—measured usually in volt-amperes, and has little or no effect on the size of core adopted, this now being almost wholly determined by the necessity to make provision for the major insulation between windings and earth.

There is another aspect in which the voltage-transformer differs from the power-transformer. In the latter the selection of winding conductor sizes is determined by the permissible temperature rise of the windings and cooling arrangements are somewhat elaborate in such transformers.

In the voltage-transformer the gauge of the primary winding conductor, for the higher-rated primary voltages, is not determined from these thermal considerations because a conductor size so determined would be such that it is too small and weak to be wound.

Some companies may, in fact, place a somewhat arbitrary lower limit to the conductor gauge they would attempt to wind, remembering too that the associated number of turns may be relatively high, such a limit may be 32 s.w.g. or thereabouts. As a corollary to this the primary winding conductor may be the same for 6·6 kV and 11 kV rated primary voltages. Thus probably the most important factor in determining the size of a voltage-transformer is the primary voltage and usually the provision of adequate cooling presents no real difficulties. In fact, oil-immersion employed with voltage-transformers is usually for the purpose of insulation rather than cooling, when rated primary voltages are high—say 3·3 kV and upwards.

In many cases, such as voltage-transformers being used in metal-clad switchgear, the designer may well encounter requirements with reference to limiting dimensions which will force him to use core dimensions or proportions not producing the optimum design from the economic viewpoint. Here again there is a difference between the voltage-transformer and the power-transformer. With the latter type there is the well-known relationship between the cost of the iron core and the cost of the winding copper such that when these are equal one has the minimum total cost of active material. However, because the primary winding conductor is possibly determined by other considerations than its current-carrying requirement, this equality between iron and copper cost is no longer valid and one expects to find in an economic design of voltage-transformer a copper cost twice that of the iron core, or thereabouts. Obviously it is dangerous to generalise on this particular aspect because local conditions vary—one must certainly take into account relative labour costs for the various manufacturing operations before claiming that a design is the economic optimum, and it is probably better to think in terms of finished core cost and finished coil cost rather than in the costs of the basic materials, iron and copper.

Many designers prefer to use magnetic characteristic curves which give watts-loss and magnetising volt-amperes rather than those giving I_w and I_m as used in the text. Similarly, the total leakage reactance referred to the primary side is frequently calculated as a percentage, so that the total impedance and resistive are then expressed as a percentage.

All the error equations that have been derived are quite easily converted should the reader so desire into those using these alternative units, but the decision is really based simply on personal preference.

CHAPTER 19

FURTHER THEORETICAL CONSIDERATIONS

The construction of the Möllinger and Gewecke diagram for current-transformers was described in chapter 5 and it was explained how this may be used either in the calculation of the errors or how, if the diagram is obtained from test data on a current-transformer, one is able to determine from it the turns ratio and the secondary winding leakage reactance. The Möllinger and Gewecke diagram may also be used for voltage-transformers and again for either purpose, but in the case of voltage-transformers it bears considerable similarity with the well-known Kapp regulation diagram. In the construction of this M. & G. diagram there is some advantage in using all the quantities concerned referred to the secondary side and not as previously to the primary side, but the modification to the error equations is quite simple.

It will be remembered that the total resistance referred to the primary side, R_p, was given by

$$R_p = R_{pw} + K_t^2 R_{sw},$$

R_{pw} and R_{sw} being the resistances of primary and secondary windings respectively.

Thus

$$R_p = K_t^2 \left(\frac{R_{pw}}{K_t^2} + R_{sw} \right),$$

but

$$\left(\frac{R_{pw}}{K_t^2} + R_{sw} \right) = R_s,$$

where R_s is the total resistance referred to the secondary side, thus $R_p = K_t^2 R_s$ and similarly $X_p = K_t^2 X_s$, that is,

$$X_p = K_t^2 \left(\frac{X_{pw}}{K_t^2} + X_{sw} \right).$$

The basic equation for the equivalent primary circuit was given by eq. (133), which reiterated, was

$$V_p = -K_t V_s + (R_p + jX_p)I_p' + (R_{pw} + jX_{pw})I_e.$$

Also, from previously,

$$I_p' = \frac{I_s}{K_t}.$$

Dividing eq. (133) throughout by K_t

$$\frac{V_p}{K_t} = -V_s + \left(\frac{R_p + jX_p}{K_t}\right)I_p' + \left(\frac{R_{pw} + jX_{pw}}{K_t}\right)I_e.$$

Now substitution in the second term for R_p, X_p and I_p' gives, as one would expect,

$$\left(\frac{R_p + jX_p}{K_t}\right)I_p' = (R_s + jX_s)I_s$$

so that

$$\frac{V_p}{K_t} = -V_s + (R_s + jX_s)I_s + \left(\frac{R_{pw} + jX_{pw}}{K_t}\right)I_e.$$

It will be appreciated that while the second term on the right-hand side of this equation is the total impedance voltage drop in secondary values, that is, referred to the secondary side, R_{pw}, X_{pw} and I_e are still in primary values and the denominator K_t in this third term denotes that it is the voltage drop $(R_{pw} + jX_{pw})I_e$ that has been referred to the secondary side. This is the form the equation normally takes for the present purpose of constructing the M. & G. diagram.

Thus

$$\frac{V_p}{K_t} = V_s\left[-1 + (R_s + jX_s)\frac{I_s}{V_s} + \left(\frac{R_{pw} + jX_{pw}}{K_t V_s}\right)I_e\right]$$

and finally

$$\frac{V_p}{V_s} = K_t\left[-1 + (R_s + jX_s)\frac{I_s}{V_s} + \left(\frac{R_{pw} + jX_{pw}}{K_t V_s}\right)I_e\right]. \tag{161}$$

Remembering that the designer in his calculations has been able to obtain $R_s X_s$ and R_{pw} and made an estimation on how X_s is portioned to give X_{pw}, then he draws two axes as shown in Fig. 92 (p. 242). The horizontal axis represents the direction of the flux so that the vertical represents the secondary induced voltage and as the voltage drops one is concerned with are small this vertical may also be taken as the direction of the secondary terminal voltage V_s. Having established the core size the designer calculates the flux density and from the usual magnetic characteristic curves he then obtains I_m, I_w and I_e and also the core power factor angle ϕ. This enables him to plot I_e at the angle $90 - \phi$ to the flux axis and along this line he can then measure off $R_{pw}I_e/K_t$. Perpendicular to the exciting current line he then draws $X_{pw}I_e/K_t$ giving him the point A. It is assumed throughout that V_s is constant and these two quantities are plotted as percentages of this. The scale of the axes which are now %R.E. for the vertical axis and phase error for the horizontal are easily established and as the secondary voltage reversed is as shown dotted then the percentage ratio error with respect to the turns ratio is given by OC and the phase error by OB for the no-load condition. As the core flux density is sensibly independent of load current, then OA still represents the drop due to the exciting current when the transformer is loaded. From the point A he now draws the line AD parallel to the voltage axis, that is, the %R.E. axis, equal in length to I_sR_s and from D he draws DE representing I_sX_s. These are then the voltage drops due to secondary load current with a unity power factor burden and the projection of the point E to the axes give the errors, that is, OF gives the phase error and OG the %R.E.

Now AE represents I_sZ_s and if a semi-circle of this radius is drawn with A as its centre this is the locus of the point E for all values of power factor for the particular burden (in VA) so that these power factor angles may be lightly drawn as shown.

For any other burden value another semi-circle, again with A as its centre, is drawn, but having radius of I_sZ_{s1}, where Z_{s1} is the new value of total impedance referred to the secondary side.

Now if the turns ratio is not equal to the nominal ratio, that is, turns correction has been adopted, then the measurement of %R.E. from the M. & G. diagram must be made from a second origin, O_1 in Fig. 92, where

$$OO_1 = \left(\frac{K_n}{K_t} - 1 \right) 100 \%.$$

The M. & G. diagram may also be used in the opposite way—by plotting an M. & G. diagram from test results one is able to obtain an indication of the magnitude of X_{ws}. One method is shown in Fig. 93 (p. 243), where a variable resistor is in series with the primary winding of the voltage-transformer. When this resistor is zero and with the secondary winding open-circuited, rated primary voltage is applied and the %R.E. and phase error measured by some means and these then determine the location of the point A relative to the previously discussed axes of the M. & G. diagram.

With the secondary winding still open-circuited the external resistor is varied and the exciting current held constant by slight variation of the applied voltage. For each resistor value the %R.E. and phase error are measured and plotted on the diagram and it will be found all the points lie on the same straight line as shown in the figure. One is therefore able to determine the point A, because the lengths $A_1 A$, and $A_2 A$, and so on are proportional to the total resistance in the primary circuit, that is, $A_1 A \propto R_{pw}$, and $A_2 A \propto (R_{pw} + r)$, r being the external series resistance, r and R_{pw} are measured separately so the point A can be determined.

Having established the position of point A, the perpendicular dropped from this point cuts the vertical axis at O and enables both the turns ratio K_t and the primary leakage reactance X_{sw} to be found.

NOTES ON THE OPERATION OF VOLTAGE-TRANSFORMERS

Up to the present little or no comment has been made on the error equations that have been evolved, but a closer examination of these in conjunction with the M. & G. diagram readily indicates certain aspects of the operation of voltage-transformers.

From eq. (152) it is immediately obvious that if the turns ratio, K_t, is made equal to the nominal voltage ratio, K_n, the %R.E. is always negative (unless the primary winding possesses high

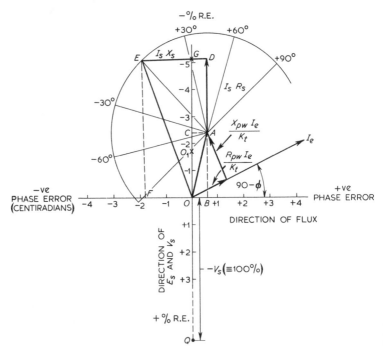

Fig. 92. Möllinger and Gewecke diagram for voltage-transformers.

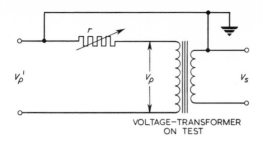

VOLTAGE–TRANSFORMER
ON TEST

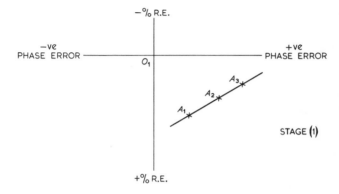

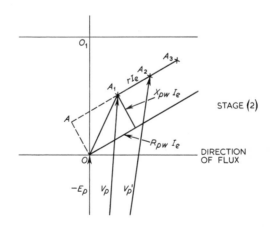

Fig. 93. Connections and vector diagram for determination of
X_{pw} and K_t.

capacitance) or, in other words, the actual voltage ratio K_v is always greater than K_n, when the secondary winding is open-circuited. When the voltage-transformer is connected to its burden the %R.E. is again always negative except when the burden is highly capacitive. For any particular burden value one may easily compensate for the ratio error by adopting turns correction, making the turns ratio less than the nominal voltage ratio either by reducing the number of primary turns or preferably by increasing the secondary turns. Such turns correction only modifies the ratio error and there is no similar simple method of reducing the phase error.

While the phase error equations do not immediately indicate how the phase errors vary as the factors influencing them change, the M. & G. diagram of Fig. 92 offers some assistance in this. When the secondary winding is open-circuited the phase error is always positive and remains so for low u.p.f. burdens. As this u.p.f. burden increases, the phase error becomes negative, and if the burden is capacitive the phase error simply becomes negative at a higher burden than in the u.p.f. case, or if the burden is inductive this then occurs at a lower burden. The burden value at which the algebraic sign of the phase error changes, that is, when the phase error is zero, depends on a number of factors as examination of the M. & G. diagram shows. This diagram also indicates that when the phase error is zero, the percentage ratio error is very nearly at its maximum value. Figure 94 shows how the errors vary with secondary power factors but with a constant burden, while Fig. 95 shows how the errors vary for a constant power factor but at difficult burden values.

Mention has already been made of the fact that there is no simple way of modifying the phase error. In order to reduce the phase error of a voltage-transformer, one must also reduce those factors concerned, namely the exciting current and all resistances and reactances. The exciting current may be reduced in a number of ways, the use of the highest possible grade of electrical steel, the shortest possible mean length of magnetic circuit (that is, the minimum volume and weight of core) and somewhat lower flux densities than are used for power-transformers. The resistances of the windings are reduced by using the lowest possible mean length per turn in the primary and secondary coils, and this is also desirable when considering the reactances. Other factors influencing the reactances are the radial depths of the coils and inter-coil duct and the axial lengths of these coils. Obviously the design of any voltage-transformer is a compromise because many of these factors are interrelated and in opposition to each other.

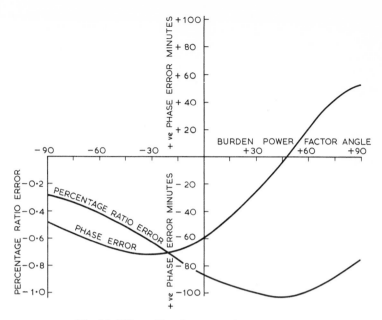

Fig. 94. Effect of burden power factor on errors.

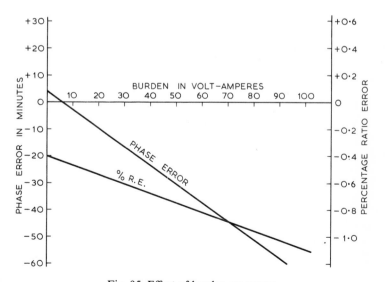

Fig. 95. Effect of burden on errors.

From the foregoing remarks it is obvious that the burden at which the errors are specified must be a realistic value and should include not only the instrument or relay burden but that of any connecting leads between the voltage-transformer and the instrument, but it is even more important that the burden power factor be correctly specified as this plays an important part in the determination of the voltage-transformer performance.

Now, many voltage-transformers are required to work at only one value of nominal primary voltage, but with some used in laboratory work, while the burden impedance is constant, the voltage-transformer is used over a possibly wide range of primary voltage. In such a transformer the flux density is very nearly directly proportional to the applied voltage, but because of the non-linearity of the magnetising characteristic of the core material, as the primary voltage decreases there will be some increase in both the %R.E. and the phase error in both the loaded and no-load conditions, although the variation in these errors over quite a wide range of applied voltage is generally very small.

As a general rule the majority of voltage-transformers are required to operate at only one supply frequency and they are expected to maintain their accuracy for only a small variation in this frequency. Should there be a reduction in frequency then for a particular value of primary applied voltage there will be a corresponding increase in the flux density and hence an increase in the exciting current so. that the %R.E. increases; or to be more precise, becomes more negative for all burden values. The effect of change of frequency on the phase error is more complex and depends on the relative increases in the watt-loss component and the magnetising component of the exciting current with reduction of frequency, but in general terms the reduction of frequency leads to an almost constant change in phase error over a range of burden values such that the phase error is more positive. The change in phase error is more marked than that in the %R.E., in many cases a voltage-transformer designed for 60 c.p.s. operation, if used at 50 c.p.s., will show little increase in the %R.E., but there is a significant increase in the phase error.

The flux density at which a voltage-transformer normally operates, as already mentioned, is somewhat lower than that used in power-transformers and there is little departure from sinusoidal conditions. It has been shown that even with a 30% third harmonic content in the primary voltage waveform there is a very small change in the ratio error determined on a sine-wave basis and furthermore the waveform of the secondary voltage shows little or no distortion from that of the primary voltage.

The manner in which the errors of voltage-transformers affect

the overall accuracy of metering circuits has already been discussed in chapter 9, when current-transformer performance in
such circuits was the main subject for discussion and there is
no need for further elaboration here on this point.

Three-phase voltage-transformers

When discussing three-phase voltage-transformers it is first of
all essential that one distinguishes between the true three-phase
voltage-transformer, that is, one in which the primary and secondary coils for all three phases are mounted on the usual form of
three-limbed core, and the alternative three-phase bank of interconnected single-phase units. As will be shown later, there is the
special case when a three-phase voltage-transformer is required
to have a tertiary winding for earth-fault protection purposes and
in such a case one must use either a three-phase bank of single-
phase units or a five-limbed core.

Ignoring for the moment tertiary windings, when the errors of
a three-phase voltage-transformer are being calculated, it is
common practice to do so for each individual phase and the basic
problem is the proper subdivision of the core's magnetic length
and numerous empirical or arbitrary rules are applied to overcome this. One quite common technique is to assume that each
of the phases on the two outer limbs of the core require an exciting
current based on the assumption that the flux path concerned is
the limb length plus the two yoke lengths to the centre limb plus
the two interleaved corners, while the phase on the centre limb
is assumed to require an exciting current corresponding to a
magnetic path of the limb length plus the two centre interleaved
junctions with the yoke. While such an analysis may not be precise it enables one to gauge the probable difference between the
exciting currents of the two 'outer' phases with that of the 'centre'
phase, such a dissimilarity in the exciting currents being reflected
in the errors of the three phases. The degree of magnetic asymmetry
that occurs therefore depends on the proportions of the core
being used and will be increased as the ratio of the leg length
to the leg centres decreases, but it must be emphasised that this
asymmetry is always present in a three-phase core of conventional
design.

The use of interconnected single-phase voltage-transformers
in three-phase banks has both advantages and disadvantages.
While, for instance, they use more material and are therefore
more expensive in first-cost, replacement, should damage occur,
is far easier than with the three-phase transformer. Similarly,
although interconnected separate, single-phase units occupy more

space, the adoption of such transformers enables one to use constructional methods offering considerable advantages at the higher voltage ratings and in many such cases at a lower cost than for a three-phase voltage-transformer using a common core.

When the application is the metering of three-phase power or energy the type of voltage-transformer to be adopted depends on the three-phase system being used. If the primary system is three-phase three-wire with an insulated neutral the two-wattmeter method of measurement is normally used, and thus one would use two single-phase voltage-transformers in 'Vee'-connection

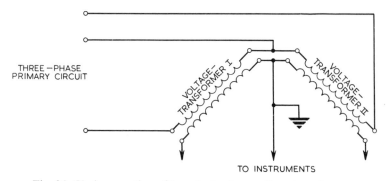

Fig. 96. 'Vee'-connection of two single-phase voltage-transformers.

as shown in Fig. 96. For a three-phase three-wire system with an earthed neutral or a three-phase four-wire system, then three single-phase voltage-transformers must be used with their primary and secondary windings both connected in star, both neutrals being earthed. Contrary to the normal practice with a star-connected bank of three single-phase power-transformers with voltage-transformers it is preferable to connect the primary neutral to the supply neutral in order to give a path for any third-harmonics appearing in the exciting current waveform so that no third harmonic voltage appears at the secondary terminals.

Obviously in a star-connected bank of three single-phase voltage-transformers the errors will not be identical in all the transformers and as no simple method exists whereby the line-to-line ratio and phase errors may be measured these must be computed from tests on the individual transformers which normally give of course, line-to-neutral values of the errors.* The vector diagram is shown in Fig. 97 and if γ_1, γ_2 and γ_3 are the phase errors of the voltage-transformers in phases 1, 2 and 3 respectively

* 'Instrument Transformers', by Hobson, *J.I.E.E.* **91** (1944), part II, p. 182.

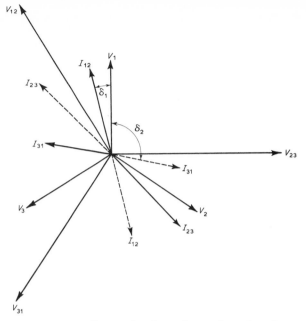

Fig. 97. Vector diagram for three-phase voltage-transformer supplying unbalanced burden.

and similarly $\%$R.E.$_1$ $\%$R.E.$_2$ and $\%$R.E.$_3$ are the corresponding percentage ratio errors, then it can be shown that the $\%$R.E. and phase error for line 1 to line 2 are given by

$$\%\text{R.E.}_{12} = 0\cdot5(\%\text{R.E}_1 + \%\text{R.E}_2) + 0\cdot289(\gamma_1 - \gamma_2) \tag{162}$$

and

$$\gamma_{12} = 0\cdot5(\gamma_1 + \gamma_2) - 0\cdot289(\%\text{R.E.}_1 - \%\text{R.E.}_2). \tag{163}$$

Similarly for line 2 to line 3

$$\%\text{R.E.}_{23} = 0\cdot5(\%\text{R.E.}_2 + \%\text{R.E.}_3) + 0\cdot289(\gamma_2 - \gamma_3) \tag{164}$$

and

$$\gamma_{23} = 0\cdot5(\gamma_2 + \gamma_3) - 0\cdot289(\%\text{R.E.}_2 - \%\text{R.E.}_3). \tag{165}$$

For line 3 to line 1 the expressions are

$$\%\text{R.E.}_{31} = 0\cdot5(\%\text{R.E.}_3 + \%\text{R.E.}_1) + 0\cdot289(\gamma_3 - \gamma_1) \tag{166}$$

and

$$\gamma_{31} = 0\cdot5(\gamma_3 + \gamma_1) - 0\cdot289(\%\text{R.E.}_3 - \%\text{R.E.}_1). \tag{167}$$

Obviously in all these equations the phase error cannot be in minutes but must be converted into percentages—thus, for instance,

$$\gamma_1 \text{ in the previous expressions} = \frac{\gamma_1 \text{ in minutes} \times 100}{3438}.$$

Now it has been shown that the errors of a voltage-transformer are comprised of a constant no-load error and a variable error which for a given power factor is proportional to the burden.

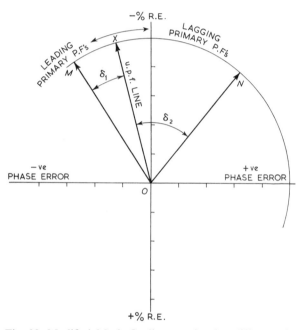

Fig. 98. Modified M. & G. diagram showing difference in errors.

Thus if a voltage-transformer is tested at zero burden, and at its rated burden the constant error is obtained immediately; the difference between the two ratio errors is a measure of the voltage-transformer resistance and the difference between the two phase errors is indicative of the transformer reactance so that the errors under any condition of loading may be readily calculated. In the single-phase case there is no need for further comment, but in the three-phase voltage-transformer certain points must be mentioned, but before doing so a modified M. & G. diagram must be introduced as shown in Fig. 98. Here at zero burden and at a known burden and unity power factor the ratio errors and phase errors of a voltage-transformer (or one phase of a three-phase transformer) have been determined by test and the differences in these errors plotted on a M. & G. grid as the point X. The line XO is then taken as the unity power factor line from which any other power factor angle is measured as shown, so that the arc of the circle with XO as radius and O its centre is the locus of the *variable* part of the errors at the same burden value used in the test for other power factors and the appropriate division of the line XO gives the *variable* part of the errors at other burden values —that is, for any given power factor the *change in errors* is proportional to the burden.

To find the total errors, these errors found from this modified M. & G. diagram must be added to the no-load or zero-burden errors. When determining the three-phase errors from line to neutral test results, no great inaccuracy is caused by assuming that the resistances and leakage reactances of the three phases are equal, so that the changes in error are the same for each phase so only one M. & G. diagram need be drawn. One other point to remember is that if the test figures relate to phase-neutral burden values, the phase-phase burdens at which the errors are to be calculated must be divided by $\sqrt{3}$ to obtain the corresponding phase-neutral value.

Let it be assumed that the phase-neutral errors of a three-phase transformer are obtained by test at zero burden and some u.p.f. burden of P volt-amperes. The change in phase error and ratio error is immediately found and as already explained should be the same for the three phases and the point X plotted on the modified M. & G. diagram.

From Fig. 97

the current in phase $1 = I_{12} - I_{31}$,
in phase $2 = I_{23} - I_{12}$,
in phase $3 = I_{31} - I_{23}$,

and the currents I_{12}, I_{23} and I_{31} are of course proportional to the line-to-line burden values which may or may not be balanced and at which the errors are required, namely P_{12}, P_{23} and P_{31} respectively.

Knowing the burden power factors gives the angle between each current and the corresponding phase-neutral voltage, and it is this angle that is used in the modified M. & G. diagram. Limiting discussion to one phase, say phase 1, the two currents are I_{12} and $-I_{31}$ and let it be assumed that the burden power factors of P_{12} and P_{31} are such that I_{12} leads V_1 by an angle of δ_1 and $-I_{31}$ lags V_1 by an angle δ_2.

From the modified M. & G. diagram, as already explained, the change in both ratio error and phase error for a burden equal in value to that used in the test but for a leading angle of δ_1 are found quite simply by rotating the u.p.f. line XO anti-clockwise through the angle δ_1 and the new changes of errors, as shown in Fig. 98, are given by the point M. Thus for the actual burden $P_{12}/\sqrt{3}$ the change of errors are those found on the M. & G. diagram multiplied by $P_{12}/\sqrt{3}$ and the resultant change of errors is that caused by I_{12}. A similar technique is used to determine the change of errors caused by I_{31}, first of all rotating XO clockwise through an angle δ_2, obtaining point N and then multiplying the change of errors so found by $P_{31}/\sqrt{3}$. The ratio error of phase 1 (phase-to-neutral) is then given by the algebraic sum of the change of error due to I_{12}, the change of error due to $-I_{31}$ and the zero-burden error. Similarly, for the phase error and of course the errors for the other two phases are similarly determined using the corresponding currents and phase-to-neutral burden and burden power factors.

It is these phase-neutral errors which are then substituted in eqs. (162) to (167) in order to determine the required phase-phase errors.

Tertiary windings

In three-phase systems the voltage-transformer is used to supply the voltage coils of energy meters and such relays as those of the directional I.D.M.T.L. type and in many cases a tertiary winding is included in the voltage-transformer for the detection of earth-faults. This application must not be confused with the use of a three-phase voltage-transformer (which may not possess tertiary windings) as an earthing transformer in a three-phase three-wire system when its primary and secondary neutral points are connected together and to earth. Such a voltage-transformer will simultaneously be used for its normal measuring function.

Consider first the case of a three-phase bank of single-phase transformers. The primary and secondary windings will be normally connected in star and on each transformer there is a tertiary winding, these then being connected in 'open delta', or 'broken delta'.

The vector diagram under healthy conditions in the primary circuit is shown in Fig. 99a, from which it is seen that the voltage appearing across the open-delta terminals is zero. Should an earth-fault occur on the primary system the symmetry of the voltages impressed on the primary windings of the voltage-transformer bank is disturbed, this dissymmetry is reflected on the secondary

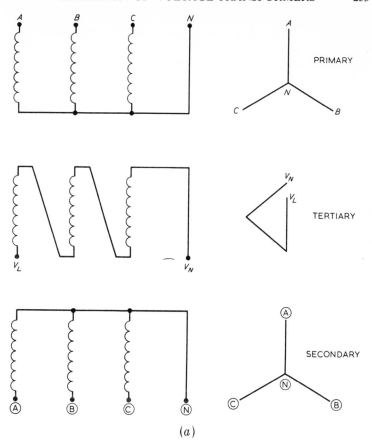

(a)

Fig. 99 a. Three-phase voltage-transformer with tertiary winding.

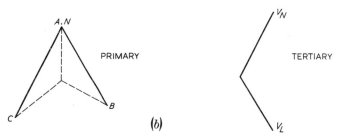

(b)

Fig. 99 b. Vector diagrams for primary and tertiary windings with primary system earth-fault.

side and, as shown in Fig. 99b, there is now a finite voltage appearing across the open-delta tertiary terminals, the magnitude of this voltage depending ultimately on the turns ratio primary to tertiary.

This tertiary voltage is frequently termed the residual voltage and the tertiary winding is called the residual voltage winding.

It will of course be appreciated that these terms apply only when the tertiary winding is being used for the detection of primary system earth-faults.

The three-limbed three-phase core is not used for this duty and should the previously mentioned three-phase bank of single-phase voltage-transformers not be used then the three-phase five-limbed core must be adopted, the primary and secondary windings being on the three centre limbs and the tertiary winding on the two outer limbs. In such a core the outer limbs carry only a small flux when the primary system is healthy, but if a primary earth-fault occurs this flux increases considerably, giving the desired residual voltage to operate on earth-fault relay.

B.S. 3941 no longer uses the categories 'W', 'X', 'Y' and 'Z' for protective voltage-transformers as did B.S. 2046, employing a different technique.

It has kept the classes of accuracy given in B.S. 81 for measuring voltage-transformers (except class 'BL') and introduced two new classes, 'E' and 'F', for dual-purpose voltage-transformers.

Details of these classes of accuracy are given in the next chapter but here, in the context of residual voltage windings one is more interested in the fact that the dual-purpose voltage-transformers have *voltage factors*, shown in Table 12, which are applied to the rated primary voltage to determine the maximum voltage at which the accuracy limits and specified thermal requirements must still be met but which also determine the test circuit with which the errors of the residual voltage winding are established.

Table 12. *Voltage factors to B.S. 3941*

Voltage factor	Duration	V.T. primary winding	System
1·1	Not limited	Non-earthed	Effectively or non-effectively earthed
1·5	30 sec	Earthed	Effectively earthed
1·9	30 sec or 8 hours	Earthed	Non-effectively earthed

Table 13. *Limits of errors for a three-phase residual voltage-transformer to B.S. 3941*

Applied primary voltage (per cent of rated voltage)	Residual burden at u.p.f. (per cent of rated value)	Voltage error	Phase error
100	100 to 25	$\pm 10\%$	± 10 degrees

It is of some interest to point out that when testing the residual voltage winding the secondary winding must be connected to its burden and in addition to the test for voltage and phase errors, with balanced three-phase rated voltage applied to the primary winding the voltage appearing across the residual winding terminals must not exceed 5 volts.

Obviously in the case of a three-phase bank of single-phase transformers the space required for a tertiary winding on those transformers is going to have some effect on the performance of the normal secondary winding. The tertiary winding is placed next to the core so that the mean lengths of both the primary and secondary windings increase, thus increasing numerous factors determining the errors. In service, under normal operating conditions, the small current taken by the indicator or relay connected to the tertiary residual voltage winding has a negligible effect on the errors of the normal secondary winding.

CHAPTER 21

TYPES OF VOLTAGE-TRANSFORMERS

The magnetic alloys most commonly used in the manufacture of voltage-transformers are the electrical steels, both the hot-rolled type and the cold-rolled oriented steels being used, the latter in increasing quantity because of their higher saturation flux density and permeability together with their lower iron losses. The nickel-iron alloys and the cobalt-iron alloy, Permendur, are only infrequently used for special applications. Data on all these magnetic alloys were given in chapter 3, and there is no point in repeating this here.

For the smaller single-phase voltage-transformers the core is usually made up of the normal 'T' and 'U', 'E' and 'I', or 'L' laminations when hot-rolled electrical steel is employed, while 'E' and 'I' laminations are preferable if oriented electrical steel is being used. For the larger single-phase units and most three-phase designs the mode of construction is to use cut-and-punched rectangular stampings, although the cut-wound core (the 'C' core described in chapter 3 has also been used in voltage-transformers, the material being one of the oriented electrical steels.

For single-phase transformers there are three core-forms that may be used: the shell-type construction, the core-type construction, and the so-called simple construction, although the first two named are the most popular. Examples of single-phase transformers are shown in Figs. 100a and b. The relative advantages and disadvantages of the shell-type over the core-type construction are well-known: while in the former the core cost tends to be greater, there is only one primary and secondary coil to be made, generally giving a lower copper and winding cost, but it also has the advantage over the core-type construction in that one is not faced with the need for inter-coil connections between the windings on the one limb with those on the other limb. However, one frequently finds that the manufacturer's preferred type of construction is based simply on tradition—he has, for instance, always used the shell-type. One advantage of the core-type construction which must not be overlooked is that in general it does

Fig. 100*a*. Single-phase A.N. voltage-transformer. Core-type construction complete with H.V. fuses. (*The English Electric Co. Ltd.*)

Fig. 100*b*. Single-phase 20 kV cast-resin voltage-transformer for indoor service. 'Simple' construction. (*Dr.-Ing. Hans Ritz.*)

make for better use of available space than the two other forms of construction.

The major insulation used in voltage-transformers may be synthetic resin-bonded paper (Bakelite) or one of the press-boards, although the latter is normally limited to oil-insulated transformers.

All types of conductor insulation are used—silk, cotton and paper, while the modern synthetic enamel coverings are becoming increasingly popular. Interlayer insulation in the coils may be paper or silk. Coils are usually former-wound and cylindrical

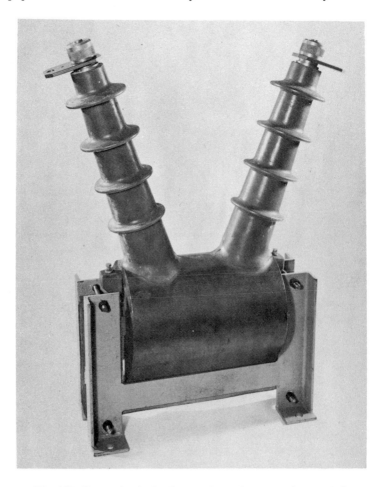

Fig. 101. Cast-resin single-phase 16 kV voltage-transformer. (*The English Electric Co. Ltd.*)

(and circular) in shape as with power-transformers, and in the same manner the primary windings for voltage-transformers having a high-rated primary voltage are section-wound, that is, made of a number of separate coils connected in series, thus minimising the inter-layer voltage. For dry-type (air-insulated) transformers all coils are normally vacuum-impregnated with varnish, while for oil-immersed voltage-transformers the same

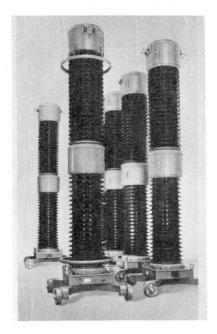

Fig. 102. Combined voltage and current-transformer units. 400 kV. Outdoor service. (*Dr.-Ing. Hans Ritz.*)

process is adopted, or alternatively, they are vacuum-impregnated with oil immediately prior to final immersion. In general, the dry-type voltage-transformer is limited to primary rated voltages not exceeding 3·3 kV although, as with the current-transformer, encapsulation of coils or complete transformers in epoxy resin enable one to use the dry-type form of construction for greater voltages and this resin encapsulation is becoming increasingly popular as it conveniently enables one to insulate the coil and at the same time provide a suitable entry terminal all in the one integral casting, a typical example being shown in Fig. 101. The

Fig. 103. Five-limb three-phase voltage-transformer. (*Foster Transformers Ltd.*)

greatest advantage in encapsulated and dry-type transformers lies in the elimination of the fire-risk occurring with all oil-immersed equipment—voltage-transformers being no exception, but for the higher voltage ratings this is usually done by the adoption of porcelain-clad voltage-transformers suitable both for outdoor and indoor use, frequently coupled with the cascade technique. Such transformers may be oil-filled or dry-type, the latter even for very high primary voltages. (It will, of course, be appreciated that the usual open-type construction cannot be used outdoors and any voltage-transformer for outdoor service must be oil- or compound-immersed or porcelain-clad.)

Numerous cascading techniques have been employed but the basic principle is common to all of them, namely that the primary voltage is subdivided between a number of transformers whose primary windings are in series, so that these windings require far less insulation from their corresponding cores than when a simple transformer orthodox construction is used, thus the use of the cascade principle leads to considerable savings in both weight and volume. Figure 102 shows a combined voltage-transformer and current-transformer and this idea of incorporating both a voltage-transformer and current-transformer into the

Fig. 104. Three-phase voltage-transformers in tanks for use in metal-clad switchgear. (*The English Electric Co. Ltd.*)

same mechanical construction obviously has a great deal of attraction from both the space and material saving viewpoints and from technical considerations and many such combined units have been developed. Figures 103–105 show further examples of voltage-transformers.

One type of voltage-transformer so far not discussed is the capacitator voltage-transformer, but it is intended here only to give a brief outline of this type. Capacitor voltage-transformers are used in high-voltage circuits from 66 kV and upwards because the cost of the normal electromagnetic type for such voltage tends to be prohibitive.

Basically two capacitors connected in series act as a voltage-transformer or divider and provided the current taken by the burden is negligible compared with the current passing through the series-connected capacitors, the error of division would also be negligible and one would have a highly efficient voltage-trans-former. Unfortunately this is never true and as the burden current

Fig. 105. Three-phase dry-type 3·3 kV voltage-transformer with H.R.C. fuses mounted in H.V. bushings. (*Foster Transformers Ltd.*)

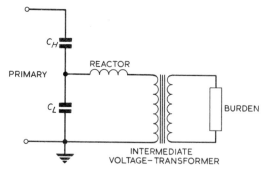

Fig. 106. Basic capacitor voltage-transformer diagram.

becomes proportionately larger so does the error of division in that the 'secondary' voltage decreases and there is also a phase error introduced.

Compensation can be carried out by 'tuning' which is done by connecting a reactor in series with the burden of such a value that at the supply frequency it is in resonance with the sum of the two capacitors. Complete elimination of the errors is not possible and a further component is added, namely an intermediate voltage-transformer (step-down) as shown in Fig. 106, the purpose of this being to reduce the burden current flowing in the capacitor transformer.

Accuracy classes and uses

In the new standard, B.S. 3941, there are five classes of accuracy, including one so-called 'laboratory' class which follow in general terms those given in B.S. 81. In addition there are two classes for dual-purpose voltage-transformers and details of all these classes are given in Tables 14 and 15. It must be pointed out that dual-purpose voltage-transformers (class E or F) must also meet the accuracy limits of one of the classes, A, B or C, and is designated class 'AE', 'AF' or 'BE' and so on.

Various fault and other abnormal conditions

While considerable emphasis is laid on the efficiency of the insulation used in voltage-transformers and in fact insulation levels employed in these are normally extremely liberal, breakdowns do occur and some protection must be given. Faults, when they occur, may be short-circuits in the primary or secondary windings or earth-faults in these windings and as a voltage-transformer is usually directly coupled to the primary system bus-bars, such faults cause such large primary fault currents that fuses on their own would not clear the fault sufficiently rapidly, so that a high resistance must be included in series with primary fuses in order to limit the fault current, but a full description of the various types of such fuses and resistances is outside the scope of this book.

The presence of this resistance in series with the primary winding increases the voltage drop and therefore causes some increase in the no-load and load %R.E. together with some increase in the no-load phase error. The phase error on load may be decreased or increased depending on the type of load. These fuses, together with secondary fuses which are used to give protection against faults on the secondary side external to the voltage-transformer, are frequently mounted on the voltage-transformer, or within the same tank, under oil.

Table 14. *Limits of errors for all voltage-transformers to B.S. 3941*

Class	0·9 to 1·1 times rated primary voltage, 0·25 to 1·0 times rated output at u.p.f.		0·8 to 1·2 times rated primary voltage and at any output not exceeding rated output and at u.p.f.	
	Voltage error (per cent + or −)	Phase error (minutes + or −)	Voltage error (per cent + or −)	Phase error (minutes + or −)
AL	−	−	0·25	10
A	0·5	20	—	—
B	1·0	30	—	—
C	2·0	60	—	—
D	5·0	—	—	—

Table 15. *Additional limits of errors for dual-purpose voltage-transformers to B.S. 3941*

Class	0·05 to 0·9 times rated primary voltage		From 1·1 to V_f times rated primary voltage	
	Voltage error (per cent + or −)	Phase error (minutes + or −)	Voltage error (per cent + or −)	Phase error (minutes + or −)
E	3	120	3	120
F	5	250	10	300

Note: These limits apply to an output of 0·25 to 1·0 rated output at u.p.f. V_f is the appropriate voltage factor.

The voltage-transformer, in common with other shunt-connected transformers, may be subjected to transient primary voltages, these transients occurring during switching operations, arcing earths and the like, but the most onerous or severe transient are those caused by lightning. It is impossible to discuss within the compass of this book the subject of lightning phenomena, interesting though it may be, or the allied subject of impulse generation whereby one artificially obtains a transient voltage wave similar to that caused by the operational condition already mentioned. It has become common practice for voltage-transformers to be tested not only at a power frequency test voltage but also under specified impulse conditions, and most manufacturers possess the required impulse generator. Furthermore, many of these are carrying out experimental works with both impulse generators and particularly with recurrent-surge oscillographs.

The impulse wave consists of a very steep 'front' or 'head' in which the voltage rises very rapidly to its maximum value, the time interval from zero to this maximum value being measured in microseconds. Once the maximum value has been reached the voltage then dies away slowly, this period being called the 'tail'. It is the front portion of the wave which is the destructive part and has the same impact or shock nature of the transient current tending to 'burst' the windings of a current-transformer, except that in the voltage-transformer the effect of this steep front is to cause non-uniform voltage distribution in the windings. This is due to the fact that the front of the impulse wave is the same as a part of a very high-frequency oscillation and when this impinges on the primary terminal of a voltage-transformer the resulting voltage distribution through the winding is determined by the capacitance of the primary winding and not its inductance. The inductance becomes the determining factor when the voltage decays (i.e. during the impulse 'tail' period) as this is equivalent to a lower frequency oscillation.

The capacitance of the primary winding is a complex network consisting of inter-turn and inter-layer capacitances together with the capacitance between each turn and earth (i.e. the frame or clamps of the voltage-transformer), but these are closely approximated by a lumped capacitance across each coil or section coil making up the primary winding and a capacitance between each coil termination and earth. When subjected to an impulse voltage these coil and earth capacitances are a low impedance path and give rise to an initial voltage distribution throughout the coil so non-uniform that the end-turns near the line terminal of the winding may well be subjected to a large percentage of the applied volts. Thus the first 5% of the turns may well be subjected to a voltage gradient of 70% of the applied voltage. Unfortunately, once the impulse voltage has decayed, the voltage distribution through the winding does not become immediately uniform because the winding may be subjected to oscillation such that turns at the neutral end will also be subjected to a high voltage gradient and even worse, turns nearer the centre of the coil may be subjected to a voltage gradient in excess of the applied impulse as shown in Fig. 107. In the example chosen, during oscillation and depending on the relative values of the inductance and capacitance of the windings, the maximum voltage appearing across the first

5% turns (from either end) may be 110% or more of the applied voltage, while the maximum voltage appearing anywhere in the coil may have a magnitude of 130% of the applied voltage and this could occur at say, 20% inside the winding (again measured from both ends).

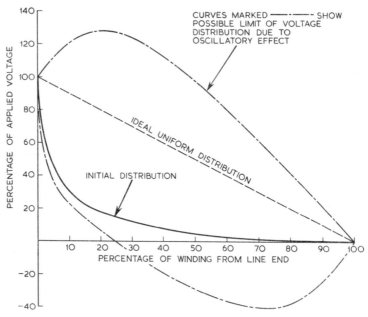

Fig. 107. Diagram showing distribution of surge voltages.

The figures given are only typical and have been given to show that the technique commonly adopted of reinforcing the end-turn insulation may do no good whatsoever to improve the ability of the voltage-transformer to withstand impulse voltages.

Again, it is impossible to describe in detail the various methods used to overcome this problem, but they fall within two broad categories—the use of protective devices external to the winding such as an auxiliary surge or choking coil, or the incorporation in the transformer design of shields and barriers so that the self-capacitances of the windings are increased.

There is another abnormal operating condition that must be mentioned, that of neutral-point inversion or displacement which is usually described in some detail in most textbooks on Electro-technology. Within the context of voltage-transformers, if a star-star connected voltage-transformer has its H.V. neutral earthed on an otherwised unearthed system, then due to the third harmonic voltages generated there is oscillation of the neutral point and almost certain neutral point inversion. This inversion, as is well known, leads to over-voltages occurring accompanied by high exciting currents due to core saturation and considerable departure from sinusoidal waveform. Some manufacturers offer special designs which give almost complete protection against neutral inversion, but one simple method of preventing 'inversion' is to use a ballast load on each secondary winding, this ballast being a resistor taking an in-phase current equal to the exciting current at rated voltage. While this method does not completely eliminate inversion it increases the voltage level at which inversion occurs and therefore it gives a high level of protection against inversion.

When primary fuses, secondary fuses and ballast loads are adopted the ratio and phase errors are measured with these in circuit if one is also using the working burden, but are omitted when a voltage-transformer is being tested with its rated burden to prove compliance with the requirements of the specified class of accuracy.

CHAPTER 22

THE TESTING OF
VOLTAGE-TRANSFORMERS

As in the case of current-transformers, discussion here is limited to those testing techniques used to determine the ratio and phase errors of voltage-transformers and no mention is made of the methods used to prove the insulation level of these transformers as these follow general practice. The method used in the testing of voltage-transformers for the determination of errors are almost as numerous as those used for the same purpose with current-transformers [see p. 202], but like them may be subdivided into two main categories:

(i) Those in which the primary and secondary voltages are precisely measured and compared, and

(ii) comparison of the voltage-transformer being tested with a standard or master voltage-transformer having known errors.

In order to determine the ratio error only, all one need do is take simultaneous readings of two voltmeters, one in the primary circuit, the other in the secondary circuit of the voltage-transformer, but the main disadvantage of this method is that it is necessary

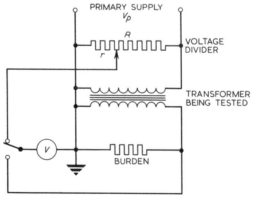

Fig. 108. Method of testing for ratio error only.

to calibrate the two voltmeters and high accuracy is not readily attained.

Figure 108 shows a method, again for ratio error only, in which an electrostatic voltmeter is first connected across the secondary terminals and then across a portion r of a resistor R which is in parallel with the primary, the value of r being adjusted so that the two voltmeter readings are approximately the same. Thus if V_1 is the voltmeter reading when connected to the primary side and V_2 is the reading when connected to the secondary, then

$$V_P = \frac{R}{r}V_1 \quad \text{and} \quad V_S = V_2,$$

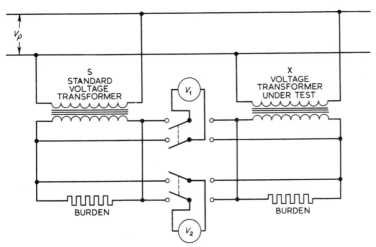

Fig. 109. Relative method of testing for ratio error only.

so that

$$K_v = \frac{R}{r}\frac{V_1}{V_2}$$

and no calibration of the instrument is required.

Numerous methods exist whereby one may also obtain the phase error using either one or two dynamometers with phase shifter or a three-phase supply to excite the dynamometers. Similarly, numerous bridge null methods exist for the measurement of both ratio and phase errors employing resistance or capacitance voltage dividers and various forms of compensation for phase error, but later on two commercially available test-sets will be described in some detail.

The simplest relative method is that shown in Fig. 109 where 'S' is the standard voltage-transformer of which the errors are known and 'X' is the voltage-transformer on test and is, of course, similar to the two-ammeter method of checking the ratio error of a current-transformer described in chapter 14. Such a method eliminates the need for meter calibration and if K_x is the ratio of the transformer under test and K_s is the known ratio of the standard transformer it can be easily shown that

$$K_x = K_s \sqrt{\left/\left(\frac{V_1 V_2}{V_1' V_2'}\right)\right.}$$

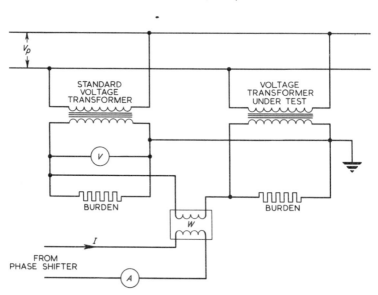

Fig. 110. Method for determining ratio and phase error using dynamo-meter wattmeter.

where V_1 and V_2 are the readings of voltmeter (1) and voltmeter (2) respectively when the former is across the secondary of the standard transformer and the latter is across the 'unknown' transformer, while V_1' and V_2' are the respective readings when the voltmeters are switched over such that voltmeter (1) is across the 'unknown' transformer and voltmeter (2) is across the standard transformer.

A very useful test-circuit, as shown in Fig. 110, employs a dynamometer wattmeter—recordings are taken when the current coil takes a current in-phase with the primary voltage V_p and then when this current leads V_p by 90°. If the two readings are W_1

and W_2 respectively, then it can be shown that the ratio of the voltage-transformer under test, K_x, is given by

$$K_x = K_s\left(1 - \frac{W_1}{V_s I}\right),$$

where K_s is the known ratio of the standard transformer and, if γ_x is the phase error of the unknown transformer and γ_s the known phase error of the standard

$$\gamma_x - \gamma_s = -\left(\frac{W_2}{V_s I}\right).$$

In using this method one must know which voltage-transformer has the smaller errors, both ratio and phase. The two readings are first taken with the unknown voltage-transformer unloaded and then connected to its rated burden. If W_1, the reading with in-phase current, increases when the load is applied, the ratio of the unknown transformer is less than that of the standard at no-load. If W_2, the reading with the current in quadrature, increases when the load increases, then the phase error of the standard transformer is the lesser of the two.

Little need be written on the use of a.c. potentiometers in the testing of voltage-transformers as the method is very similar to that already described for current-transformers, except to point out that they may be used in association with suitable voltage dividers for both comparative and absolute methods of testing.

Mention was made in chapter 14 of the Petch-Elliott current-transformer test-set manufactured by Elliott Bros. (London) Ltd. The same company also manufacture a voltage-transformer test-set using basically the same circuitry in that the difference in secondary voltages of a standard voltage-transformer and the voltage-transformer being tested is used to energise a toroidal core.

The difference volts may be considered to consist of two components, one in-phase with the secondary voltage of the standard voltage-transformer and the other in quadrature to this voltage. The former is therefore proportional to the difference in ratio errors of the two transformers, while the latter is proportional to the difference in the phase errors. As with the current-transformer test-set, two windings on the toroids are fed through calibrated potentiometers and when the two components of the 'difference voltage' are counterbalanced a null reading is obtained on a vibration galvanometer, as shown in Fig. 111a, fed from a winding on the toroidal core.

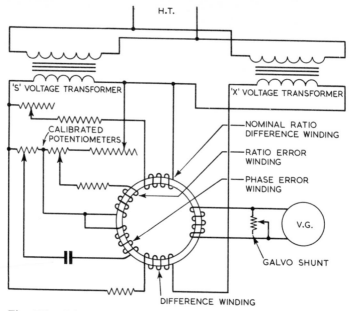

Fig. 111a. Schematic diagram for Petch-Elliott voltage-transformer test-set.

Once this null reading is obtained the difference in errors between the standard and unknown voltage-transformers are read directly from the respective potentiometer calibrated dial.

One interesting facet of this test-set is its ability to test voltage-transformers having dissimilar rated secondary voltages, that is, one is able to test voltage-transformers having a 100 volt rated secondary voltage against a 110 volt master or *vice versa*. This is achieved by a fifth winding on the toroid termed the 'nominal ratio difference winding' which in effect supplies to the toroid a voltage in-phase with the secondary voltage of the standard transformer which is proportional to the difference in the nominal ratio of the master and of the transformer under test. When the nominal ratios are equal, the test-set at the point of balance does not add any burden to the transformer being tested, but with unequal ratios there is an additional burden on both the standard and unknown voltage-transformers. It is of interest to note that when the nominal secondary voltage of the unknown transformer is less than that of the standard, this additional burden is in fact negative in sign and therefore one must actually increase the burden in the secondary of the unknown voltage-transformer in order to obtain the correct rated burden value. As the 100 volt standard

Fig. 111*b*. Petch-Elliott voltage-transformer test-set. (*Elliott Bros. (London) Ltd.*)

rated secondary voltage is rarely met the 100/110 and 110/100 volt versions of this set is likely to become obsolete.

The second commercially available voltage-transformer test-set to be discussed is, in fact, a modification to the Arnold current-transformer test-set described in chapter 14, this modification being due to Hobson.* It will be remembered that the Arnold bridge method requires a potentiometer consisting of a mutual inductor and a slide-wire resistor together with low-value four-terminal resistances, a vibration galvanometer and an ammeter. Figure 112, which shows the basic Hobson modification, immediately indicates how some of these original components are used and the additional ones that are required, these latter being a non-inductive resistance R (100 ohms), two voltmeters and a difference voltage-

* 'Instrument Transformers', by Hobson, *J.I.E.E.* **91** (1944), part II, p. 182.

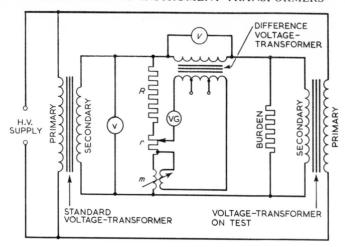

Fig. 112. Hobson variation to Arnold test-set for measuring voltage-transformer errors.

transformer. This difference voltage-transformer has connected across its primary winding one of the voltmeters, having a full scale deflection of about 10 volts, this voltmeter giving a check on the circuit connections, the ratio of the standard transformer and the polarity. If all these are correct this difference voltmeter will give a reading under 2 volts or thereabouts. The secondary tappings on the difference voltage-transformer give three ranges of measurement, namely 2% and 100 minutes, 1% and 50 minutes, and 0·2% and 10 minutes. Details are not required here but it is

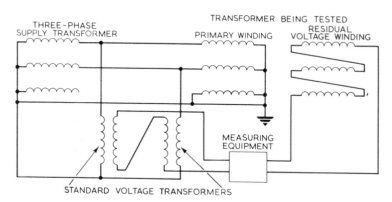

Fig. 113. Test circuit for residual voltage winding of voltage-transformer having a voltage factor of 1·5.

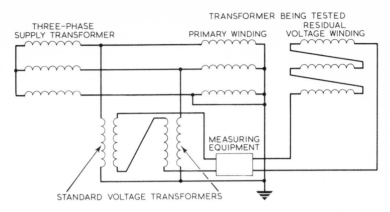

Fig. 114. Test circuit for residual voltage winding of voltage-transformer having a voltage factor of 1·9.

now possible to obtain the apparatus mentioned in one self-contained box for connection to the Arnold current-transformer set which requires only one slight alteration, this alteration simply requires the breaking of the connections between the secondary of the 5/5 isolating transformer and the potentiometer elements and the resulting four leads reconnected to terminals on the 'voltage-transformer box'.

A further modification to the basic circuit which reduces the burden on the standard transformer and increases the overall sensitivity is the provision of a step-down transformer having a primary voltage the same as the nominal secondary voltage of the standard and 'unknown' voltage-transformers and a secondary voltage of 5·5 volts, this interposing transformer being used to supply the potentiometer elements. The resistance R must of course be changed to a lower value, of the order of 2 ohms.

It may be shown that at balance the difference in the ratio error between the standard and the transformer under test is given by nr/R and the difference in their phase errors by $2\pi fmn/R$, where n is the transformation ratio of the difference voltage-transformer, the other symbols being self-explanatory.

Finally, Figs. 113 and 114 show the test connections necessary for checking the residual voltage windings of voltage-transformers to B.S. 3941.

CHAPTER 23

SOME NOTES ON OTHER NATIONAL SPECIFICATIONS

The American Standards Association specification for instrument-transformers C.57.13–1954 has already been mentioned with reference to current-transformers, but this also deals with potential transformers. As in the case of current-transformers, it is not the intention here to discuss the thermal ratings, insulation tests and the like, but simply to limit discussion to those requirements dealing with the accuracy of transformation. However, in this American standard, potential transformers are divided into three groups.

(1) Those transformers which may be connected line-to-line on a system of a specified voltage or connected line-to-neutral on a system having $\sqrt{3}$ times this voltage. In this case the primary voltage rating is given, for example, as 2400/4160 Y.

(2) Those transformers which are limited by insulation to line-to-neutral connection on the same voltage as that when connected line-to-line. Here the primary voltage rating would be given as 2400/2400 Y.

(3) Those transformers which have reduced insulation at the neutral end which must therefore be directly connected to ground but also possess a second ratio given by a tertiary winding giving the same nominal voltage in the secondary from line-to-line as from line-to-neutral.

Five standard burdens are specified in Table 16, but these are based on 120 volts (nominal secondary voltage) for transformers in groups (1) and (2), also on 120 volts for the main secondary windings of transformers in group (3) but on only 69·3 volts for the tertiary windings and such transformers. However, the standard ratios are such that while this nominal secondary voltage of 120 volts applies to primary line-to-line voltages of 24 kV or less, this becomes 115 volts for primary voltages from 34·5 kV to 345 kV. Similarly, the tertiary winding voltage is modified to 66·4 volts for the higher primary voltage range.

Table 16. *Standard burdens in the American Standards Association*
C.57.13–1954

Burden designation	Secondary volt-amperes	Burden power factor
W	12·5	0·10
X	25	0·70
Y	75	0·85
Z	200	0·85
ZZ	400	0·85

There are three standard accuracy classes which can be best described by the control parallelograms shown in Fig. 115.

These are based on exactly the same principle as for the current-transformer accuracy classes as described in chapter 15. The limits of accuracy are based on a secondary voltage of 120 volts and in the case of the tertiary winding for group 3 transformers on 69·3

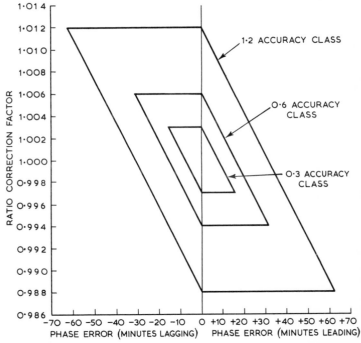

Fig. 115. Accuracy class for voltage-transformers to American Standards Association C.57.13–1954.

volts and apply from 10% below to 10% above rated primary voltage at rated frequency and from zero burden to the specified burden and would be designated, for instance, by 0·6 W, i.e. the accuracy class followed by the burden letter.

In the transformers having a tertiary winding the accuracy limits for this winding shall be for the same burden as for the main secondary winding, but when both windings are loaded the total burden must not exceed the specified burden (of the main secondary winding).

Table 17. *Accuracy classes for voltage-transformers to VDE 0414/12.62*

Accuracy class	Primary voltage	Voltage error $\pm \%$	Phase difference $\pm$ minutes
0·1	$0·8–1·2\ V_{pn}$	0·1	5
0·2	$0·8–1·2\ V_{pn}$	0·2	10
0·5	$0·8–1·2\ V_{pn}$	0·5	20
1	$0·8–1·2\ V_{pn}$	1·0	40
3	$1·0\ V_{pn}$	3·0	—

The German specification, VDE 0414/12.62, previously mentioned in chapter 15, also covers voltage-transformers and here, as in the B.S. 81, the errors are specified as % ratio error (but called % voltage error) and the phase difference in minutes. Five classes of accuracy are given, as shown in Table 17, and the limits of errors, in the case of the first four classes, apply to the primary voltage 20% below to 20% above the nominal or rated value. For accuracy class 3 only the voltage error is specified and only at the nominal primary voltage. For the first four classes the errors apply to burdens from one-quarter to full-rated burden and for class 3 from one-half to full-rated burden, but in all cases at a burden power factor of 0·8 lagging.

This VDE specification also defines the various supply systems and the basic rated secondary voltage for three-phase systems is either 100 volts or $100/\sqrt{3}$ volts, while for tertiary windings it is 100/3 volts depending on the type of system. (For one class it is $200/\sqrt{3}$ volts for the main secondary winding.) For single-phase systems the rated secondary voltages are either 100 volts or 100/2 volts for the main-secondary winding and 100/2 volts for a tertiary winding. The term 'basic' nominal secondary voltage has been used here because this specification caters for series-parallel secondary windings giving either 2×100 volts or for some types 2×200 volts.

BIBLIOGRAPHY

For those readers wishing to study further some aspects of instrument-transformer practice, the following references will prove of interest:

Instrument Transformers, by Hobson, *J.I.E.E.* **91** (1944), part II, p. 182.

The Predetermination of Current Transformer Errors, by Freeman, *J.I.E.E.* **91** (1944), part II, p. 190.

The Design of a Capacitor Voltage Transformer, by Billig, *Proc. I.E.E.* **96** (1949), part II, p. 793.

Dielectric Admittances in Current Transformers, by Arnold, *Proc. I.E.E.* **97** (1950), part II, p. 727.

The Effect of Capacitance on the Design of Toroidal Current Transformers, by Arnold, *Proc. I.E.E.* **97** (1950), part II, p. 797.

The Protection of Electrical Power Systems: A critical review of present-day practice and recent progress, by Leyburn and Lackey, *Proc. I.E.E.* **99** (1952), part II, p. 47.

Voltage Transformers and Current Transformers Associated with Switchgear, by Gray and Wright, *Proc. I.E.E.* **100** (1953), part II, p. 223.

Current Summations with Current Transformers, by Hobson, *Proc. I.E.E.* **102**A (1955), p. 581.

Also, for those having access to the *Transactions of the American Institute of Electrical Engineers*, the following references will prove of interest:

A High Speed Relay for Generator Protection, by Sonnemann (1940).

Current Transformer Design, by Camilli (1940), p. 835.

A Proposed Method of Determination of Current Transformer Errors, by Camilli and Tenbroek (1940), p. 547.

Overcurrent Performance of Bushing-type Current Transformers, by Woods and Bottonari (1940), p. 554.

Computation of Accuracy in Current Transformers, by Sinks (1940), p. 663.

A Simple Method for Determination of Ratio Error and Phase Angle in Current Transformers, by Wentz (1941), p. 949.

Biased Core Current Transformer Design Method, by Specht (1945), p. 635.

Overvoltages in Saturable Series Devices, by Boyajian and Camilli, **70** (1951), part II, pp. 1845–51.

Typical of articles in the technical press, are:

Differential Protection. Some Notes on Theory and Practice, by C. Onyemelukwe (24. 12. 59 and 31. 12. 59).

Balanced Current Protective Systems, by J. Rushton (3. 9. 59).

Switched Distance Protection, by A. Salzmann (3. 12. 59).

High-speed Directional Relaying, by A. Salzmann (24. 9. 59).

Co-ordination of Feeder and Transformer Protection, by A. Salzmann (17. 11. 60).

Pilot Wire Protection with Long Pilot Circuits, by J. Rushton (6. 6. 63, 13. 6. 63, 18. 7. 63, 25. 7. 63).

Current Transformers and their Operation, by A. A. Halacsy (26. 6. 52).
Current Transformers under Overload Conditions, by A. A. Halacsy (11. 9. 52).
[All the above appeared in the *Electrical Times*.]

Current Transformers. Their Behaviour in Balanced Circuits, by J. H. Toule (15. 7. 55).
[This appeared in the *Electrical Review*.]

Finally, books of interest, are:

Instrument Transformers, by Hague (Pitman, 1936).
Protective Current Transformers and Circuits, by Mathews (Chapman and Hall, 1955).
The Johnson and Phillips Transformer Book.
The Johnson and Phillips Switchgear Book.
Magnetic Alloys and Ferrites, consulting editor M. G. Say (George Newnes, 1954).
Magnetic Amplifiers and Saturable Reactors, consulting editor M. G. Say (George Newnes, 1954).

INDEX